SCHOOL CERTIFICATE
ALGEBRA

G. Bell and Sons Ltd
Portugal Street, London

Calcutta, Bombay & Madras
Orient Longmans Private Ltd

Toronto
Clarke, Irwin & Co. Ltd

Melbourne
John Cochrane, P.O. Box 2478 V

Accra
E. A. Kinder, P.O. Box 959

Johannesburg
N. E. H. Chance, 17 Sauer's Bldg.

SCHOOL CERTIFICATE ALGEBRA

AN ALTERNATIVE VERSION OF
"A NEW ALGEBRA FOR SCHOOLS"

By

CLEMENT V. DURELL, M.A.

AUTHOR OF "GENERAL ARITHMETIC," "A NEW GEOMETRY FOR SCHOOLS,
"MATRICULATION TRIGONOMETRY," ETC.

LONDON

G. BELL AND SONS LTD

THIS book is issued with
or without answers; it
is available complete and
also in two parts.

PART I. First published 1937
Reprinted: 1937, 1938 (*twice*), 1939, 1940, 1941, 1942,
1943, 1944, 1945 (*thrice*), 1946, 1947, 1948, 1950, 1951, 1952,
1953, 1954, 1956, 1957, 1959, 1960

PART II. First published 1937
Reprinted: 1937, 1938 (*twice*), 1939, 1940, 1941, 1942,
1943, 1944, 1945 (*thrice*), 1946, 1947, 1948, 1950, 1951, 1952,
1953, 1954, 1955, 1957, 1958, 1960

Printed in Great Britain by
The Camelot Press Ltd., London and Southampton

PREFACE

THIS Alternative Version of my *New Algebra for Schools* has been prepared in order to meet the views of some teachers, who have suggested to me that modifications within the framework of the existing book would make it more suitable to their requirements. I gratefully acknowledge the many valuable suggestions which have been made to me, and in accordance with them I have made the following changes in this Alternative Version.

1. The number of purely drill examples in the main text has been increased, thus rendering the provision of "extra practice" drill exercises unnecessary.

2. Revision exercises are given at frequent suitable intervals throughout the book instead of being collected in an appendix.

3. A set of "Tests in Manipulation" has been added; these not only serve to disclose weakness in elementary technique but help to overcome it and consolidate the pupil's knowledge.

4. Examples are classified in the same way as in the author's *General Arithmetic*:

   (i) A first course, which may be worked entire by all pupils: plain numbers;

   (ii) a parallel course which does not extend the scope of (i), but merely gives extra practice, when this is needed: numbers enclosed in brackets;

   (iii) harder examples intended for those pupils who run ahead of the class: asterisked numbers.

Great care has been taken to secure that the examples suggested for the first course are *straightforward* applications of the bookwork, and special attention has been given to their grading. In cases where the drill element is of primary importance, practice is given in examples of a single type before another type is introduced, mixed types being included later in the exercise. I am deeply indebted to Mr. J. A. Hodge for help in the arrangement and construction of the exercises and revision papers.

The initial difficulties in Algebra are mainly due to the novelty of the notation. These are best overcome by training the pupil to think in numbers when using letters and by demonstrating the practical utility of the notation by applications to formulae and problems. These two principles, as in the *New Algebra for Schools*, have determined the selection of the subject-matter of the early chapters. Throughout the book illustrations have been drawn from practical geometry, physics, and mechanics to increase the interest in the theory and to secure variety in problems, and this object is furthered by a free use of diagrams.

The volume, divided into two Parts, contains all that is required for *elementary mathematics* in School Certificate examinations, as laid down by the syllabuses and interpreted by the papers of the various examining Boards; it does not include any topic which is not required for at least one of these examinations.

C. V. D.

April, 1937

CONTENTS

PART I

CONTENTS

⁎ This book is issued *with* or *without* Answers.

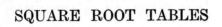

SQUARE ROOT TABLES

SQUARE ROOTS

	0	1	2	3	4	5	6	7	8	9	1 2 3	4 5 6	7 8 9
10	1000	1005	1010	1015	1020	1025	1030	1034	1039	1044	0 1 1	2 2 3	3 4 4
11	1049	1054	1058	1063	1068	1072	1077	1082	1086	1091	0 1 1	2 2 3	3 4 4
12	1095	1100	1105	1109	1114	1118	1122	1127	1131	1136	0 1 1	2 2 3	3 4 4
13	1140	1145	1149	1153	1158	1162	1166	1170	1175	1179	0 1 1	2 2 3	3 3 4
14	1183	1187	1192	1196	1200	1204	1208	1212	1217	1221	0 1 1	2 2 2	3 3 4
15	1225	1229	1233	1237	1241	1245	1249	1253	1257	1261	0 1 1	2 2 2	3 3 4
16	1265	1269	1273	1277	1281	1285	1288	1292	1296	1300	0 1 1	2 2 2	3 3 4
17	1304	1308	1311	1315	1319	1323	1327	1330	1334	1338	0 1 1	2 2 2	3 3 3
18	1342	1345	1349	1353	1356	1360	1364	1367	1371	1375	0 1 1	1 2 2	3 3 3
19	1378	1382	1386	1389	1393	1396	1400	1404	1407	1411	0 1 1	1 2 2	3 3 3
20	1414	1418	1421	1425	1428	1432	1435	1439	1442	1446	0 1 1	1 2 2	2 3 3
21	1449	1453	1456	1459	1463	1466	1470	1473	1476	1480	0 1 1	1 2 2	2 3 3
22	1483	1487	1490	1493	1497	1500	1503	1507	1510	1513	0 1 1	1 2 2	2 3 3
23	1517	1520	1523	1526	1530	1533	1536	1539	1543	1546	0 1 1	1 2 2	2 3 3
24	1549	1552	1556	1559	1562	1565	1568	1572	1575	1578	0 1 1	1 2 2	2 3 3
25	1581	1584	1587	1591	1594	1597	1600	1603	1606	1609	0 1 1	1 2 2	2 3 3
26	1612	1616	1619	1622	1625	1628	1631	1634	1637	1640	0 1 1	1 2 2	2 2 3
27	1643	1646	1649	1652	1655	1658	1661	1664	1667	1670	0 1 1	1 2 2	2 2 3
28	1673	1676	1679	1682	1685	1688	1691	1694	1697	1700	0 1 1	1 1 2	2 2 3
29	1703	1706	1709	1712	1715	1718	1720	1723	1726	1729	0 1 1	1 1 2	2 2 3
30	1732	1735	1738	1741	1744	1746	1749	1752	1755	1758	0 1 1	1 1 2	2 2 3
31	1761	1764	1766	1769	1772	1775	1778	1780	1783	1786	0 1 1	1 1 2	2 2 3
32	1789	1792	1794	1797	1800	1803	1806	1808	1811	1814	0 1 1	1 1 2	2 2 2
33	1817	1819	1822	1825	1828	1830	1833	1836	1838	1841	0 1 1	1 1 2	2 2 2
34	1844	1847	1849	1852	1855	1857	1860	1863	1865	1868	0 1 1	1 1 2	2 2 2
35	1871	1873	1876	1879	1881	1884	1887	1889	1892	1895	0 1 1	1 1 2	2 2 2
36	1897	1900	1903	1905	1908	1910	1913	1916	1918	1921	0 1 1	1 1 2	2 2 2
37	1924	1926	1929	1931	1934	1936	1939	1942	1944	1947	0 1 1	1 1 2	2 2 2
38	1949	1952	1954	1957	1960	1962	1965	1967	1970	1972	0 1 1	1 1 2	2 2 2
39	1975	1977	1980	1982	1985	1987	1990	1992	1995	1997	0 1 1	1 1 2	2 2 2
40	2000	2002	2005	2007	2010	2012	2015	2017	2020	2022	0 0 1	1 1 1	2 2 2
41	2025	2027	2030	2032	2035	2037	2040	2042	2045	2047	0 0 1	1 1 1	2 2 2
42	2049	2052	2054	2057	2059	2062	2064	2066	2069	2071	0 0 1	1 1 1	2 2 2
43	2074	2076	2078	2081	2083	2086	2088	2090	2093	2095	0 0 1	1 1 1	2 2 2
44	2098	2100	2102	2105	2107	2110	2112	2114	2117	2119	0 0 1	1 1 1	2 2 2
45	2121	2124	2126	2128	2131	2133	2135	2138	2140	2142	0 0 1	1 1 1	2 2 2
46	2145	2147	2149	2152	2154	2156	2159	2161	2163	2166	0 0 1	1 1 1	2 2 2
47	2168	2170	2173	2175	2177	2179	2182	2184	2186	2189	0 0 1	1 1 1	2 2 2
48	2191	2193	2195	2198	2200	2202	2205	2207	2209	2211	0 0 1	1 1 1	2 2 2
49	2214	2216	2218	2220	2223	2225	2227	2229	2232	2234	0 0 1	1 1 1	2 2 2
50	2236	2238	2241	2243	2245	2247	2249	2252	2254	2256	0 0 1	1 1 1	2 2 2
51	2258	2261	2263	2265	2267	2269	2272	2274	2276	2278	0 0 1	1 1 1	2 2 2
52	2280	2283	2285	2287	2289	2291	2293	2296	2298	2300	0 0 1	1 1 1	2 2 2
53	2302	2304	2307	2309	2311	2313	2315	2317	2319	2322	0 0 1	1 1 1	2 2 2
54	2324	2326	2328	2330	2332	2335	2337	2339	2341	2343	0 0 1	1 1 1	1 2 2

Find the first significant figure and the position of the decimal point by inspection.

	0	1	2	3	4	5	6	7	8	9	1 2 3	4 5 6	7 8 9
10	3162	3178	3194	3209	3225	3240	3256	3271	3286	3302	2 3 5	6 8 9	11 12 14
11	3317	3332	3347	3362	3376	3391	3406	3421	3435	3450	1 3 4	6 7 9	10 12 13
12	3464	3479	3493	3507	3521	3536	3550	3564	3578	3592	1 3 4	6 7 8	10 11 13
13	3606	3619	3633	3647	3661	3674	3688	3701	3715	3728	1 3 4	5 7 8	10 11 12
14	3742	3755	3768	3782	3795	3808	3821	3834	3847	3860	1 3 4	5 7 8	9 11 12
15	3873	3886	3899	3912	3924	3937	3950	3962	3975	3987	1 3 4	5 6 8	9 10 11
16	4000	4012	4025	4037	4050	4062	4074	4087	4099	4111	1 2 4	5 6 7	9 10 11
17	4123	4135	4147	4159	4171	4183	4195	4207	4219	4231	1 2 4	5 6 7	8 10 11
18	4243	4254	4266	4278	4290	4301	4313	4324	4336	4347	1 2 3	5 6 7	8 9 10
19	4359	4370	4382	4393	4405	4416	4427	4438	4450	4461	1 2 3	5 6 7	8 9 10
20	4472	4483	4494	4506	4517	4528	4539	4550	4561	4572	1 2 3	4 6 7	8 9 10
21	4583	4593	4604	4615	4626	4637	4647	4658	4669	4680	1 2 3	4 5 6	8 9 10
22	4690	4701	4712	4722	4733	4743	4754	4764	4775	4785	1 2 3	4 5 6	7 8 9
23	4796	4806	4817	4827	4837	4848	4858	4868	4879	4889	1 2 3	4 5 6	7 8 9
24	4899	4909	4919	4930	4940	4950	4960	4970	4980	4990	1 2 3	4 5 6	7 8 9
25	5000	5010	5020	5030	5040	5050	5060	5070	5079	5089	1 2 3	4 5 6	7 8 9
26	5099	5109	5119	5128	5138	5148	5158	5167	5177	5187	1 2 3	4 5 6	7 8 9
27	5196	5206	5215	5225	5235	5244	5254	5263	5273	5282	1 2 3	4 5 6	7 8 9
28	5292	5301	5310	5320	5329	5339	5348	5357	5367	5376	1 2 3	4 5 6	7 7 8
29	5385	5394	5404	5413	5422	5431	5441	5450	5459	5468	1 2 3	4 5 5	6 7 8
30	5477	5486	5495	5505	5514	5523	5532	5541	5550	5559	1 2 3	4 4 5	6 7 8
31	5568	5577	5586	5595	5604	5612	5621	5630	5639	5648	1 2 3	3 4 5	6 7 8
32	5657	5666	5675	5683	5692	5701	5710	5718	5727	5736	1 2 3	3 4 5	6 7 8
33	5745	5753	5762	5771	5779	5788	5797	5805	5814	5822	1 2 3	3 4 5	6 7 8
34	5831	5840	5848	5857	5865	5874	5882	5891	5899	5908	1 2 3	3 4 5	6 7 8
35	5916	5925	5933	5941	5950	5958	5967	5975	5983	5992	1 2 2	3 4 5	6 7 8
36	6000	6008	6017	6025	6033	6042	6050	6058	6066	6075	1 2 2	3 4 5	6 7 7
37	6083	6091	6099	6107	6116	6124	6132	6140	6148	6156	1 2 2	3 4 5	6 7 7
38	6164	6173	6181	6189	6197	6205	6213	6221	6229	6237	1 2 2	3 4 5	6 6 7
39	6245	6253	6261	6269	6277	6285	6293	6301	6309	6317	1 2 2	3 4 5	6 6 7
40	6325	6332	6340	6348	6356	6364	6372	6380	6387	6395	1 2 2	3 4 5	6 6 7
41	6403	6411	6419	6427	6434	6442	6450	6458	6465	6473	1 2 2	3 4 5	5 6 7
42	6481	6488	6496	6504	6512	6519	6527	6535	6542	6550	1 2 2	3 4 5	5 6 7
43	6557	6565	6573	6580	6588	6595	6603	6611	6618	6626	1 2 2	3 4 5	5 6 7
44	6633	6641	6648	6656	6663	6671	6678	6686	6693	6701	1 2 2	3 4 5	5 6 7
45	6708	6716	6723	6731	6738	6745	6753	6760	6768	6775	1 1 2	3 4 4	5 6 7
46	6782	6790	6797	6804	6812	6819	6826	6834	6841	6848	1 1 2	3 4 4	5 6 7
47	6856	6863	6870	6877	6885	6892	6899	6907	6914	6921	1 1 2	3 4 4	5 6 7
48	6928	6935	6943	6950	6957	6964	6971	6979	6986	6993	1 1 2	3 4 4	5 6 6
49	7000	7007	7014	7021	7029	7036	7043	7050	7057	7064	1 1 2	3 4 4	5 6 6
50	7071	7078	7085	7092	7099	7106	7113	7120	7127	7134	1 1 2	3 4 4	5 6 6
51	7141	7148	7155	7162	7169	7176	7183	7190	7197	7204	1 1 2	3 4 4	5 6 6
52	7211	7218	7225	7232	7239	7246	7253	7259	7266	7273	1 1 2	3 3 4	5 6 6
53	7280	7287	7294	7301	7308	7314	7321	7328	7335	7342	1 1 2	3 3 4	5 5 6
54	7348	7355	7362	7369	7376	7382	7389	7396	7403	7409	1 1 2	3 3 4	5 5 6

Find the first significant figure and the position of the decimal point by inspection.

SQUARE ROOTS

	0	1	2	3	4	5	6	7	8	9	1	2	3	4	5	6	7	8	9
55	2345	2347	2349	2352	2354	2356	2358	2360	2362	2364	0	0	1	1	1	1	1	2	2
56	2366	2369	2371	2373	2375	2377	2379	2381	2383	2385	0	0	1	1	1	1	1	2	2
57	2387	2390	2392	2394	2396	2398	2400	2402	2404	2406	0	0	1	1	1	1	1	2	2
58	2408	2410	2412	2415	2417	2419	2421	2423	2425	2427	0	0	1	1	1	1	1	2	2
59	2429	2431	2433	2435	2437	2439	2441	2443	2445	2447	0	0	1	1	1	1	1	2	2
60	2449	2452	2454	2456	2458	2460	2462	2464	2466	2468	0	0	1	1	1	1	1	2	2
61	2470	2472	2474	2476	2478	2480	2482	2484	2486	2488	0	0	1	1	1	1	1	2	2
62	2490	2492	2494	2496	2498	2500	2502	2504	2506	2508	0	0	1	1	1	1	1	2	2
63	2510	2512	2514	2516	2518	2520	2522	2524	2526	2528	0	0	1	1	1	1	1	2	2
64	2530	2532	2534	2536	2538	2540	2542	2544	2546	2548	0	0	1	1	1	1	1	2	2
65	2550	2551	2553	2555	2557	2559	2561	2563	2565	2567	0	0	1	1	1	1	1	2	2
66	2569	2571	2573	2575	2577	2579	2581	2583	2585	2587	0	0	1	1	1	1	1	2	2
67	2588	2590	2592	2594	2596	2598	2600	2602	2604	2606	0	0	1	1	1	1	1	2	2
68	2608	2610	2612	2613	2615	2617	2619	2621	2623	2625	0	0	1	1	1	1	1	2	2
69	2627	2629	2631	2632	2634	2636	2638	2640	2642	2644	0	0	1	1	1	1	1	2	2
70	2646	2648	2650	2651	2653	2655	2657	2659	2661	2663	0	0	1	1	1	1	1	2	2
71	2665	2666	2668	2670	2672	2674	2676	2678	2680	2681	0	0	1	1	1	1	1	1	2
72	2683	2685	2687	2689	2691	2693	2694	2696	2698	2700	0	0	1	1	1	1	1	1	2
73	2702	2704	2706	2707	2709	2711	2713	2715	2717	2718	0	0	1	1	1	1	1	1	2
74	2720	2722	2724	2726	2728	2729	2731	2733	2735	2737	0	0	1	1	1	1	1	1	2
75	2739	2740	2742	2744	2746	2748	2750	2751	2753	2755	0	0	1	1	1	1	1	1	2
76	2757	2759	2760	2762	2764	2766	2768	2769	2771	2773	0	0	1	1	1	1	1	1	2
77	2775	2777	2778	2780	2782	2784	2786	2787	2789	2791	0	0	1	1	1	1	1	1	2
78	2793	2795	2796	2798	2800	2802	2804	2805	2807	2809	0	0	1	1	1	1	1	1	2
79	2811	2812	2814	2816	2818	2820	2821	2823	2825	2827	0	0	1	1	1	1	1	1	2
80	2828	2830	2832	2834	2835	2837	2839	2841	2843	2844	0	0	1	1	1	1	1	1	2
81	2846	2848	2850	2851	2853	2855	2857	2858	2860	2862	0	0	1	1	1	1	1	1	2
82	2864	2865	2867	2869	2871	2872	2874	2876	2877	2879	0	0	1	1	1	1	1	1	2
83	2881	2883	2884	2886	2888	2890	2891	2893	2895	2897	0	0	1	1	1	1	1	1	2
84	2898	2900	2902	2903	2905	2907	2909	2910	2912	2914	0	0	1	1	1	1	1	1	2
85	2915	2917	2919	2921	2922	2924	2926	2927	2929	2931	0	0	1	1	1	1	1	1	2
86	2933	2934	2936	2938	2939	2941	2943	2944	2946	2948	0	0	1	1	1	1	1	1	2
87	2950	2951	2953	2955	2956	2958	2960	2961	2963	2965	0	0	1	1	1	1	1	1	2
88	2966	2968	2970	2972	2973	2975	2977	2978	2980	2982	0	0	1	1	1	1	1	1	2
89	2983	2985	2987	2988	2990	2992	2993	2995	2997	2998	0	0	1	1	1	1	1	1	2
90	3000	3002	3003	3005	3007	3008	3010	3012	3013	3015	0	0	0	1	1	1	1	1	1
91	3017	3018	3020	3022	3023	3025	3027	3028	3030	3032	0	0	0	1	1	1	1	1	1
92	3033	3035	3036	3038	3040	3041	3043	3045	3046	3048	0	0	0	1	1	1	1	1	1
93	3050	3051	3053	3055	3056	3058	3059	3061	3063	3064	0	0	0	1	1	1	1	1	1
94	3066	3068	3069	3071	3072	3074	3076	3077	3079	3081	0	0	0	1	1	1	1	1	1
95	3082	3084	3085	3087	3089	3090	3092	3094	3095	3097	0	0	0	1	1	1	1	1	1
96	3098	3100	3102	3103	3105	3106	3108	3110	3111	3113	0	0	0	1	1	1	1	1	1
97	3114	3116	3118	3119	3121	3122	3124	3126	3127	3129	0	0	0	1	1	1	1	1	1
98	3130	3132	3134	3135	3137	3138	3140	3142	3143	3145	0	0	0	1	1	1	1	1	1
99	3146	3148	3150	3151	3153	3154	3156	3158	3159	3161	0	0	0	1	1	1	1	1	1

Find the first significant figure and the position of the decimal point by inspection.

	0	1	2	3	4	5	6	7	8	9	1 2 3	4 5 6	7 8 9
55	7416	7423	7430	7436	7443	7450	7457	7463	7470	7477	1 1 2	3 3 4	5 5 6
56	7483	7490	7497	7503	7510	7517	7523	7530	7537	7543	1 1 2	3 3 4	5 5 6
57	7550	7556	7563	7570	7576	7583	7589	7596	7603	7609	1 1 2	3 3 4	5 5 6
58	7616	7622	7629	7635	7642	7649	7655	7662	7668	7675	1 1 2	3 3 4	5 5 6
59	7681	7688	7694	7701	7707	7714	7720	7727	7733	7740	1 1 2	3 3 4	5 5 6
60	7746	7752	7759	7765	7772	7778	7785	7791	7797	7804	1 1 2	3 3 4	4 5 6
61	7810	7817	7823	7829	7836	7842	7849	7855	7861	7868	1 1 2	3 3 4	4 5 6
62	7874	7880	7887	7893	7899	7906	7912	7918	7925	7931	1 1 2	3 3 4	4 5 6
63	7937	7944	7950	7956	7962	7969	7975	7981	7987	7994	1 1 2	3 3 4	4 5 6
64	8000	8006	8012	8019	8025	8031	8037	8044	8050	8056	1 1 2	2 3 4	4 5 6
65	8062	8068	8075	8081	8087	8093	8099	8106	8112	8118	1 1 2	2 3 4	4 5 5
66	8124	8130	8136	8142	8149	8155	8161	8167	8173	8179	1 1 2	2 3 4	4 5 5
67	8185	8191	8198	8204	8210	8216	8222	8228	8234	8240	1 1 2	2 3 4	4 5 5
68	8246	8252	8258	8264	8270	8276	8283	8289	8295	8301	1 1 2	2 3 4	4 5 5
69	8307	8313	8319	8325	8331	8337	8343	8349	8355	8361	1 1 2	2 3 4	4 5 5
70	8367	8373	8379	8385	8390	8396	8402	8408	8414	8420	1 1 2	2 3 4	4 5 5
71	8426	8432	8438	8444	8450	8456	8462	8468	8473	8479	1 1 2	2 3 4	4 5 5
72	8485	8491	8497	8503	8509	8515	8521	8526	8532	8538	1 1 2	2 3 4	4 5 5
73	8544	8550	8556	8562	8567	8573	8579	8585	8591	8597	1 1 2	2 3 3	4 5 5
74	8602	8608	8614	8620	8626	8631	8637	8643	8649	8654	1 1 2	2 3 3	4 5 5
75	8660	8666	8672	8678	8683	8689	8695	8701	8706	8712	1 1 2	2 3 3	4 5 5
76	8718	8724	8729	8735	8741	8746	8752	8758	8764	8769	1 1 2	2 3 3	4 5 5
77	8775	8781	8786	8792	8798	8803	8809	8815	8820	8826	1 1 2	2 3 3	4 4 5
78	8832	8837	8843	8849	8854	8860	8866	8871	8877	8883	1 1 2	2 3 3	4 4 5
79	8888	8894	8899	8905	8911	8916	8922	8927	8933	8939	1 1 2	2 3 3	4 4 5
80	8944	8950	8955	8961	8967	8972	8978	8983	8989	8994	1 1 2	2 3 3	4 4 5
81	9000	9006	9011	9017	9022	9028	9033	9039	9044	9050	1 1 2	2 3 3	4 4 5
82	9055	9061	9066	9072	9077	9083	9088	9094	9099	9105	1 1 2	2 3 3	4 4 5
83	9110	9116	9121	9127	9132	9138	9143	9149	9154	9160	1 1 2	2 3 3	4 4 5
84	9165	9171	9176	9182	9187	9192	9198	9203	9209	9214	1 1 2	2 3 3	4 4 5
85	9220	9225	9230	9236	9241	9247	9252	9257	9263	9268	1 1 2	2 3 3	4 4 5
86	9274	9279	9284	9290	9295	9301	9306	9311	9317	9322	1 1 2	2 3 3	4 4 5
87	9327	9333	9338	9343	9349	9354	9359	9365	9370	9375	1 1 2	2 3 3	4 4 5
88	9381	9386	9391	9397	9402	9407	9413	9418	9423	9429	1 1 2	2 3 3	4 4 5
89	9434	9439	9445	9450	9455	9460	9466	9471	9476	9482	1 1 2	2 3 3	4 4 5
90	9487	9492	9497	9503	9508	9513	9518	9524	9529	9534	1 1 2	2 3 3	4 4 5
91	9539	9545	9550	9555	9560	9566	9571	9576	9581	9586	1 1 2	2 3 3	4 4 5
92	9592	9597	9602	9607	9612	9618	9623	9628	9633	9638	1 1 2	2 3 3	4 4 5
93	9644	9649	9654	9659	9664	9670	9675	9680	9685	9690	1 1 2	2 3 3	4 4 5
94	9695	9701	9706	9711	9716	9721	9726	9731	9737	9742	1 1 2	2 3 3	4 4 5
95	9747	9752	9757	9762	9767	9772	9778	9783	9788	9793	1 1 2	2 3 3	4 4 5
96	9798	9803	9808	9813	9818	9823	9829	9834	9839	9844	1 1 2	2 3 3	4 4 5
97	9849	9854	9859	9864	9869	9874	9879	9884	9889	9894	1 1 2	2 3 3	4 4 5
98	9899	9905	9910	9915	9920	9925	9930	9935	9940	9945	0 1 1	2 2 3	3 4 4
99	9950	9955	9960	9965	9970	9975	9980	9985	9990	9995	0 1 1	2 2 3	3 4 4

Find the first significant figure and the position of the decimal point by inspection.

Logarithm and Anti-Logarithm Tables
are given on pages 396–399

CHAPTER I

FIRST NOTIONS

General Statements

THE following example, illustrating the use of letters to generalise statements, is intended for oral discussion.

Example 1. Part of a post is painted black, namely the shaded portion in the figures below; the rest is white. What is the length of the white portion?

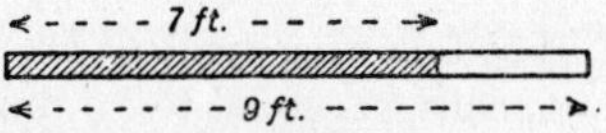

The post is 9 feet long, and the black portion is 7 feet long;

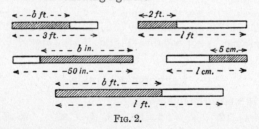

FIG. 1.

∴ the white portion is 9 feet − 7 feet long or 2 feet long.

Repeat with the following figures:

FIG. 2.

The general statement is as follows:

If the length of the post is l feet and if the length of the part painted black is b feet, then the length of the remainder, painted white, is l feet − b feet.

These statements can be shortened by using *brackets*.

Instead of 9 feet − 7 feet, we may write $(9 − 7)$ feet; and instead of l feet − b feet, $(l − b)$ feet. The contents of a bracket are then regarded as equivalent to a single number.

Letters are used to represent numbers. *Do* not *use them to represent quantities, i.e. numbers-of-things.*

Do not say the length of a rod is l, but say that its length is l inches or l feet or l cm., etc.

Symbols and Notation

The symbols $+$, $-$, $\times$, $\div$ have the same meanings in Algebra as in Arithmetic.

The operation "multiply the number N by 5" might be written $N \times 5$, but to save time it is written 5N, although in Arithmetic 57 means 5 tens $+7$, and $5\frac{3}{4}$ means $5 + \frac{3}{4}$. But in Algebra,

ab always means a × b.

In Arithmetic, $2 \div 3$ is written $\frac{2}{3}$; similarly in Algebra, $a \div b$ is written $\frac{a}{b}$.

The following symbols are in common use:

$=$ means "is equal to"; thus $5 - 2 = 3$.

$\therefore$ means "therefore"; thus 1 yard $= 3$ feet, $\therefore$ 4 yards $= 3 \times 4$ feet.

Do not confuse $=$ with $\therefore$; use the symbol $=$ as a *verb*.

The following symbols are also useful:

$>$ means "is greater than"; thus $5 > 2$.

$<$ means "is less than"; thus $1\frac{1}{2} < 2\frac{1}{4}$.

$\simeq$ means "is approximately equal to"; thus $3\frac{1}{7} \simeq 3 \cdot 14$.

$\neq$ means "is not equal to"; thus if $x = 5$ and $y = 2$, $x \neq y$.

EXERCISE I. a (Oral)

State in words the following:

1. $3 \times 4 = 12$.
2. $x \times 2 = 10$.
3. $3y = 18$.
4. $ab = 6$.
5. $7 > 4$.
6. $5 < 8$.
7. $1\frac{1}{3} \simeq 1 \cdot 33$.
8. $24 \neq 2 \times 4$.
9. $3 < 4 < 5$.
10. $10 > 8 > 7$.
11. $\frac{1}{3} \neq 0 \cdot 3$.
12. $1 \cdot 6 < 1\frac{2}{3}$.
13. $N > 3$.
14. $A < 8$.
15. $x = y = 5$.
16. $5\frac{2}{7} \simeq 5 \cdot 3$.
17. $z \neq 1$.
18. $6 > b$.
19. $5 < c < 8$.
20. $4 > b > 3$.

Write in symbols the following:

21. Twice b equals six.
22. Five times x equals twenty.
23. 3^2 is greater than 3.
24. $\frac{1}{2} \times \frac{1}{2}$ is less than $\frac{1}{2}$.
25. N is greater than 5.
26. n is less than 4.
27. x is not equal to nought.
28. y and z are equal.
29. c and d are unequal.
30. a and b each equal 6.
31. 8 kilometres is approximately equal to 5 miles.

32. 1·4 × 1·4 is approximately equal to 2.

33. Twice N equals 14, therefore N equals 7.

34. The sum of x and 3 is 8, therefore x equals 5.

35. If t minus 4 equals 6, then t equals 10.

EXERCISE I. b

1. Find the total weight of two parcels (i) if one weighs 5 lb. and the other 8 lb., (ii) if one weighs P lb. and the other Q lb.

2. How much can the water-level rise in each of the glasses shown in Fig. 3 before the water overflows?

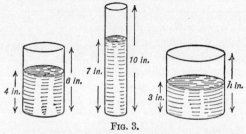

Fig. 3.

How much if (i) a glass 5 inches high contains water d inches deep;

(ii) a glass h inches high contains water d inches deep?

[3] A boy is now 12 years old; how old will he be (i) in 5 years' time, (ii) in n years' time?

[4] I have to make a journey of 30 miles. How much farther have I to go after travelling (i) 10 miles, (ii) s miles?

5. Part of a rod (see Fig. 4) is painted red, another part white, and the rest black. Find the total length of the rod in the following cases:

	(i)	(ii)	(iii)	(iv)
Length of red part	2 in.	r in.	3 in.	r in.
Length of white part	3 in.	4 in.	w in.	w in.
Length of black part	4 in.	5 in.	7 in.	b in.

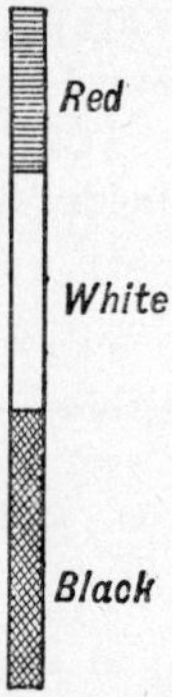

Red

White

Black

Fig. 4.

6. Find the length of the black part of the rod (see Fig. 4 repeated here) in the following cases:

	(i)	(ii)	(iii)	(iv)
Total length of rod -	14 cm.	b cm.	9 cm.	l cm.
Length of red part -	3 cm.	2 cm.	r cm.	r cm.
Length of white part	5 cm.	3 cm.	4 cm.	w cm.

7. A man is now 50 years old; how old was he (i) 8 years ago, (ii) p years ago?

8. Write down *without multiplying up*
(i) the number of pence in 9 shillings, in P shillings;
(ii) the number of feet in 14 yards, in x yards.

[9] Write down *without multiplying up*
(i) the number of shillings in £7, in £y;
(ii) the number of ounces in 5 lb., in W lb.

10. 1 golf ball costs 2 shillings. Find the cost of (i) 5 golf balls, (ii) n golf balls, of the same kind.

[11] A watch loses 20 seconds a day; how many seconds does it lose in 7 days, in z days?

12. (i) Express in shillings: 11 pence, z pence.
    (ii) Express in lb.: 13 oz., w oz.

[13] (i) Express in £: 7 shillings, N shillings.
    (ii) Express in feet: 5 inches, l inches.

14. A ticket for a cinema costs 2 shillings; how many tickets can I buy for (i) 18 shillings, (ii) p shillings?

[15] A packet of chocolate costs 3 shillings; how many packets can I buy for (i) 15 shillings, (ii) r shillings?

16. Fig. 5 gives the dimensions in yards of three rectangular fields; find the total length of fencing necessary to enclose each field.

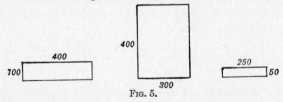

Fig. 5.

A rectangular field is l yards long, b yards broad; find its perimeter, *i.e.* the sum of the lengths of its sides.

[17] Find how much a man saves each year in the following cases:

	(i)	(ii)	(iii)	(iv)
Income - -	£700	£I	£800	£I
Expenditure -	£500	£400	£E	£E

[18] A man walks 4 miles an hour; how far does he go (i) in 3 hours, (ii) in t hours?

19. Find the height of a pile of equal notebooks in the following cases:

	(i)	(ii)	(iii)	(iv)
Number of notebooks -	12	n	12	p
Thickness of each book -	2 cm.	3 cm.	t cm.	d cm.

20. Write down the size of each unmarked angle in Fig. 6.

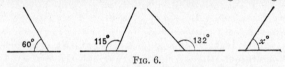

FIG. 6.

*21. The area of the floor of a rectangular room is 180 sq. ft. Copy the given table and complete it.

Length of room - -	18 ft.		l ft.	
Breadth of room - -		12 ft.		b ft.

*22. Fig. 7 represents a rectangular shed in the corner of a rectangular garden; the dimensions are given in feet. What is the length (i) of **AE,** (ii) of **CG**?

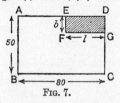

FIG. 7.

FIG. 8.

*23. Fig. 8 represents a rectangular enclosure; the dimensions are given in yards. Write down (i) the length of **PC,** (ii) the distance of **A** from **P** measured round the enclosure through **B** and **C**.

*24. Each step in a staircase is 6 ins. high. How many steps are there if the height of the staircase is (i) 7 feet, (ii) h feet?

*25. A piece of soap costs n pence; how many pieces can I buy for two shillings?

*26. When a man is 40 years old his son is 10 years old. Copy the given table (ages in years) and complete it.

Age of Father -		50		f	
Age of Son -	6		s		$x+10$

*27. How many hours is a person in bed (i) if he goes to bed at 9 p.m. and gets up at 7 a.m., (ii) if he goes to bed at x p.m. and gets up at y a.m.?

Operations

Just as $6 \times 1 = 1 \times 6 = 6$, so $N \times 1 = 1 \times N = N$; we therefore write N instead of 1N.

Also just as $\dfrac{6}{1} = 6 \div 1 = 6$, so $\dfrac{N}{1} = N \div 1 = N$; we therefore write N instead of $\dfrac{N}{1}$.

Just as $7 \times \dfrac{1}{2} = \dfrac{7}{2}$, so $N \times \dfrac{1}{2} = \dfrac{N}{2}$; this is also written $\tfrac{1}{2}N$.

Just as $7 \times \dfrac{3}{4} = \dfrac{7 \times 3}{4}$, so $N \times \dfrac{3}{4} = \dfrac{N \times 3}{4}$; this is written $\dfrac{3N}{4}$ or $\tfrac{3}{4}N$.

Similarly $N \times 1\tfrac{2}{3} = N \times \dfrac{5}{3} = \dfrac{N \times 5}{3}$; this is written $\dfrac{5N}{3}$ or $\tfrac{5}{3}N$ or $1\tfrac{2}{3}N$.

Apart from the fact that in Algebra ab always means $a \times b$, notation in Algebra is the same as in Arithmetic:

$5 \times 5 \times 5$ is written 5^3; $N \times N \times N$ is written N^3.

$2 \times 2 \times 2 \times 2 \times 3 \times 3 \times 7 = 2^4 \cdot 3^2 \cdot 7$; $x \times x \times x \times x \times y \times y \times z = x^4 y^2 z$.

$\dfrac{3}{7} + \dfrac{2}{7}$ is written $\dfrac{3+2}{7}$; $\dfrac{a}{x} + \dfrac{b}{x}$ is written $\dfrac{a+b}{x}$.

$\sqrt{9}$ means the square root of 9; $\sqrt{y}$ means the square root of y.

But $2xy$ means $2 \times x \times y$ although 237 means 2 hundreds $+$ 3 tens $+$ 7.

Example 2. What is the meaning of $3N - 7$? What is its value if N stands for 5?

$3N$ means "multiply N by 3."

To obtain the value of $3N - 7$, multiply N by 3 and then subtract 7 from the result.

If N stands for 5, $3N - 7 = 3 \times 5 - 7 = 15 - 7$
$$= 8.$$

Example 3. If r stands for 8, what is the value of $\dfrac{r+2}{r}$?

$$\text{If } r = 8, \quad \frac{r+2}{r} = \frac{8+2}{8} = \frac{10}{8}$$
$$= 1\tfrac{1}{4}.$$

EXERCISE I. c

State in words the meanings of the expressions, Nos. 1–5, and *afterwards* find their values if $N = 8$.

1. $3N$.   **2.** $N + 3$.   **3.** $5N + 5$.   **4.** $\dfrac{N}{4}$.   **5.** N^2.

Find the values of the expressions, Nos. 6–30, if $N = 6$, $a = 2$, $b = 1$.

6. $2N + 2$.   **7.** aN.   **8.** ab.   **9.** $a + b$.   **10.** $2N - 6a$.

[11] $4a + 4$.   **[12]** bN.   **[13]** $b + N$.   **[14]** $5a - N$.   **[15]** $a - 2b$.

16. $\dfrac{N}{a}$.   **17.** $\dfrac{a}{N}$.   **18.** $\dfrac{N}{b}$.   **19.** $\dfrac{2}{3}N$.   **20.** $\dfrac{a+b}{N}$.

[21] $\dfrac{1}{2}N$.   **[22]** $\dfrac{b}{N}$.   **[23]** $\dfrac{3}{4}N$.   **[24]** $\dfrac{a}{b}$.   **[25]** $\dfrac{N+3}{3}$.

26. $5aN$.   **27.** $3a^2$.   **28.** a^3.   **29.** abN.   **30.** $b + aN$.

If $x = 3$, $y = 5$, $z = 8$, $c = 0$, find the values of the following:

31. $2xy$.   **32.** $3z + c$.   **33.** $2cx$.   **34.** $2x^2$.   **35.** $5x - 3y$.

[36] $4yz$.   **[37]** $2y - 4c$.   **[38]** $3cy$.   **[39]** $y^2 - x^2$.   **[40]** $8y - 5z$.

*41. $4x + 3y - 3z$.   ***42.** $2zy - 3cx + 3$.   ***43.** $xyz + xy - yz$.

Write down the results of the following operations:

44. Add 2 to a.   **45.** Multiply b by 3.

46. Subtract 5 from c.   **47.** Divide d by 4.

48. Seven times l.   **49.** Half of m.

50. Add n to 1.   **51.** Subtract 2 from $2p$.

52. Divide 12 by r.

53. Two-thirds of t.

54. Square z.

55. Increase y by 4.

[56] Add $3c$ to 3.

[57] Subtract d from 10.

[58] Multiply 4 by e.

[59] Divide 1 by g.

[60] Three-quarters of h.

[61] Decrease k by 2.

*62. Multiply n by 4 and subtract 2 from the result.

*63. Multiply together a, b, c and double the result.

*64. Multiply d by 3 and subtract the result from 6.

*65. Divide e by 5 and subtract the result from $\frac{1}{2}$.

*66. Square f and multiply the result by $2g$.

*67. Take half the sum of k and 6.

*68. Divide $a + b$ by n.

Like and Unlike Terms

A straight fence (see Fig. 9) is made up of 5 hurdles, each 9 feet long.

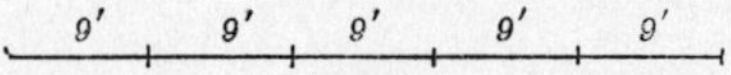

| $9'$ | $9'$ | $9'$ | $9'$ | $9'$ |

FIG. 9.

Its total length $= (9 + 9 + 9 + 9 + 9)$ feet $= 9$ feet $\times 5 = (5 \times 9)$ feet.

If a straight fence **AB** is made of 5 hurdles, each x feet long, the length of **AB** $= (x + x + x + x + x)$ feet $= x$ feet $\times 5 = 5x$ feet.

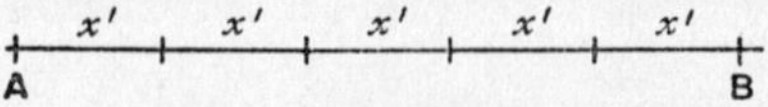

| x' | x' | x' | x' | x' |

A   B

FIG. 10.

Thus $\qquad \mathbf{x} + \mathbf{x} + \mathbf{x} + \mathbf{x} + \mathbf{x} = \mathbf{x} \times 5 = 5\mathbf{x}.$

Now add 3 more hurdles of the same length to the fence **AB** to form the fence **ABC** as in Fig. 11.

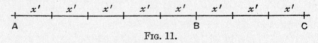

| x' | x' | x' | x' | x' | x' | x' | x' |

A   B   C

FIG. 11.

The lengths of **AB** and **BC** are $5x$ feet and $3x$ feet. But there are in all $(3 + 5)$ hurdles $= 8$ hurdles.

∴ the length of **ABC** is x feet $\times 8$, or $8x$ feet.

Thus $\qquad\qquad 5\mathbf{x} + 3\mathbf{x} = 8\mathbf{x}.$

This is simply a short-hand statement:

$$5x = x + x + x + x + x \quad \text{and} \quad 3x = x + x + x,$$
$$\therefore \ 5x + 3x = x + x + x + x + x + x + x + x = 8x.$$

If, however, each of the 3 hurdles added to the fence **AB** is y feet long (see Fig. 12) the length of **AB** is $5x$ feet, and the length of **BC** is $3y$ feet.

$\therefore$ the length of **ABC** is $(5x + 3y)$ feet.

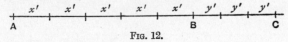

FIG. 12.

This is a short-hand statement:

$$x + x + x + x + x + y + y + y = 5x + 3y.$$

We cannot write $5x + 3y$ in any shorter way unless we know the values of x and y or the connection between them.

If an expression consists of various parts, some of which are connected by $+$ or $-$ signs and others by $\times$ or $\div$ signs, the parts connected by $+$ or $-$ signs are called **terms**.

For example, $5 \times x + 3 \times x$ or $5x + 3x$ contains 2 terms, namely $5x$ and $3x$; so also does the expression $5x + 3y$.

We call $5x$ and $3x$ **like** terms because $5x + 3x$ can be replaced by the single term $8x$.

We call $5x$ and $3y$ **unlike** terms because $5x + 3y$ cannot be replaced by a single term.

Similarly the expression $5x + 3y - 4$ contains 3 terms, and these are all unlike because the expression cannot be replaced by one containing less than 3 terms.

Example 4.   Simplify $7x - 2x$.

Suppose a fence is made of 7 hurdles, each x feet long; its total length is $7x$ feet. Now remove two of the hurdles; then the length of the part removed is $2x$ feet.

$\therefore$ the length of the remainder is $(7x - 2x)$ feet.

But 5 hurdles remain; therefore the remainder is $5x$ feet long.

Thus $\mathbf{7x - 2x = 5x.}$

This is simply a short-hand statement:

$$x + x + x + x + x + x + x - x - x = x + x + x + x + x = 5x.$$

Expressions containing several like terms are simplified in the same way as in arithmetic by *collecting together terms with the same sign*:

Just as in arithmetic, we have

$$12 - 8 + 4 - 5 = 12 + 4 - 8 - 5$$
$$= 16 - 13 = 3;$$

so in algebra,

$$7x - 5x + 3x - 4x = 7x + 3x - 5x - 4x$$
$$= 10x - 9x$$
$$= x.$$

Example 5.   Simplify $5y + 9z - 2y + y - 4z - 2z$.

Collect like terms and arrange together those which have the same sign:

$$5y + 9z - 2y + y - 4z - 2z = 5y + y - 2y + 9z - 4z - 2z$$
$$= 6y - 2y + 9z - 6z$$
$$= 4y + 3z.$$

EXERCISE I. d

Write down shorter forms for the following:

1. $a + a + a + a$.   [2] $b + b + b + b + b$.   3. $c + c + c - c$.

4. $d + d - d - d$.   [5] $e - e + e - e + e$.   6. $f + f - f + f + f$.

7. $g + g + g - g - g + g$.   [8] $h + h + h - h + h - h + h$.

9. $2a + 3a$.   10. $4b + b$.   11. $6c - 2c$.   12. $5d - 4d$.

[13] $5e + e$.   [14] $6g + 4g$.   [15] $9h - 3h$.   [16] $4k - 4k$.

17. $r + r + 2r$.   18. $3s + 2s + s$.   19. $4t + t + 4t$.

[20] $5x + x + 3x$.   [21] $y + 2y + 4y$.   [22] $2z + 2z + 2z$.

23. $a + 5a - 3a$.   24. $4b + 2b - 5b$.   25. $6c + 6c - 3c$.

26. $9d - 3d - 3d$.   27. $8e - 4e - 4e$.   28. $6f - 2f - 3f$.

[29] $7g + 2g - 3g$.   [30] $h + 7h - 8h$.   [31] $16k - 4k - 4k$.

32. $8n - 2n + n$.   33. $5m - 4m + m$.   34. $6p - 2p + 3p$.

35. $10r - 5r + 5r$.   36. $10s - 2s + 5s$.   37. $8t - 7t + t$.

[38] $5x - 4x + x$.   [39] $12y - 6y + 6y$.   [40] $9z - 3z + 2z$.

41. $5a + a - 3a + a - 2a$.   42. $2b + 8b - 4b - b + 2b$.

[43] $c + 7c - 2c - 3c + c$.   [44] $8d - 2d - 3d + 4d - 7d$.

Write down (if possible) shorter forms for the following expressions. *If there is no shorter form, say so.*

45. $a + b + b + a$.

46. $c + d + c + c$.

[47] $e + f + e + f$.

48. $g + g - h + g - h - h - h$

[49] $m + n + m + n - n + n$.

50. $r + r + s - r + s - r - s$.

[51] $x + y + y + y + x - y - x$.

52. $5a + 2b + 3b + a$.

53. $6c + 4d - 2c - d$.

54. $2e + 2f$.

55. $7g + 4h + g - 3h$.

56. $5r + 6s - r - 3s$.

57. $8m - 6n - 2m - 2n$.

58. $4x - 2y - 2y - y$.

59. $8x - 4z - 4$.

60. $8y + 6 - 4y - 3$.

[61] $9a + 3b + 2a + 3b$.

[62] $7c - 2d - 3d - 2d$.

[63] $5e + 5f - 5$.

[64] $7g - 3h - 4h$.

[65] $6k + 5m - 4m + m$.

[66] $9n - 2p - 3n + 2p$.

67. $p + q + r - p + q - r$.

68. $3x - 5y - 4z - 2x - y - z$.

69. $3a + 6b - 3b + 2a - 5$.

70. $1 + 4c + 2d - 3c + d$.

[71] $6e + f - 2e + f - f$.

[72] $8g - 2h + 2g - 2 - h$.

Multiplication and Division

Example 6. Write more shortly:

　　(i) $5a \times 3$;　　(ii) $2b \times 3c$;　　(iii) $4x \times 5xy$

(i) $5a \times 3 = 5 \times a \times 3 = 5 \times 3 \times a$
$= 15a$.

Note that $5a \times 3 = 5a + 5a + 5a = 15a$.

(ii) $2b \times 3c = 2 \times b \times 3 \times c = 2 \times 3 \times b \times c$
$= 6bc$.

(iii) $4x \times 5xy = 4 \times x \times 5 \times x \times y = 4 \times 5 \times x \times x \times y$
$= 20x^2y$.

In Algebra fractions are simplified by the same processes as are used in Arithmetic.

Example 7. Simplify (i) $6a \div 2$; (ii) $6b \div 4c$.

$$\text{(i) } 6a \div 2 = \frac{6 \times a}{2} = 3 \times a$$
$$= 3a.$$

$$\text{(ii) } 6b \div 4c = \frac{6 \times b}{4 \times c} = \frac{3 \times b}{2 \times c}$$
$$= \frac{3b}{2c}.$$

Example 8. Simplify (i) $1\frac{1}{6}a \times 4$; (ii) $\dfrac{2b^2}{9} \div \dfrac{1}{6} bc$.

(i) $1\frac{1}{6}a \times 4 = \dfrac{7}{6} \times a \times 4 = \dfrac{7 \times a \times 4}{6}$

$$= \dfrac{7 \times a \times 2}{3}$$

$$= \dfrac{14a}{3}.$$

(ii) $\dfrac{2b^2}{9} \div \dfrac{1}{6}bc = \dfrac{2b^2}{9} \div \dfrac{bc}{6}$

$$= \dfrac{2 \times b \times b}{9} \times \dfrac{6}{b \times c} = \dfrac{2 \times b \times 2}{3 \times c}$$

$$= \dfrac{4b}{3c}.$$

EXERCISE I. e

Write more shortly the following :

1. $a \times 3$.
2. $b \times 1$.
3. $c \times 3 \times 4$.
4. $d \times 1 \times 2$.

5. $3e \times 2$.
6. $4f \times 0$.
7. $3 \times g \times 2$.
8. $7 \times 3h$.

[9] $4k \times 5$.
[10] $6 \times 6m$.
[11] $5n \times 1$.
[12] $3p \times 0$.

13. $r \times s$.
14. $t \times t$.
15. $x \times x \times x$.
16. $y \times z \times y$.

[17] $3a \times 3a$.
18. $4b \times 4b$.
[19] $2c \times 5d$.
20. $3 \times e \times 4f$.

[21] $gh \times h$.
22. $pq \times 2r$.
[23] $st \times ts$.
24. $3yz \times 3z$.

[25] $ab \times 2a$.
[26] $4cd \times 4c$.
[27] $ef \times eg$.
[28] $2hk \times 3km$.

29. $3ab \times 4ac$.
30. $2d^2 \times 2e^2$.
31. $5gh \times 4gh$.
32. $3xyz \times 3xz$.

33. $6a \div 3$.
34. $4b \div 1$.
35. $5c \div 5$.
36. $d \div d$.

37. $\dfrac{12e}{3}.$
38. $\dfrac{6f}{6}.$
39. $\dfrac{12g}{8}.$
40. $\dfrac{2h}{2h}.$

[41] $\dfrac{8m}{4}.$
[42] $\dfrac{n}{n}.$
[43] $\dfrac{5p}{5}.$
[44] $\dfrac{6r}{9}.$

[45] $\dfrac{s}{4} \times 6.$
[46] $1\frac{1}{2}t \times 2.$
47. $2 \times \dfrac{3x}{4}.$
48. $1\frac{1}{4}y \times 8.$

[49] $z \div 1$.
[50] $3v \div \frac{1}{2}$.
51. $8a \div 6$.
52. $3b \div \frac{3}{4}$.

53. $\dfrac{cd}{ce}.$
54. $\dfrac{f}{fg}.$
55. $\dfrac{h}{h^2}.$
56. $\dfrac{k^2m^2}{km}.$

[57] $\dfrac{mn}{m}$.   [58] $\dfrac{p^2}{pq}$.   [59] $\dfrac{r}{nr}$.   [60] $\dfrac{rs^2}{rs}$.

[61] $\dfrac{a}{5} \times 5a$.   [62] $1\frac{3}{4}b \times 2b$.   63. $\dfrac{c}{2} \times 6c$.   64. $1\frac{1}{3}d \times \frac{2}{8}d$.

*65. $\dfrac{6ab}{5} \div \dfrac{9ac}{10}$.   *66. $\dfrac{2d^2}{3} \div \dfrac{de}{6}$.   *67. $\dfrac{8fg}{3} \div \dfrac{12g^2}{5}$.

*68. $\dfrac{4h^2}{9} \div \dfrac{2k^2}{3}$.   *69. $\dfrac{rst}{2r} \div \dfrac{s^2}{3t}$.   *70. $\dfrac{p}{q} \times \dfrac{q}{r} \times \dfrac{r}{s} \div \dfrac{p}{s}$.

Numbers and Quantities

Letters in Algebra are used to represent numbers, not numbers-of-things.

A letter may stand for 2, 15, $\frac{3}{4}$, etc., but *not* for 2 pence, 15 days, $\frac{3}{4}$ mile, etc.

A number-of-things is called a **quantity**.

When dealing with quantities, **always state what the unit is**, as in the following examples :

A parcel weighs **W** lb. ; a book costs **C** shillings ; a room is h feet high ; a tank holds n gallons.

EXERCISE I. f

1. How far does a man travel in a day if the distances travelled in the morning and afternoon are as follows: (i) morning 4 miles, afternoon 20 miles; (ii) morning s miles, afternoon 20 miles; (iii) morning $2x$ miles, afternoon $6x$ miles; (iv) morning y miles, afternoon z miles ?

[2] A box weighs **W** lb.; I put two parcels into it. Find the total weight if the parcels weigh (i) 4 lb., 6 lb.; (ii) 2**W** lb., 3**W** lb.

3. I have to make a journey of 30 miles. How much farther have I to go after travelling d miles ? What is the value of the answer if $d = 10$?

[4] A milkman starts with 20 gallons of milk. How much is left after he has sold n gallons ? What is the value of the answer if $n = 16$?

5. A bus fare is 3 pence. What is the cost of (i) 5 journeys, (ii) m journeys, (iii) $7n$ journeys ?

6. I can walk 4 miles an hour. How far can I walk in (i) 3 hours, (ii) t hours, (iii) $2p$ hours ?

[7] A car uses 1 gallon of petrol every 20 miles. How far can the car run on (i) 4 gallons, (ii) k gallons, (iii) $3n$ gallons, (iv) $\frac{1}{2}p$ gallons?

Find the cost of the following, Nos. 8–12:

8. 5 lb. of butter at r pence per lb.

[9] W lb. of tea at 2 shillings per lb.

10. $4n$ yards of silk at $3t$ shillings per yard.

[11] $3m$ gallons of oil at $2p$ shillings per gallon.

12. N dozen notebooks at P pence each book. Answer in shillings.

13. If I cycle at 12 miles an hour, it takes me n hours to get from my house to the station. How far away is the station? What is this distance if $n = \frac{3}{4}$?

14. Express in shillings as simply as possible (i) 8 pence, (ii) $6c$ pence, (iii) $9e$ pence.

[15] Express in £ as simply as possible (i) 12 shillings, (ii) $5n$ shillings, (iii) $8n$ shillings.

16. Some apples are shared equally between 6 boys. How many does each get if the total number of apples is (i) 30, (ii) $12m$, (iii) $9n$, (iv) $2p$?

[17] A tank contains 40 gallons of water. How many pails can be filled from it if each pail holds (i) 2 gallons, (ii) p gallons, (iii) $5n$ gallons?

18. How long does a man take to walk 12 miles if his speed is (i) 4 miles an hour, (ii) v miles an hour, (iii) $4n$ miles an hour?

[19] A car uses 1 gallon of petrol every 20 miles. How much petrol is used for (i) 1 mile, (ii) 12 miles, (iii) d miles?

20. Express in inches (i) 4 feet, (ii) l feet, (iii) 4 feet 9 inches, (iv) m feet n inches.

[21] Express in shillings (i) £3, 7s., (ii) £x, y shillings.

22. Find the total length in inches of the wire used to make the grid in Fig. 13. What is the value of the answer if $a = 2$, $b = 8$? Check the result direct from the figure.

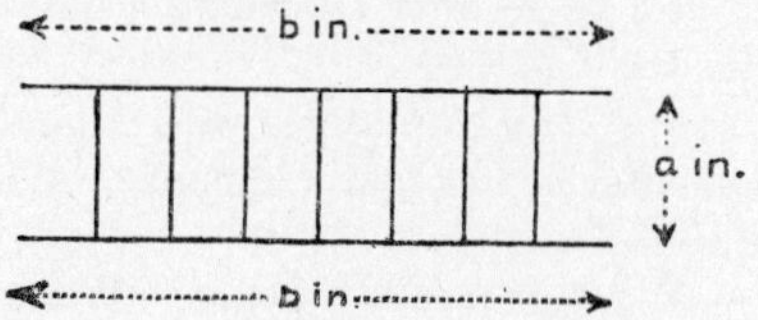

Fig. 13.

[23] A man pays 1d. for his daily paper and 2d. for his Sunday paper. How much does he pay for n weeks? Give the answer (i) in pence, (ii) in shillings.

[24] The price of coal on October 1 is p pence per cwt. more than it was on September 1, when it was 2 shillings per cwt. What is the price of coal in pence per cwt. on October 1?

25. Fig. 14 represents a short flight of steps from A to B. Each step is h inches high and d inches from front to back. What length of carpet is needed to run from A to B? What is the answer

Fig. 14.

if each step is $2x$ inches high and $5x$ inches from front to back?

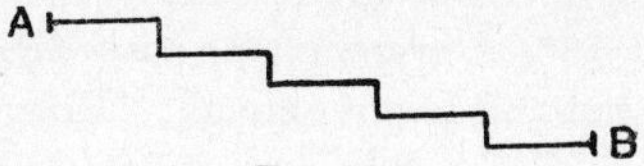

[26] There are two exit doors from a hall. People pass out through one door at x per minute and through the other door at y per minute. How many go out in 5 minutes?

[27] What length of wire is obtained (i) from m coils of wire each containing x yards, (ii) altogether from n coils of wire each containing y yards, and p coils of wire each containing z yards?

28. At an entertainment N people buy one-shilling tickets and n people buy sixpenny tickets. How much money is taken altogether? Give the answer (i) in pence, (ii) in shillings.

29. (i) I buy $3c$ apples and then buy 3 more apples; how many altogether?

   (ii) Rewrite the question taking $c = 4$, and find the answer in this case.

   (iii) What is the value of your answer to (i) if $c = 4$?

30. (i) I buy a bunch of $4t$ bananas and cut off 4 bananas; how many are left?

   (ii) Rewrite the question, taking $t = 6$, and find the answer in this case.

   (iii) What is the value of your answer to (i) if $t = 6$?

[31] How many shillings have I left if I spend (i) 5s. out of £2, (ii) 5s. out of £N, (iii) x shillings out of £y, (iv) $(10p)$ shillings out of £$(2p)$?

[32] A man buys a horse for £$(5k)$. Find his profit if he sells it for (i) £$(7k)$, (ii) £$(4n)$, (iii) £60.

33. I gained $3p$ shillings by selling a watch. Find how much the watch cost me if I sold it for (i) $12p$ shillings, (ii) $4x$ shillings, (iii) £2.

34. A ship starts with W tons of coal as fuel and uses n tons per day. How many tons are left after (i) 1 week, (ii) t days, (iii) r weeks?

[35] A man buys 100 cigarettes and smokes n cigarettes a day. How many are left after (i) 1 week, (ii) $2k$ days?

[36] A gramophone costs £P; n boys each contribute 2 shillings, but this is not enough. How many more shillings are required?

37. (i) A basket, weighing W lb. when empty, contains $6n$ lb. of apples. If $2n$ lb. of apples are then sold, find the weight of the basket and the remaining apples.

(ii) Rewrite the question taking W $=4$ and $n=5$ and find the answer in this case.

(iii) What is the value of your answer to (i) if W $=4$ and $n=5$?

38. (i) Fig. 15 represents a carpet on the floor of a room; there is a margin 2 feet wide all the way round. What is the length and breadth of the carpet?

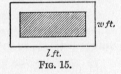

(ii) Copy Fig. 15, marking on it the data if $l=30$, $w=15$, and find the answers in this case.

l ft.

Fig. 15.

(iii) What are the values of your answers to (i) if $l=30$, $w=15$?

*39. A railway porter is paid b shillings a week and receives in tips n shillings a day. How much does he get altogether each week, working 6 days?

*40. It is now a quarter past ten; in how many minutes will it be (i) 25 minutes past ten, (ii) t minutes past ten, (iii) 20 minutes to eleven, (iv) n minutes to eleven?

*41. A boy is now y years old and his father is now three times as old. (i) How old will each be in 5 years' time? (ii) What will be the sum of their ages in 10 years' time?

*42. A drives at 30 miles an hour. How far will B go in 3 hours if he drives (i) 10 miles an hour faster than A, (ii) v miles an hour faster than A, (iii) t miles an hour slower than A?

*43. My stride is $4p$ *inches*; how many *yards* do I go in $6q$ strides?

*44. A man walks from **A** to **B**, s miles, at 4 miles an hour (see Fig. 16); how long does he take? He stays 2 hours at **B** and then returns to **A** at 3 miles an hour. How long is he away from **A** altogether?

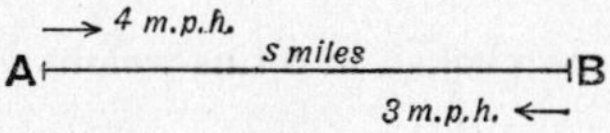

FIG. 16.

*45. A boy goes to bed at 10 p.m. and stays in bed t hours where $2 < t < 12$. At what time does he get up? *First answer the question if $t = 9$.*

Meaning of Brackets

The contents of a bracket may be regarded as equivalent to a single number.

Thus $(7 + 3)$ means the number obtained by adding 3 to 7; and $(N + 5)$ means the number obtained by adding 5 to N.

The product of 9 and $(7 + 3)$ is written $9(7 + 3)$; the product of a and $(x + y)$ is written $a(x + y)$.

Similarly $(p - q) \div 7$ means "subtract q from p and divide the result by 7." It is usually written $\dfrac{p - q}{7}$ or $\dfrac{1}{7}(p - q)$. Just as $a \times a$ is written a^2, so $(x + y) \times (x + y)$ is written $(x + y)^2$ and means "add y to x and multiply the result by itself."

Brackets show the order in which operations must be performed

Thus $5 + 2(3 + 4)$ means "add 4 to 3, double the sum, add the result to 5":

$$5 + 2(3 + 4) = 5 + 2 \times 7 = 5 + 14 = 19.$$

But $(5 + 2)3 + 4$ means "add 2 to 5, multiply the sum by 3, add 4 to the result":

$$(5 + 2)3 + 4 = 7 \times 3 + 4 = 21 + 4 = 25.$$

And $(5 + 2)(3 + 4)$ means "add 2 to 5, add 4 to 3, multiply the first sum by the second sum:

$$(5 + 2)(3 + 4) = 7 \times 7 = 49.$$

Example 9. 8 oz. of cocoa are packed in a tin which weighs t oz. when empty. What is the weight of 5 tins of cocoa?

One tin when full of cocoa weighs $(t+8)$ oz.

$\therefore$ 5 full tins weigh $5(t+8)$ oz.

Or we could say,

5 empty tins weigh $5 \times t$ oz.

The cocoa packed in 5 tins weighs 5×8 oz.

$\therefore$ 5 full tins weigh $(5 \times t + 5 \times 8)$ oz.

Thus $\qquad\qquad\qquad 5(t+8) = 5 \times t + 5 \times 8.$

This illustrates the fact that

If an expression in a bracket is multiplied by a number, each term in the bracket must be multiplied by that number when the bracket is removed.

For example, $\qquad\qquad 7(4+6) = 7 \times 10 = 70,$

and $\qquad\qquad 7 \times 4 + 7 \times 6 = 28 + 42 = 70,$

thus $\qquad\qquad\qquad 7(4+6) = 7 \times 4 + 7 \times 6.$

The general statement may be illustrated geometrically:

Fig. 17 represents a rectangle, a inches high, $(x+y)$ inches long; its area is $a(x+y)$ sq. in. But the areas of the two compartments are ax sq. in., ay sq. in.;

thus $\qquad\qquad\qquad a(x+y) = ax + ay.$

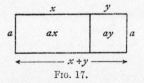

FIG. 17.

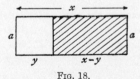

FIG. 18.

Similarly in Fig. 18, the area of the shaded rectangle is $a(x-y)$ sq. in.; and this is equal to the result of subtracting the area of the rectangle on the left, ay sq. in., from the area of the whole rectangle, ax sq. in.;

thus $\qquad\qquad\qquad a(x-y) = ax - ay.$

Example 10. Remove the brackets from the following:

(i) $2a(3b-4)$; (ii) $a(p+2q)+3b(4x-2y)$.

(i) $2a(3b-4) = 2a \times 3b - 2a \times 4$
$= 6ab - 8a$.

(ii) $a(p+2q)+3b(4x-2y) = a \times p + a \times 2q + 3b \times 4x - 3b \times 2y$
$= ap + 2aq + 12bx - 6by$.

EXERCISE I. g

State in words the meanings of the following expressions, and *afterwards* evaluate them (*i.e.* find their values) for the given special cases:

1. $2(a+3)$; $a=5$.   [2] $(b-3)c$; $b=5$, $c=4$.

3. $(d+4)(e-2)$; $d=2$, $e=5$.   [4] $d+4(e-2)$; $d=2$, $e=5$.

Evaluate the following, if $x=3$, $y=5$, $c=8$:

5. $2(c-x)$.   **6.** $c(y-x)$.   [7] $3(c-y)$.   [8] $y(c+x)$.

9. $(x-2)y$.   **10.** $\dfrac{x+y}{c}$.   [11] $(2y-c)x$.   [12] $\dfrac{c-x}{y}$.

13. $4(x+y)-(4x+4y)$.   **14.** $(x+y)(c-y)$.

[15] $5(x+y)-(5x+y)$.   [16] $(3y-5x)(2c-x)$.

Evaluate the following:

17. $3(2l+1)$ and $6l+3$, when $l=4$.

18. $5x(y-2z)$ and $5xy-10xz$, when $x=4$, $y=5$, $z=2$.

19. $a(x-y+1)$ and $ax-ay+a$, when $a=7$, $x=5$, $y=2$.

[20] $a(b+3)$ and $ab+3a$, when $a=4$, $b=1$.

[21] $3c(d-3e)$ and $3cd-9ce$, when $c=5$, $d=4$, $e=1$.

[22] $2k(p-2q-2)$ and $2kp-4kq-4k$ when $k=4$, $p=10$, $q=3$.

Remove the brackets from the following:

23. $5(2a+3)$.   **24.** $4(3b-2c)$.   **25.** $7(2e-3f+1)$.

26. $d(e-f)$.   **27.** $3r(4s-1)$.   **28.** $2n(p+3q)$.

[29] $6(3x-5)$.   [30] $5x(2y-3)$.   [31] $8(3x-5y-1)$.

32. $2(4b-3)+3(b-1)$.   **33.** $3p(2x+y)+2p(2a+b)$.

[34] $5(c+4)+2(3c-8)$.   [35] $x(a-2b)+3y(3a+b)$.

Evaluate the following, if $a=3$, $b=2$, $c=6$, $d=5$:

36. $a+b(c+d)$.   **37.** $(a+b)(c+d)$.   **38.** $(a+b)c+d$.

[39] $a+(b+c)d$.   [40] $a+bc+d$.   [41] $(b+c)\div a$.

42. $b+c\div a+d$.   **43.** $(b+c)\div(a+d)$.   **44.** $(a+b)^2+(c-d)^2$.

[45] $b+c\div(a+d)$.   [46] $(a+b+c)^2$.   [47] $a^2+b^2+c^2$.

Use of Brackets

Example 11. Express by means of brackets the result of subtracting twice the sum of x and y from three times the sum of a and b.

Three times the sum of a and b is represented by $3(a+b)$; twice the sum of x and y is represented by $2(x+y)$.

$$\therefore \text{ required result} = 3(a+b) - 2(x+y).$$

Example 12. 8 oz. of cocoa are packed in a tin which weighs t oz. when empty; 30 such tins of cocoa are packed in a box weighing W oz. Find the total weight.

One tin of cocoa weighs $(8+t)$ oz.

$\therefore$ 30 tins of cocoa weigh $30(8+t)$ oz.

But the box, when empty, weighs W oz.

$\therefore$ the box, when packed, weighs W oz. $+30(8+t)$ oz.

It is simpler to write this answer in the form

$$[\text{W} + 30(8+t)] \text{ oz.}$$

Note.—If one set of brackets is enclosed as here inside another set, different shapes of brackets should be used, because this makes it easier to see what the expression means.

EXERCISE I. h

Throughout this exercise, express the answers by using brackets. *Do not remove the brackets.*

1. Add $2b$ to a and multiply the result by 5.

2. Subtract d from $3c$ and multiply the result by 4.

3. Multiply $3f - g$ by e.

4. Divide $r + s + t$ by 3.

[5] Six times the sum of $2m$ and $3n$.

[6] Subtract $3x$ from $3z$ and multiply the result by 5.

[7] The product of $2a$ and $b - 3c$.

[8] Divide $2d + 3e + 5$ by 6.

9. Half the sum of $3f$ and $7g$.

10. Subtract $h - 2k$ from $2p - q$.

11. The product of $r - x$ and $t - y$.

12. The number by which x exceeds $y - z$.

[13] One-third of the sum of $5a$ and $4b$.

[14] Subtract $c + 2d$ from $e - 2$.

[15] The square of the sum of x and y.

16. The number of pence in $(p + q)$ shillings.

[17] The number of shillings in £$(r - 2s)$.

18. The number of yards in $(m - n)$ feet.

[19] The number of feet in $(2y - z)$ inches.

20. Add 3 times the sum of a and $2b$ to 4 times the sum of $3c$ and d.

21. Subtract 5 times the sum of $2e$ and 4 from 3 times the sum of $4f$ and 1.

22. Subtract 1 from h, and add 2 to k; then write down the product of the two numbers thus obtained.

[23] Subtract x from y and halve the result.

[24] Subtract a from 2, and subtract the result from twice the sum of $5b$ and $4c$.

25. Subtract the square of the sum of a and b from the sum of the squares of b and c.

26. The product of two consecutive whole numbers, the smaller of which is n.

[27] The product of two consecutive even numbers, the larger of which is p.

28. The product of three consecutive odd numbers, the largest of which is r.

[29] The product of three consecutive whole numbers, the smallest of which is t.

30. A jar, which weighs w lb. when empty, holds 10 lb. of jam when full. What is the weight of 12 full jars? The 12 full jars are packed in a box weighing P lb.; what is the total weight?

31. A box full of sugar weighs W lb., and when empty weighs w lb. What is the weight of the sugar in the box? What is the weight of the sugar in n boxes of the same kind?

32. I have 10 coins; n of them are sixpences and the rest are shillings. What is (i) the number of shillings, (ii) the total value of all the coins in pence?

[33] I have 12 coins; *m* of them are half-crowns and the rest are florins. What is (i) the number of florins, (ii) the total value of all the coins in shillings?

[34] A man buys *x* knives; he pays 2 shillings each for 12 of them and 3 shillings each for the rest. How many knives does he buy at 3 shillings each? What is the *total* amount he pays in shillings?

*35. A journey by car takes 5 hours. For the first *t* hours the speed is 30 miles per hour and for the rest of the time it is 40 miles per hour. Find the length of the journey.

*36. Find the *total* number of pence in $(a+b)$ shillings $(c+d)$ pence.

*37. A book costs *x* shillings *y* pence. Find the cost of *n* copies of the book. Answer (i) in pence, (ii) in shillings.

*38. The length of   hurdle is *c* feet *d* inches. Find the length of a straight fence containing *n* of these hurdles. Answer (i) in inches, (ii) in feet.

*39. At a hotel a man is charged 15 shillings a day for the first 4 days and only 12 shillings a day afterwards. Find the total charge in shillings if he stays (i) 7 days, (ii) *n* days, where $n > 4$.

*40. A man's rate of pay is as follows: ordinary time, up to 8 hours a day, 15 pence an hour; over-time for any hours after the first eight, 2 shillings an hour. Find in shillings the amount he receives for a day on which he works (i) 10 hours, (ii) *t* hours, if $t > 8$.

*41. A spoon costs *b* shillings, and the same spoon with 3 forks costs *c* shillings. What is the cost of (i) 3 forks, (ii) 1 fork, (iii) *n* forks, (iv) 5 spoons and 2 forks?

*42. In Fig. 19, AB is 10 inches long, AP is *b* inches long. PB is divided into three equal parts. Find the length of each part.

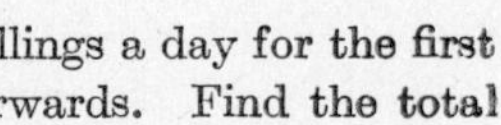

*43. In Fig. 19, AB is *x* inches long, AP is 2 inches long, and PB is divided

FIG. 19.

at Q, R into 3 equal parts. Find lengths of (i) PQ, (ii) PR, (iii) AR.

*44. A cask when empty weighs P lb. and when full of beer weighs Q lb. (i) Find the weight of the beer in a full cask. (ii) Find the weight of the cask and its contents when half-full of beer.

CHAPTER II

FORMULAE

Construction of Formulae

THE following illustrative examples are intended for oral discussion.

Example 1. The Area of a Rectangle.

If you have a rectangle 4 inches long, 3 inches broad, you can divide it as in Fig. 20, so that there are 3 rows and each row contains 4 one-inch squares. Therefore there are 4×3 one-inch squares altogether. But the area of a one-inch square is called 1 sq. in.

$\therefore$ the area of the rectangle is 4×3 sq. in.

It would be a waste of time to use this process whenever the area of a rectangle is required. We therefore look for *the general method*.

Fig. 20.

Suppose a rectangle is l inches long and b inches broad. Show, by repeating the argument used above, that, if l and b are whole numbers, its area is $l \times b$ sq. in. Call the area A sq. in.

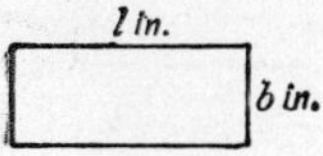

l in.

b in.

Fig. 21.

Then $A = l \times b$.

This relation is called a formula. Although **only** proved here for integral values of l and b, it can be shown to be true for all values; we therefore use it whenever we wish to find the area of a rectangle.

We say that this formula **expresses A in terms of l and b.**

Example 2. Measurement of average Speed.

If a motorist travels 60 miles in 3 hours, his average speed is $\frac{60}{3}$ miles per hour, or 20 m.p.h.

If a cyclist travels 25 miles in 2 hours, his average speed is $\frac{25}{2}$ miles per hour, or $12\frac{1}{2}$ m.p.h.

23

Similarly, if a man travels s miles in t hours, his average speed is $\frac{s}{t}$ miles per hour.

Call the average speed v miles per hour, then

$$v = \frac{s}{t}$$

and we say that this is a formula which expresses **v** in terms of **s and t**.

By using this formula we can find the average speed when the distance travelled in a given time is known.

For example, suppose a train travels 60 miles in $1\frac{1}{2}$ hours, then

$$v = \frac{60}{1\frac{1}{2}} = \frac{60 \times 2}{3}$$

$$= 40.$$

∴ the average speed is 40 miles per hour.

EXERCISE II. a

If brackets occur in the answer, do not remove them.

1. (i) What is the perimeter (*i.e.* the sum of the lengths of the sides) of a rectangle 7 inches long, 3 inches broad?

    (ii) If the perimeter of the rectangle in Fig. 22 is p inches, complete the formula, $p = \ldots$, which expresses p in terms of l, b.

FIG. 22.

2. (i) The perimeter of an isosceles triangle is 11 inches and the lengths of the two equal sides are each 4 inches; find the length of the third side.

    (ii) If the perimeter of the triangle in Fig. 23 is p inches, complete the formula, $b = \ldots$, which expresses b in terms of p, y.

[3] (i) Two angles of a triangle are 60°, 80°; find the third angle.

    (ii) Two angles of a triangle are $x°$, $y°$. If the third angle is $z°$, complete the formula, $z = \ldots$, which expresses z in terms of x, y.

4. In Fig. 24, **ABC** is a straight line.

    (i) If $p = 40$, find the value of q.

    (ii) Complete the formula, $q = \ldots$, which expresses q in terms of p.

[5] Fig. 25 represents a closed box x inches long, x inches wide, y inches high.

    (i) Find the sum of the lengths of its edges if $x = 5$ and $y = 3$.

    (ii) If the sum of the lengths of its edges is s inches, complete the formula, $s = \ldots$, which expresses s in terms of x and y.

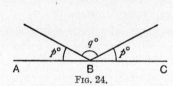

FIG. 24.

FIG. 25.

6. (i) Fig. 25 represents a closed box x inches long, x inches wide, y inches high; find its volume if $x = 5$ and $y = 4$.

    (ii) If the volume of the box is **V** cu. in., complete the formula, **V** $= \ldots$, which expresses **V** in terms of x and y.

7. Each edge of a rectangular block is l inches long.

    (i) Find the sum of the areas of all the faces of the block if $l = 5$.

    (ii) If the sum of the areas of all the faces of the block is **A** sq. in., complete the formula, **A** $= \ldots$, for **A** in terms of l.

[8] If the sum of the areas of all the faces of a rectangular block x inches long, x inches wide, y inches deep (see Fig. 25) is **A** sq. in., complete the formula, **A** $= \ldots$, for **A** in terms of x, y.

9. A man has now £50 in the bank. If he puts £20 into the bank every year and draws nothing out, how much will he have in the bank after 3 years?

If he has £**A** in the bank after t years, complete the formula, **A** $= \ldots$, which expresses **A** in terms of t.

[10] There are 10 gallons of water in a bath. When a tap is turned on, water runs into the bath at the rate of g gallons per minute. How much water is there in the bath after 4 minutes?

If there are V gallons of water in the bath when the tap has been turned on for t minutes, complete the formula, $V = ...,$ which expresses V in terms of t.

11. To roast a leg of mutton, allow 15 minutes for each lb. weight of the joint and then 18 minutes more. What time should be allowed if the joint weighs 6 lb.?

If t minutes should be allowed for a joint which weighs W lb., complete the formula, $t = ...,$ which expresses t in terms of W.

12. Eggs cost 2 pence each. If n eggs cost p pence, complete the formula, $p = ...,$ which expresses p in terms of n.

[13] Silk costs 3 shillings a yard. If l yards cost m shillings, complete the formula, $m = ...,$ which expresses m in terms of l.

14. Pears are sold at two for 3 pence. If n pears cost r pence, complete the formula, $r = ...,$ which expresses r in terms of n.

[15] Cloth is sold at 3 yards for 10 shillings. If k yards cost x shillings, complete the formula, $x = ...,$ which expresses x in terms of k.

16. p inches is the same length as l feet.
    (i) What is the value of p if $l = 5$?
    (ii) Complete the formula, $p = ...,$ which expresses p in terms of l.

17. £x is equal to y shillings.
    (i) What is the value of x if $y = 60$?
    (ii) Complete the formula, $x = ...,$ which expresses x in terms of y.

18. (i) What must be added to 17 to make 100?
    (ii) What must be added to b to make c?

[19] (i) By how much does 30 exceed 14?
    (ii) By how much does p exceed q?

20. (i) By what must 8 be multiplied to make 24?
    (ii) By what must x be multiplied to make y?

[21] (i) By what must 36 be divided to give 9?
    (ii) By what must r be divided to give t?

22. (i) A piece of cotton is wound 10 times round a cylinder. When unwound it measures 30 inches. Find the girth of the cylinder.

   (ii) A piece of cotton is wound n times round a cylinder. When unwound it measures l inches. If the girth of the cylinder is g inches, complete the formula, $g = ...$, which expresses g in terms of l, n.

[23] (i) The wheel of a car makes 10 revolutions when the car travels 120 feet. What is the circumference of the wheel?

   (ii) The wheel of a car makes r revolutions when the car travels d feet. If the circumference of the wheel is c feet, complete the formula, $c = ...$, which expresses c in terms of r, d.

24. A photograph (see Fig. 26) is mounted on a card so that there is a margin t inches wide all the way round. Write down (i) the height, (ii) the length of the photograph. If the area of the photograph is A sq. in., complete the formula, A $= ...$, which expresses A in terms of h, l, t.

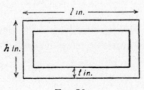

Fig. 26.

*25. A telegram containing 9 words costs 6 pence, and the charge for extra words is a penny a word. If the charge for a telegram containing n words (where n is greater than 9) is p pence, complete the formula, $p = ...$, for p in terms of n.

*26. A member of a club receives 3 free tickets and is charged 5s. for each extra ticket. If he has to pay x shillings for p tickets (where p is greater than 3), complete the formula, $x = ...$, for x in terms of p.

*27. A spiral spring is 30 inches long when unstretched; and it stretches 2 inches for each lb. weight of the load it carries.

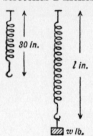

(i) What is the total length when the load is 7 lb.?

(ii) If the total length is l inches when the load is w lb., complete the formula, $l = \ldots$, for l in terms of w.

*28. Letter postage is $1\frac{1}{2}$d. up to 2 oz. and $\frac{1}{2}$d. for each extra 2 oz. What is the postage on an 8-oz. letter?

FIG. 27.

If the postage on a letter weighing $2w$ oz., where w is a whole number, is p pence, complete the formula, $p = \ldots$, for p in terms of w.

*29. The prices of various sizes of vases of the same shape are given in a catalogue:

Size	1	2	3	4
Height	6 in.; (3×2)	9 in.; (3×3)	12 in.; (3×4)	15 in.; (3×5)
Price	2s.; $(3 \times 1 - 1)$	5s.; $(3 \times 2 - 1)$	8s.; $(3 \times 3 - 1)$	11s.; $(3 \times 4 - 1)$

The catalogue shows only what is printed in thick type; the rest is added to help you.

(i) What is the probable height of size 5, of size 8, of size N?

(ii) What is the probable price of size 5, of size 8, of size N?

*30. If you start with 4 and count up by 3's, you obtain the set of numbers, 4, 7, 10, 13, 16, ...

What is the 8th number in this set? What is the rth number in this set?

*31. A book is t inches thick, each cover is c inches thick, and there are 120 sheets in the book. What is the thickness of each sheet?

*32. There are 3 whole numbers *between* 6 and 10, namely 7, 8, 9. How many whole numbers are there (i) *between* 3 and 11, (ii) between the whole numbers b and c, if b is smaller than c?

Substitution

The process of finding the numerical value of an expression, when the letters it contains stand for given numbers, is called substitution. It is required for making use of formulae.

Example 3. If $x = 3$, $y = 2$, find the values of

$$\text{(i) } 4x^2 ; \text{ (ii) } 5xy^3 ; \text{ (iii) } (x-y)^4.$$

(i) $4x^2 = 4 \times x^2 = 4 \times x \times x.$

$\therefore$ if $x = 3$, $4x^2 = 4 \times 3 \times 3 = 36.$

(ii) If $x = 3$, $y = 2$,

$5xy^3 = 5 \times x \times y \times y \times y = 5 \times 3 \times 2 \times 2 \times 2$

$= 120.$

(iii) If $x = 3$, $y = 2$,

$(x-y)^4 = (3-2)^4 = 1^4$

$= 1 \times 1 \times 1 \times 1 = 1.$

Example 4. If $a = \frac{1}{2}$, $b = \frac{1}{3}$, $c = 0$, find the values of

$$\text{(i) } 2a^2b + 3b^2c ; \text{ (ii) } \frac{1}{a} + \frac{2}{b}.$$

(i) $2a^2b + 3b^2c = 2 \times \frac{1}{2} \times \frac{1}{2} \times \frac{1}{3} + 3 \times \frac{1}{3} \times \frac{1}{3} \times 0$

$= \frac{1}{6} + 0 = \frac{1}{6}.$

(ii) $\dfrac{1}{a} + \dfrac{2}{b} = (1 \div \frac{1}{2}) + (2 \div \frac{1}{3})$

$= (1 \times 2) + (2 \times 3) = 2 + 6$

$= 8.$

EXERCISE II. b

If $x = 4$, $y = 3$, evaluate:

1. $3x + 3$.	2. $4x - 5y$.	3. $\frac{1}{2}x + y$.	4. $\frac{1}{4}x - \frac{1}{3}y$.
[5] $5y - 5$.	[6] $6x + 2y$.	[7] $3x - 4y$.	[8] $x - \frac{2}{3}y$.
9. $3y^2$.	10. $2xy^2$.	11. $xy - x$.	12. $y(x - y)$.
[13] $2x^3$.	[14] $\frac{1}{2}xy$.	[15] $x(x + y)$.	[16] $x^2 - y^2$.

If $a = 5$, $b = 1$, $c = 0$, evaluate:

17. $2ab$.	18. $4abc$.	19. $a^2 - b^2$.	20. $a(2b - c)$.
[21] $3bc$.	[22] $3b + 2c$.	[23] $(a - b)^2$.	[24] $4ab^2$.

If $r = 3$, $s = 5$, $t = 4$, evaluate:

25. $2st^2$.	26. $s^2 - 2rt$.	[27] $r + s - 2t$.	[28] $\frac{1}{2}rst$.

If $x=6$, $y=0$, $z=3$, evaluate:

29. $2xy+yz$.　　**30.** $x(x-2z)$.　　[31] $3y+xz^2$.　　[32] $x(z-2y)$.

33. $\dfrac{x}{2z}$.　　**34.** $\dfrac{x+2}{x-2}$.　　**35.** $\dfrac{1}{z}-\dfrac{1}{x}$.　　**36.** $\dfrac{2y}{xz}$.

[37] $\dfrac{2z^2}{x}$.　　[38] $\dfrac{x+3}{z+3}$.　　[39] $\dfrac{yz}{x}$.　　[40] $\dfrac{x+y}{x-y}$.

If $f=3$, $g=6$, $h=2$, $k=0$, evaluate:

41. $\dfrac{f}{12}$.　　**42.** $\dfrac{g^2}{f^2}$.　　**43.** $\dfrac{g-1}{f+h}$.　　**44.** $\dfrac{1}{h}-\dfrac{1}{g}$.

[45] $\dfrac{18}{f}$.　　[46] $\dfrac{24}{gh}$.　　[47] $\dfrac{g-h}{g+h}$.　　[48] $\dfrac{1}{f}+\dfrac{1}{g}$.

49. $1\frac{1}{2}fg+3hk$.　　**50.** $5hk^2+\frac{2}{3}f^2$.　　**51.** $\frac{1}{4}(g-h)^2+\frac{1}{2}(h-k)^2$.

[52] $\frac{3}{4}ghk$.　　[53] $2\frac{1}{2}h^2+3gk$.　　[54] $2\frac{1}{4}gh+2\frac{1}{2}fk$.

If $d=1$, $e=\frac{1}{2}$, evaluate:

55. d^3.　　**56.** $3d-6e$.　　**57.** $1-\frac{1}{2}e$.　　**58.** $2d^2e^2$.

[59] $2e^3$.　　[60] $1\frac{1}{2}de$.　　[61] $\frac{1}{2}d+3e$.　　[62] d^2+2e^2.

If $x=\frac{1}{2}$, $y=\frac{1}{3}$, evaluate:

63. $4xy$.　　**64.** $1-1\frac{1}{2}y$.　　[65] $x-y$.　　[66] $6y^2$.

67. $\dfrac{x}{y}$.　　**68.** $\dfrac{3}{x}-\dfrac{2}{y}$.　　[69] $\dfrac{4}{xy}$.　　[70] $\dfrac{5}{x}-\dfrac{3}{y}$.

If $l=5$, $m=9$, $n=1$, evaluate:

71. $\dfrac{m+3n}{2l-4}$.　　**72.** $\dfrac{l^2-n^2}{m+3}$.　　[73] $\dfrac{m+n}{l^2}$.　　[74] $\left(\dfrac{3l+n}{m-1}\right)^2$.

[75] $l\div(m+n)+6$.　　　　[76] $(m-2n)\div(4l-2m)$.

[77] $2(3l-m)(l+3n)$.　　　　**78.** $m-2n\div(4l-2m)$.

79. $4l^2n(2l-m-n)$.　　　　**80.** $(m-n)^2-(l-n)^2$.

If $c=\frac{2}{5}$, $d=1\frac{1}{4}$, evaluate:

*81. $d-2\frac{1}{2}c$.　　*82. c^2d.　　*83. $4cd^2$.　　*84. $4d^2-5c^2$.

*85. $\dfrac{1}{c}-\dfrac{1}{d}$.　　*86. $\dfrac{1}{c^2}-3d$.　　*87. $\dfrac{d-c}{d\div c}$.　　*88. $\dfrac{c+d}{cd}$.

89. If $a=3b$ and $b=4$, find a.

90. If $r=\frac{1}{2}d$ and $d=5$, find r.

91. If $y=2x+3$ and $x=4$, find y.

92. If $y=x^2$ and $x=5$, find y.

[93] If $s = 5t$ and $t = 1$, find s.

[94] If $y = 20 - 3x$ and $x = 5$, find y.

[95] If $y = 2x^2$ and $x = \frac{1}{2}$, find y.

96. If $y = 10 - \frac{1}{2}x$ and $x = 6$, find y.

97. If $y = x^2 - 2x$ and $x = 5$, find y.

98. If $y = 3x^2 - 2x - 1$, find y if $x = 1$, $x = 2$, $x = 3$.

99. If $y = (x + 1)(3 - x)$, find y if $x = 0$, $x = 1$, $x = 2$.

[100] If $y = \frac{3}{4}x - 2$ and $x = 12$, find y.

[101] If $y = x(7 - x)$ and $x = 3$, find y.

[102] If $y = 1 + 5x^2 - 6x$, find y if $x = 0$, $x = 1$, $x = 2$.

[103] If $y = (2x - 1)(4 - x)$, find y if $x = 2$, $x = 3$, $x = 4$.

*104. If $a = 3b$ and $b = 4c$ and $c = 2$, find the values of a and ab.

*105. If $c + d = 8$ and $d = 3$, find c.

*106. If $pv = 48$ and $v = 8$, find p.

*107. If $N - n = 3$ and $n = 7$, find the values of N and $N + n$.

*108. If $y - z = 2$ and $y = 9$, find the values of z and yz.

*109. If $x + 2y = 14$ and $y = 7$, find x.

*110. If $pq = 36$ and $p = 9$, find the value of q^2.

*111. If $r - s = 8$ and $s = 5$, find the values of r and $r + s$.

*112. If $lb = 5$ and $b = 2$, find (i) l, (ii) $2(l + b)$.

*113. If $\dfrac{a}{b} = 6$ and $b = 2$, find (i) a, (ii) ab.

*114. If $\dfrac{r}{s} = 8$, find r if $s = 3$, and find s if $r = 40$.

Use of Formulae

Example 5. If a speed of x feet per second is the same as a speed of v miles per hour, v is given by the formula, $v = \dfrac{15x}{22}$. Express a speed of 33 feet per second in miles per hour.

Put $x = 33$ in the formula, then

$$v = \frac{15 \times 33}{22} = \frac{15 \times 3}{2}$$
$$= 22\tfrac{1}{2};$$

∴ 33 feet per second is the same speed as $22\frac{1}{2}$ miles per hour.

We can obtain this result by arithmetic, but it saves time to use the formula.

The process of obtaining special results from a general formula is called substituting in the formula.

The formula in the next Example cannot be proved till the reader has done more advanced work in geometry or trigonometry.

Example 6. If from a masthead h *feet* above the surface of the sea it is possible to see a distance of d *miles*, d is given by the formula, $d = \sqrt{\left(\dfrac{3h}{2}\right)}$. How far can an observer see if he is (i) at the top of a mast 54 feet above the sea, (ii) at the top of a cliff 50 yards high?

(i) Put $h = 54$ in the formula, then

$$d = \sqrt{\left(\frac{3 \times 54}{2}\right)} = \sqrt{81}$$
$$= 9;$$

∴ the distance he can see (called the distance of the horizon) is 9 miles.

(ii) In the formula, h stands for the number of *feet* above the surface of the sea; we must therefore first express 50 *yards* as 150 *feet*. Put $h = 150$ in the formula, then

$$d = \sqrt{\left(\frac{3 \times 150}{2}\right)} = \sqrt{225}$$
$$= 15;$$

∴ the distance of the horizon is 15 miles.

EXERCISE II. c

1. When a stone is dropped from the top of a tower, the distance, s feet, it falls in t seconds is given by the formula, $s = 16t^2$. Find how far it falls in 3 seconds.

2. If K kilometres is the same distance as M miles, K is given approximately by the formula, $K = \dfrac{8M}{5}$. Find the number of kilometres in 20 miles.

[3] If P pints of water weigh W lb., W is given by the formula, $W = \dfrac{5P}{4}$. Find the weight of (i) 6 pints of water, (ii) 1 gallon of water (1 gallon = 8 pints).

[4] If v miles an hour is the same speed as y feet per second, y is given by the formula, $y = \dfrac{22v}{15}$. Express in feet per second speeds of (i) 60 miles an hour, (ii) 5 miles an hour.

5. If the safe load which can be supported by a steel rope of diameter d inches is **W** tons, **W** is given by the formula, $W = 8d^2$. Find the safe load for a steel rope of diameter $1\frac{1}{2}$ inches.

6. If the circumference of a circle of radius r inches is **C** inches, **C** is given by the formula, $C = 2\pi r$, where $\pi = \frac{22}{7}$ approximately. Find the circumference of a circle of radius $10\frac{1}{2}$ inches.

[7] If the area of a circle of radius r inches is **A** sq. in., **A** is given by the formula, $A = \pi r^2$, where $\pi = \frac{22}{7}$ approximately. Find the area of a circle of radius $3\frac{1}{2}$ inches.

8. The "rise" **AB**, **R** inches, and the "tread" **BC**, **T** inches, of a staircase (see Fig. 28) are often connected by the formula, $R = \frac{1}{2}(24 - T)$. Find the rise if the tread is (i) 12 inches, (ii) 9 inches.

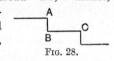

Fig. 28.

9. Fig. 29 represents a polygon with 5 sides, called a pentagon.

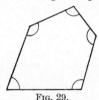

Fig. 29.

If the sum of the interior angles of a polygon with n sides is r right angles, r is given by the formula, $r = 2n - 4$. Find the sum of the angles of (i) a quadrilateral (4 sides), (ii) a pentagon, (iii) a decagon (10 sides). Does the formula give the correct answer for a triangle?

10. If **F**° Fahrenheit is the same temperature as **C**° Centigrade, **F** is given by the formula, $F = 32 + \dfrac{9C}{5}$. Express in degrees Fahrenheit the following temperatures:

    (i) 100° Centigrade (temperature at which water boils);

    (ii) 0° Centigrade (temperature at which water freezes);

    (iii) 15° Centigrade.

[11] If a cricketer scores altogether r runs in x innings, n times not out, his average is $\dfrac{r}{x - n}$ runs. Find his average if he scores 204 runs in 15 innings, 3 times not out.

[12] If $F°$ Fahrenheit is the same temperature as $C°$ Centigrade, the formula in No. 10 is equivalent to either of the formulæ: (i) $F = \frac{9}{5}(C + 40) - 40$;   (ii) $C = \frac{5}{9}(F + 40) - 40$.   Use formula (i) to express in degrees Fahrenheit, the temperatures 100° Centigrade, 15° Centigrade, 35° Centigrade. Use formula (ii) to express in degrees Centigrade the temperatures 32° Fahrenheit, 59° Fahrenheit, 212° Fahrenheit.

13. To make tea for n people for whom t teapots are required, $(n + t)$ spoonfuls of tea must be used. How much tea is used for 30 people who need 3 teapots?

14. If the engine of a motor-car has n cylinders each of diameter d inches, the horse-power H of the car is calculated for purposes of taxation by the formula, $H = \frac{2}{5}nd^2$. Find the horse-power of (i) a 4-cylinder car, diameter of each cylinder 3 inches, (ii) a 6-cylinder car, diameter of each cylinder 5 inches.

[15] If the life of an iron bar G feet in girth and weighing W lb. per foot length, submerged in sea-water, is n years, n is given by the formula, $n = \frac{8W}{G}$. Find the life in sea-water of an iron bar of girth 2 feet and weighing 30 lb. per foot length.

16. If a hemp rope is C inches in circumference, its working load W tons and its breaking load B tons are given by the formulae, $W = \frac{1}{10}C^2$ and $B = \frac{3}{5}C^2$. Make a table showing the working loads and breaking loads for circumferences of 3 inches, 4 inches, 5 inches.

[17] The marks obtained in an examination run from 20 to 70. They are changed so that an original mark p becomes n where $n = 2(p - 20)$. What is the new mark if the original mark is (i) 31, (ii) 58, (iii) 40, (iv) 70, (v) 20?

18. The price of n stamped postcards is p pence, where
$$p = n + 1, \text{ if } n \text{ is less than } 12;$$
and $p = n + 2$, if n is *between* 11 and 24.
Find the cost of (i) 8 stamped postcards, (ii) 20 stamped postcards.

19. The nth day of March is the same day of the week as the pth day of September if $p = n + 5$. If the 1st day of March is a Monday, what are the dates of the Mondays in September? What day of the week is September 1?

[20] The mth day of May is the same day of the week as the rth day of December if $r = m + 3$. If May 6 is a Saturday, what are the dates of the Saturdays in December? What day of the week is Christmas Day?

*21. If a cricket ball is thrown with a speed of *u feet per second*, across level ground, the greatest distance away of the place where it pitches is s feet where $s = \dfrac{u^2}{32}$. What is the greatest distance a boy can throw a ball if he throws it with a speed of 60 *miles per hour*?

*22. A box without a lid is l inches long, l inches wide, h inches high. If the total area of its external surface is S sq. in., then $S = l(l + 4h)$. Verify this formula for an open box 5 inches long, 5 inches wide, 3 inches high.

Use the formula to find in terms of x the area of the external surface of an open box, $4x$ inches long, $4x$ inches wide, $3x$ inches high.

*23. If you write down the numbers, 3, 7, 11, 15, 19, 23, ... the nth number is equal to $4n - 1$. Verify that this statement is correct for the 6th number, and find the 100th number.

*24. The sum of the first n odd numbers 1, 3, 5, 7, 9, ... is n^2. Verify that this statement is correct for the first 6 odd numbers and find the sum of the first 50 odd numbers.

*25. The sum of the cubes of the first n whole numbers, 1^3, 2^3, 3^3, 4^3, 5^3, ... is $\frac{1}{4}n^2(n + 1)^2$. Verify that this statement is correct for $1^3 + 2^3 + 3^3 + 4^3$, and find the sum of the cubes of the first 20 whole numbers.

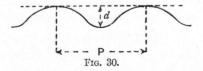

FIG. 30.

*26. For corrugated iron roofing (see Fig. 30), if the pitch is P inches and the depth is d inches, then $d = \frac{1}{4}P$. The pitch should not be less than 3 inches and not more than 5 inches; what can you say about the depth?

*27. When a railway cutting, h feet high, is faced with a brick wall, the thickness of the wall at its base is t inches where

$$t = \tfrac{1}{3}h + 3, \text{ if } h \text{ is less than } 18,$$
and $$t = \tfrac{2}{3}h - 3, \text{ if } h \text{ is greater than } 18.$$

Find the thickness of the wall at the base if the height is (i) 15 feet, (ii) 21 feet.

How would you proceed for a height of exactly 18 feet?

*28. The sum of the first n whole numbers 1, 2, 3, 4, 5, ... is $\tfrac{1}{2}n(n+1)$. Show that this statement is correct for

$$1 + 2 + 3 + 4 + 5 + 6 + 7 + 8.$$

Use this statement to find the sum of the whole numbers, $100 + 101 + 102 + 103 + \ldots + 150$.

*29. An oak beam, l feet long, b inches wide, d inches thick, is built into a wall at one end and carries a load of W cwt. at the other end (see Fig. 31). It will break if $W > \dfrac{5bd^2}{4l}$. Will such a beam 5 feet long, 8 inches wide, 3 inches thick, break under a load of 1 ton?

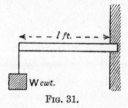

FIG. 31.

*30. The rise, R inches, and the tread, T inches, of a staircase (see No. 8, Fig. 28) are sometimes connected by the formula, $R = \dfrac{66}{T}$. The tread should not be less than 9 inches; what can you say about the rise? The tread should not be more than 12 inches; what can you say about the rise?

REVISION EXERCISE R. 1. (Ch. I–II)

If $a=2$, $b=5$, $c=0$, find the values of

1. $3a-b$.   [2] $2b^2$.   3. $3bc$.   4. $\frac{1}{2}a^3$.   [5] $5ab^2$.

6. $\dfrac{b+c}{a}$.   [7] $\dfrac{a+3}{b}$.   [8] $\dfrac{3a^2}{8}$.   [9] $\dfrac{8a+b}{a+b}$.   10. $\dfrac{a^3}{b-1}$.

11. $3(2b-4a)-2(3b-7a)$.   [12] $2(b-a)(b+a)$.

If $x=4$, $y=0$, $z=3$, find the values of

13. z^3-3xy^2.   [14] $3x-2y-4z$.   15. x^2+z^2-2xz.

Simplify:

16. $9b-3b+6c-3b-2c+b+c$.

[17] $4a \times 2b$.   18. $3cd \times 3d$.   19. $4e \div \frac{1}{2}$.   [20] $9f \div 6$.

21. $5(2x+y)+2(3x-2y)$.   [22] $3(2p-q)+4(p-2q)$.

Write down the results of the following operations:

23. Add 3 to $3x$.   [24] Subtract 4 from $4z$.

25. Divide 6 by y.   [26] Square $3t$.

If $r=\frac{1}{4}$, $t=\frac{2}{3}$, find the values of

[27] rt.   28. $1-r$.   29. $\dfrac{1}{t}$.   [30] $\dfrac{t}{r}$.

31. If $bc=36$, what is b if $c=9$?

[32] If $d+e=20$, what is d if $e=13$?

33. Express k half-crowns in pence.

34. Express $2r$ feet in yards.

[35] A rectangular field is $3x$ yards long, $2x$ yards wide; find its perimeter.

36. A car travels v miles an hour. How far does it go in (i) 3 hours, (ii) 20 minutes?

37. I buy 10 tons of coal; how much will remain when I have used $2n$ tons?

38. Find in shillings the cost of $3k$ eggs at 2 pence each.

[39] Find in shillings the cost of 1 lb. of tobacco at $6r$ pence per oz.

[40] A peach costs 4 pence. How many can I buy for z shillings?

41. A shopkeeper gained $4n$ shillings by selling a watch for $12n$ shillings. What did the shopkeeper pay for the watch? Answer (i) in shillings, (ii) in £.

[42] Five years ago I was $5n$ years old; how old shall I be in five years' time?

43. A book contains 240 pages. If I read n pages a day, how many pages remain to be read after (i) 3 days, (ii) t days?

44. How long does it take to travel $6s$ miles at 20 miles an hour?

45. If the area of a rectangular lawn $4l$ yards long, $3l$ yards wide is A sq. yards, complete the formula, $A = ...$, for A in terms of l.

46. A tank contains 100 gallons of water. If water runs into it at the rate of 20 gallons a minute, there will be n gallons of water in the tank after t minutes. Complete the formula, $n = ...$, for n in terms of t.

[47] A hotel bill for n days is

        (i) $12n$ shillings if n is less than 5,

        (ii) $10n$ shillings if n is greater than 5.

What is the bill (i) for 3 days, (ii) for 1 week?

[48] The perimeter of a rectangle is $2r$ inches. If its length is l inches, find its breadth. Find also its area.

49. A walks n miles an hour; B walks 1 mile an hour faster than A. How far does B walk in 3 hours?

[50] A man walks 3 miles an hour uphill and 4 miles an hour downhill. How long does he take altogether to walk $24k$ miles uphill and then $24k$ miles downhill?

[51] If W kilograms is the same weight as P lb., W is given approximately by the formula, $W = \dfrac{11P}{5}$. Find the number of kilograms in $2\frac{1}{2}$ lb.

52. If $C°$ Centigrade is the same temperature as $F°$ Fahrenheit, C is given by the formula, $C = \frac{5}{9}(F - 32)$. Express in degrees Centigrade (i) $212°$ Fahrenheit, (ii) $50°$ Fahrenheit.

53. If the radius of a circle, whose circumference is C inches, is r inches, r is given by the formula, $r = \dfrac{C}{2\pi}$, where $\pi = \dfrac{22}{7}$ approximately. Find the radius of a circle whose circumference is (i) 11 inches, (ii) $5\frac{1}{2}$ feet.

54. If $c = 2x - y + z$ and $d = x + y - 2z$, find the value of $2c - d$ when $x = 4$, $y = 3$, $z = 2$.

[55] If $r = 2s = 3t = 24$, find the value of $r + s + t$.

56. What must be added to t to make x?

[57] What must be subtracted from r to leave y?

58. By what must s be multiplied to make z?

59. A man on a walking tour walks 12 miles the first day and 20 miles every day afterwards. How far does he walk in n days?

60. Start with the number 2 and count up by sevens, thus obtaining 2, 9, 16, 23, ... Find in terms of n the nth number in this set of numbers, and check your answer by putting $n = 4$.

CHAPTER III

EASY PROBLEMS AND EQUATIONS

General Instructions

(i) Numbers may be represented by letters. **Do not use letters to represent quantities,** *i.e.* numbers-of-things.

(ii) In any problem which deals with quantities, **state your units clearly.**

(iii) Whenever you use a letter to represent an unknown number, first **write down a sentence, stating exactly what this letter represents.**

Example 1. Express by an equation the following statement:

I think of a number; I then double it and add 7 to it; the result is 25.

We might say

(Twice the number thought of) $+ 7 = 25$.

But it is simpler to say: denote the number thought of by n.

Then $2n + 7 = 25$.

The form in which this statement is now written is called an **equation,** and n is called "the unknown." The process of discovering the unknown number is called **solving the equation;** and the value of the unknown number is called the **root of the equation.** The reader may be able to see what this value is; methods for finding it will be given later.

Example 2. The weight of a box and its contents is 10 lb.; the contents weigh 3 lb. more than the box. Express these facts by an equation.

Suppose that the box by itself weighs **W** lb.

Then the contents of the box weigh $(W + 3)$ lb.

∴ the weight of the box and its contents is

$$W \text{ lb.} + (W + 3) \text{ lb.};$$

but this is 10 lb.;

∴ W lb. $+ (W + 3)$ lb. $= 10$ lb.

This is a relation between quantities; we can obtain from it a relation between numbers, $W + W + 3 = 10$.

∴ $2W + 3 = 10$.

EXERCISE III. a (Oral)

Correct, where necessary, the following statements:

1. Suppose that the length of the room is l.
2. Let x be the cost of the house.
3. Suppose that the weight of the parcel is w.
4. Suppose it is s miles from **A** to **B**.
5. Let the speed of the train be v.
6. $x + y = 180°$.
7. Eggs are sold at the rate of **N** for a shilling.
8. Let t be the time taken to walk a mile.
9. Let the required even number be n.
10. If the radius of a circle is r, its diameter is $2r$.
11. Let the price of butter be y.
12. If a rectangle is l inches long, b inches broad, its area is lb.

EXERCISE III. b (Oral)

In *each* of the examples Nos. 1–16, *start* with the number n and write down the result of the operation:

1. Double it.   2. Add 2 to it.   3. Halve it.
4. Subtract 2 from it.   5. Subtract it from 10.
6. Divide it by 5.   7. Diminish it by 4.
8. Increase it by 3.   9. Multiply it by 6.
10. Square it.   11. Divide 24 by it.
12. Take two-thirds of it.   13. Divide it by $\frac{3}{4}$.
14. Multiply it by 3 and subtract 3 from the result.
15. Increase it by 5 and halve the result.
16. Add to it one half of itself.

Write the statements in Nos. 17–24 as equations. If you can say *at sight* what the root of the equation is, do so.

17. I think of a number n, then subtract 9; the result is 13.
18. I think of a number n, then double it; the result is 38.
19. I think of a number n, divide it by 4, add 7; the result is 12.

20. I think of a number n, then add 15; the result is the same as multiplying the original number by 4.

21. The smaller of two consecutive whole numbers is n; their sum is 25.

22. The larger of two consecutive whole numbers is n; their sum is 37.

23. The smaller of two consecutive *odd* numbers is n; the sum of the larger and twice the smaller is 23.

24. A number n exceeds 5 by half the amount that it falls short of 17.

Express each of the equations, Nos. 25–30, as a "think of a number" problem. If you can say *at once* what the answer to the problem is, do so.

25. $n + 6 = 33$.   26. $n - 7 = 19$.   27. $20 - n = 9$.

28. $n + 18 = 3n$.   29. $n + 5n = 42$.   30. $n + (n+1) = 27$.

Write the statements in Nos. 31–38 as equations. If you can state *at sight* the root of the equation, do so.

31. A scuttle full of coal weighs 28 lb.; the coal weighs 3 times as much as the empty scuttle. Suppose the empty scuttle weighs **W** lb.

32. In Fig. 32, the length of **BP** exceeds the length of **PC** by $1\frac{1}{2}$ inches, and the length of **BC** is 5 inches. Suppose the length of **PC** is l inches.

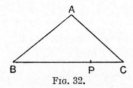

FIG. 32.

33. In Fig. 32, $\angle$ **B** $= \angle$ **C** and $\angle$ **A** $= 4 \angle$ **B**. Suppose $\angle$ **B** $= x°$.

34. In Fig. 32, **AB** $=$ **AC** and **BC** $= 1\frac{1}{2}$**AB**; also the perimeter of the triangle **ABC** is 10 inches. Suppose the length of **AB** is y inches.

35. The rods **AB** and **CD** in Fig. 33 are shortened by equal amounts so that one is just twice the length of the other. Suppose a length of x inches is cut away from each rod.

36. **A** is now 53 years old and **B** is 21 years old. In n years' time, **A** will be just twice as old as **B** will then be.

37. The sum of the angles of a polygon with k sides is 14 right angles. [If a polygon has n sides, the sum of its angles is $(2n-4)$ right angles.]

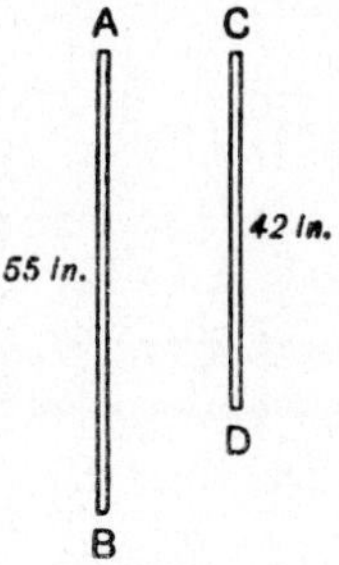

38. A man walks at 4 miles an hour from his house to the station (see Fig. 34) and then returns home at 3 miles an hour. The two journeys together take $3\frac{1}{2}$ hours.

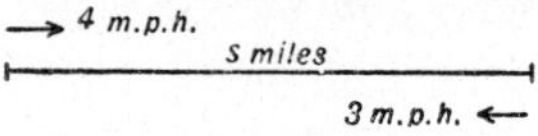

Fig. 33.

Fig. 34.

Solving Equations

Example 3.   What is n, if $n+6=19$?

I think of a number; then add 6; the result is 19.

By adding 6, I obtain 19; $\therefore$ the number $=19-6=13$.

$$\therefore\ n=13.$$

Check: $n+6=13+6=19$.

Example 4.   What is x, if $7x=63$?

I think of a number; then multiply it by 7; the result is 63.

By multiplying by 7, I obtain 63; $\therefore$ the number $=63 \div 7=9$.

$$\therefore\ x=9.$$

Check: $7x=7 \times 9=63$.

EXERCISE III. c

Express each equation as a "think of a number" problem; then find the answer and check it.

1. $n+8=17$.   2. $n-5=11$.   3. $3y=21$.

4. $\dfrac{z}{2}=9$.   5. $8x=0$.   6. $n-2\frac{1}{2}=5$.

[7] $N - 7 = 0.$ [8] $x + 1\frac{1}{2} = 2.$ [9] $\frac{y}{5} = 7.$

[10] $z + 2z = 18.$ [11] $3n - 2 = 10.$ [12] $\frac{x}{3} + 4 = 9.$

13. $4y - y = 21.$ 14. $\frac{z + 2}{4} = 5.$ 15. $\frac{z}{4} + 2 = 5.$

If a pair of scales is available, the methods for solving simple equations should be illustrated **experimentally**. Mere diagrams are valueless.

A tin containing shot (or sand) is made up so that, when placed with three 1-oz. weights in one scale pan, it is just balanced by seven 1-oz. weights in the other scale pan.

If the tin and its contents weigh W oz.,

$$W + 3 = 7.$$

The balance is still preserved when three 1-oz. weights are removed from each scale pan, thus

$$W + 3 - 3 = 7 - 3,$$
$$\therefore\ W = 4.$$

In a similar way, each of the processes used in solving a simple equation can be illustrated.

General Methods for solving Simple Equations

Example 5. Solve $n - 17 = 46.$

Since the numbers $n - 17$ and 46 are equal, if we *add* 17 *to each of them*, the results will be equal.

$$\therefore\ n - 17 + 17 = 46 + 17;$$
$$\therefore\ n = 63.$$

Example 6. Solve $x + 17 = 46.$

Since the numbers $x + 17$ and 46 are equal, if we *subtract* 17 *from each of them*, the results will be equal.

$$\therefore\ x + 17 - 17 = 46 - 17;$$
$$\therefore\ x = 29.$$

Example 7.   Solve $7y = 91$.

Since the numbers $7y$ and 91 are equal, if we *divide each number* by 7, the results will be equal.

$$\therefore\ 7y \div 7 = 91 \div 7.$$
$$\therefore\ y = 13.$$

Example 8.   Solve $\dfrac{z}{3} = 14$.

Since the numbers $\dfrac{z}{3}$ and 14 are equal, if we *multiply each number by* 3, the results will be equal.

$$\therefore\ \frac{z}{3} \times 3 = 14 \times 3;$$
$$\therefore\ z = 42.$$

The solution of every simple equation is performed by applying one or more of these four arguments, which may be summarised as follows:

(i) *Equal numbers may be added to each side.*

(ii) *Equal numbers may be subtracted from each side.*

(iii) *Each side may be multiplied by equal numbers.*

(iv) *Each side may be divided by equal numbers.*

From (i), if $x - a = b$, then $x = b + a$.

From (ii), if $x + a = b$, then $x = b - a$.

This shows that **any term may be moved from either side of an equation to the other side if the sign in front of it is changed.**

When solving an equation

Start by writing down the equation *exactly as it stands in the book*: do not try to simplify it in your head.

Be careful not to confuse the symbols $=$ and $\therefore$.

$=$ means "is equal to"; $\therefore$ means "therefore."

Thus we say: $3x = 15$; $\therefore\ x = 5$.

When checking an equation

Substitute for "the unknown" in each side *separately*, as in Example 9.

Substitute in the equation as it is given, *not* in any simplified form of it.   The object of checking is to make sure that your answer is right.   You cannot be certain that it is, unless you substitute in the actual equation given you.

Example 9. Solve $3x - 12 = \dfrac{2x}{3} + 16$.

Add 12 to each side, $\therefore 3x - 12 + 12 = \dfrac{2x}{3} + 16 + 12$;

$$\therefore 3x = \dfrac{2x}{3} + 28.$$

Subtract $\dfrac{2x}{3}$ from each side, $\therefore 3x - \dfrac{2x}{3} = \dfrac{2x}{3} + 28 - \dfrac{2x}{3}$;

$$\therefore 3x - \dfrac{2x}{3} = 28.$$

Multiply each side by 3, $\therefore 3x \times 3 - \dfrac{2x}{3} \times 3 = 28 \times 3$;

$$\therefore 9x - 2x = 84;$$
$$\therefore 7x = 84.$$

Divide each side by 7, $\therefore x = 12.$

Check: Left side $= 3x - 12 = 3 \times 12 - 12 = 36 - 12 = 24.$

Right side $= \dfrac{2x}{3} + 16 = \dfrac{2 \times 12}{3} + 16 = 8 + 16 = 24.$

$\therefore$ When $x = 12$, left side = right side.

It is sometimes convenient to reverse the order of an equation.
Thus, if $3 = x$, we can at once say $x = 3$, without using any of the
arguments (i)–(iv) on p. 45.

Example 10. Solve $\dfrac{5}{x} = \dfrac{2}{3}$.

Multiply each side by $3x$, $\therefore \dfrac{5}{x} \times 3x = \dfrac{2}{3} \times 3x$;

$$\therefore 15 = 2x; \quad \therefore 2x = 15.$$

Divide each side by 2, $\therefore x = \dfrac{15}{2} = 7\frac{1}{2}.$

EXERCISE III. d

Solve the equations in Nos. 1–11, explaining each step in the
argument as in Example 9.

1. $3n = 21;$ $\quad 8x = 64;$ $\quad 0 \cdot 3y = 1 \cdot 2.$
2. $a - 4 = 0;$ $\quad p - 2\frac{1}{2} = 6\frac{1}{2};$ $\quad w - 3 \cdot 2 = 1 \cdot 9.$
3. $l + 5 = 12;$ $\quad t + \frac{2}{5} = 1;$ $\quad x + 7 \cdot 4 = 9.$

4. $\frac{1}{8}p = 3$; $\frac{n}{3} = \frac{2}{7}$; $\frac{q}{5} = 4\cdot2$; $\frac{r}{4} = 0$.

5. $\frac{2m}{3} = 10$; $\frac{4\mathsf{R}}{5} = 2$; $\frac{3x}{5} = 1$; $\frac{5y}{7} = 0$.

6. $3 = n - 2$; $15 = 6y$; $17 = 2 + 5t$.

[7] $7 = p + 5$; $25 = 7z - 3$; $4\frac{1}{2} = 2 + 5m$.

8. $4\frac{1}{2} = t + \frac{1}{4}$; $8 = 3b + 8$; $9 = 7l - 3$.

[9] $3\frac{3}{4} = x + 1\frac{1}{4}$; $23 = 4y + 3$; $20 = 9t + 8$.

10. $0\cdot3n = 1\cdot5$; $1\cdot6p = 8$; $3\cdot8 + 2k = 6\cdot2$.

[11] $0\cdot4x = 2\cdot4$; $2\cdot5y = 15$; $3z - 1\cdot2 = 2\cdot7$.

Solve the equations in Nos. 12–26, and check each answer.

12. $2p - 8 = p - 3$.   **13.** $t + 7 = 17 - 4t$.   **14.** $3(n - 7) = 12$.

[15] $2l + 4 = 19 - l$.   **[16]** $4(2k - 1) = 20$.   **[17]** $5(2r + 3) = 15$.

18. $4(t - 5) = 0$.   **19.** $l - \frac{1}{3}l = 6$.   **20.** $10y = y$.

[21] $m + \frac{m}{5} = 12$.   **[22]** $x - \frac{2x}{7} = 10$.   **[23]** $\frac{l}{3} = 1 + \frac{l}{4}$.

24. $\frac{p}{2} - \frac{p}{3} = 1$.   **25.** $\frac{1}{2}(3x - 1) = 7$.   **26.** $5 = \frac{1}{4}(3k - 1)$.

Solve the equations in Nos. 27–50:

27. $7(3y - 1) = 28$.   **28.** $0 = 2t - 7$.   **29.** $\frac{r}{5} - \frac{2}{7} = 0$.

[30] $5 = 3n$.   **[31]** $\frac{1}{4}(2p + 1) = 3$.   **[32]** $\frac{2b}{3} - \frac{b}{2} = 1$.

33. $\frac{c}{3} + \frac{c}{5} = 0$.   **34.** $5d - 8 = \frac{3d}{7}$.   **[35]** $5 - \frac{3}{5}k = 1 + k$.

36. $2\frac{1}{2}m = 10 - 1\frac{2}{3}m$.   **37.** $\frac{1}{5}(2y - 3) = 3$.   **38.** $1 + \frac{7z}{2} = z + 6$.

[39] $\frac{6x}{7} + 2 = 11$.   **[40]** $\frac{3n}{5} - \frac{n}{2} = \frac{1}{2}$.   **[41]** $\mathsf{R} - 0\cdot7\mathsf{R} = 12$.

*42. $\frac{3}{4}m = 2\cdot7$.   ***43.** $\frac{n}{0\cdot3} = 4$.   ***44.** $\frac{5}{2p} = \frac{1}{6}$.

*45. $\frac{3}{5x} = 1\frac{1}{2}$.   ***46.** $\frac{1}{y} + \frac{1}{3y} = \frac{1}{12}$.   ***47.** $\frac{z}{3} \div 1\frac{1}{2} = 1\frac{1}{3}$.

*48. $\frac{t + 1}{5} = \frac{t + 3}{6}$.   ***49.** $\frac{d - 1}{3} = \frac{2d + 1}{7}$.   ***50.** $\frac{2r + 4}{5} = \frac{4 - r}{3}$.

General Procedure in the Solution of Problems

1. *Read the question carefully.* Do not start to try to work it out before you are sure that you understand what you are given and what you are asked to find out.

2. Take a letter to stand for some unknown *number* which the problem involves.

If the problem involves quantities, *state clearly what the unit is.*

Never say, let the length be x; a clear statement would be, let the length of the room be x feet.

Never say, let x be the cost of eggs; a clear statement would be, suppose one dozen eggs cost x pence.

3. *Check the answer by using the actual data of the problem.*

It is not sufficient to check by substituting in the equation, because your equation may be wrong.

Example 11. Share 10 shillings between two boys, **A** and **B**, so that **A** receives 1s. 6d. more than **B**.

Suppose that **B**'s share is b shillings.

Now **A** receives $1\frac{1}{2}$ shillings more than **B**.

$$\therefore \text{ A's share is } (b + 1\tfrac{1}{2}) \text{ shillings.}$$

$\therefore$ **A**'s share and **B**'s share together make

$$(b + 1\tfrac{1}{2}) \text{ shillings} + b \text{ shillings;}$$

but this is 10 shillings;

$$\therefore (b + 1\tfrac{1}{2}) \text{ shillings} + b \text{ shillings} = 10 \text{ shillings;}$$
$$\therefore b + 1\tfrac{1}{2} + b = 10;$$
$$\therefore 2b = 10 - 1\tfrac{1}{2} = 8\tfrac{1}{2};$$
$$\therefore b = 4\tfrac{1}{4}.$$
$$\therefore \text{ B's share} = 4\tfrac{1}{4}\text{s.} = 4\text{s. } 3\text{d.}$$
$$\therefore \text{ A's share} = 4\text{s. } 3\text{d.} + 1\text{s. } 6\text{d.} = 5\text{s. } 9\text{d.}$$

Check: The total sum shared out equals 4s. 3d. + 5s. 9d. = 10s.

EXERCISE III. e

Solve the following problems by Algebra, and check each answer.

1. I think of a number, divide it by 4 and add 11; the result is 17. What is the number?

2. I think of a number, add to it one-third of itself; the result is 28. What is the number?

[3] The result of adding 42 to a certain number is the same as multiplying that number by 4. What is the number?

[4] If I halve a certain number and add 1, the result is the same as dividing the number by 3 and adding 4. What is the number?

5. The sum of two consecutive numbers is 55. What are they?

[6] What number exceeds 17 by the same amount as it falls short of 55?

7. The sum of three consecutive even numbers is 72; what are they?

8. From three-quarters of a certain number, 3 is subtracted; the result is two-thirds of that number. What is the number?

[9] I think of a number, add 2 to it, multiply the sum by 5 and then subtract 7; the result is 23. What is the number?

10. In Fig. 35, AP is 3 inches longer than PB. Find the length of PB.

[11] In Fig. 35, AP is twice the length of PB. Find the length of PB.

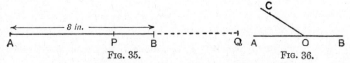

Fig. 35.   Fig. 36.

12. In Fig. 36, find ∠ AOC if ∠ BOC = 5 ∠ AOC.

[13] In Fig. 36, find ∠ AOC if ∠ BOC exceeds twice ∠ AOC by 90°.

14. The flagstaff **PQ** in Fig. 37 is one-fifth of the height **AB** of a tower; **Q** is 90 feet above the ground. Find the height **AB**.

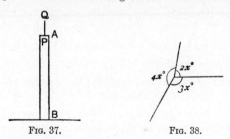

FIG. 37.   FIG. 38.

[15] With the data of Fig. 38, find x.

16. Tank **A** contains 24 gallons of water and tank **B** contains 5 gallons. Equal quantities of water are pumped into **A** and **B**. How much has been added to each when **A** contains just twice as much as **B**?

[17] A man is 30 years old when his son is 4. In how many years' time will the son be just half the age of his father?

18. I buy a house for a certain sum of money and then have to spend one-third of that amount on repairs. The total cost is £3000. What did I pay for the house?

[19] An excursion ticket is one-quarter of the ordinary fare. I save 5s. 6d. by taking an excursion ticket. What is the ordinary fare?

20. Two milk cans **A** and **B** together contain 50 pints of milk. When 2 pints are taken out of **A**, there remains in **A** half of what **B** contains. How much does **B** contain?

21. A grocer buys some eggs at 2d. each; he finds that one dozen are bad. By selling the rest at 3d. each, he makes 5s. profit. How many did he buy?

[22] I bought 20 pencils for 3s.; some cost $1\frac{1}{2}$d. each, the rest cost $2\frac{1}{2}$d. each; how many of the cheaper kind did I buy?

23. A strip of lace 6 feet long is cut into two parts so that the length of one part is three-fifths of that of the other part. Find the length of the longer part.

[24] In Fig. 35, p. 49, **AQ** is $2\frac{1}{2}$ times as long as **BQ**; find the length of **BQ**.

25. In Fig. 39 all the corners are right-angled, and the dimensions are given in *inches*. Find *l* if the perimeter of the shaded area is $2\frac{1}{2}$ feet.

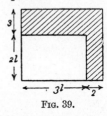

FIG. 39.

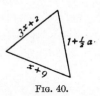

FIG. 40.

26. Fig. 40 shows the lengths in inches of the sides of a triangle. If the triangle is equilateral, find the values of *a* and *x*. Find also the perimeter of the triangle.

[27] If in Fig. 40 the triangle is isosceles and if $x = 3$, find the value of *a*. [There are two answers.]

28. Fig. 41 represents a hurdle whose *total* width is $1\frac{1}{2}$ times its *total* height. It is made of metal strips whose total length is 36 feet. Find the height of the hurdle.

FIG. 41.

[29] In Fig. 42, find $\angle$ **B** if $\angle$ **B** = $\angle$ **C** = $4 \angle$ **A**.

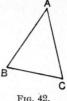

FIG. 42.

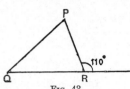

FIG. 43.

30. In Fig. 43, find $\angle$ **P** if $\angle$ **P** = $3 \angle$ **Q**.

[31] The sum of the angles of a polygon with *n* sides is $(2n - 4)$ right angles. How many sides has a polygon if the sum of its angles is 20 right angles?

32. Use the statement in No. 31 to find the number of sides of a polygon if each of its angles is 156°.

33. 12 shillings is shared between two boys **A** and **B** so that **A** gets half a crown more than twice what **B** gets. How much does **B** get?

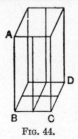

Fig. 44.

*34. Fig. 44 represents a skeleton wire cage; **AB** is twice as long as **BC**, and **BC** = **CD**. The total length of wire is $5\frac{1}{2}$ feet. What are the lengths of **AB** and **BC** in inches?

*35. If a shopkeeper sells a hat for 14s. the amount he gains is three times as much as the amount he would lose if he was forced to sell it for 8s. What did the shopkeeper pay for the hat?

*36. A lead sheet, 6 feet wide, of indefinite length is bent to form a gutter; Fig. 45 represents its vertical cross-section. The base **BC** is $2\frac{1}{2}$ times each of the sides **AB**, **CD**. Find the *height* **AB** of the gutter in inches, and the area of its cross-section in square inches.

Fig. 45.   Fig. 46.

*37. In Fig. 46, **O** is the mid-point of **AB**, and **AP** is one-fifth of **PB**; **OP** is 2 inches. Find the length of **AB**.

*38. **ABC** is a triangle. If $\angle$ **A** = $25°$ + $\angle$ **B** and if $\angle$ **B** = $10°$ + $\angle$ **C**, find $\angle$ **C**.

*39. **ABC** is a triangle. If $\angle$ **A** = $\frac{2}{3}$ $\angle$ **B** and if $\angle$ **B** = $\frac{6}{5}$ $\angle$ **C**, find $\angle$ **C**.

*40. Find k if $3k$ minutes past five is the same time as $2k$ minutes to six.

*41. The wind backs from direction **AO** to direction **BO** (see Fig. 47); if the change of direction is 100°, find its first direction.

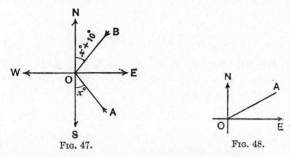

FIG. 47.   FIG. 48.

*42. In Fig. 48, the direction **OA** is $2p$ degrees E. of N.; it is also $(3p + 5)$ degrees E. of S.   What is the direction of **OA**?

CHAPTER IV

ELEMENTARY PROCESSES

Like and Unlike Terms. When simplifying, *work from the left* unless brackets or $\times$ and $\div$ signs show that operations must be performed in a different order.

Example 1. Simplify $2a(2b - 3c) + b(2c - 3a) + 3c(b - a)$.

$2a(2b - 3c) + b(2c - 3a) + 3c(b - a) = 4ab - 6ac + 2bc - 3ba + 3cb - 3ca;$

but $\qquad 3ba = 3ab$ and $3cb = 3bc$ and $3ca = 3ac,$

$\qquad \therefore$ expression $= 4ab - 3ab + 2bc + 3bc - 6ac - 3ac$
$\qquad\qquad\qquad\quad = ab + 5bc - 9ac.$

EXERCISE IV. a

Simplify (when possible) the following expressions. *If there is no shorter form, say so.*

1. $3ab + 3ab$.
2. $5bc + 2cb$.
3. $de + e$.
4. $6cd - 3dc$.
5. $3ef - ef + 2ef$.
6. $9gh - 3gh - 3gh$.
7. $4mn - m + n$.
8. $7pq - 3pq - 4qp$.
9. $rs + 2r + s$.
10. $2st - st$. tc.
11. $5xy - 5yz$.
12. $6xy - 2yz - 2xy$.
[13] $12ab - 3ba - 4ba$.
[14] $4cd - 2c + 2d$.
[15] $10ef - fe - fe$.
16. $3(2g + 1) + 2(4g - 1)$.
17. $4(4 + h) + 5(h - 3)$.
[18] $5(2k - 1) + 2(3k - 2)$.
[19] $7(3m + n) + 3(4n - 5m)$.
20. $2(3p + 7) + 5(q - 2) + 3(p - q)$.
[21] $5(3r + 2s + 4) + 3(r - 3s - 5)$.
22. $a(2x - y) + a(3x - 2y)$.
23. $b(5c + d) + b(3c - d)$.
24. $3f(3g + 4h) + 2f(h - 4g)$.
25. $3t(r - 2s) + 2s(4t - 2r)$.
[26] $2a(3e - 2f) + 3a(2e - 2f)$.
[27] $4x(2a - 3b) + 2x(3a - 4b)$.
[28] $5y(4c + 2d) + 3y(3d - 6c)$.
[29] $p(q + 2r) + q(p - s)$.
30. $a(b - c) + b(c + a) + c(a - b)$.
31. $2f(3g - h) + 2g(h - 3f) + 3h(g + 2f)$.
[32] $3x(4y - z) + y(3z - 2x) + 4z(y - x)$.
[33] $7r(s + 2t) + 2s(t - 3r) + 2t(s - 5r)$.

Write down the results of the following operations:

34. Add ab to a.   **35.** Subtract c from cd.

[36] Add gh to gk.   [37] Subtract rs from sr.

38. Decrease $2p$ by 2.   **39.** Increase $3n$ by 3.

[40] Add $R + r$ to $3r$.   [41] Subtract 1 from $3x$.

42. Add $y + 1$, y, $y - 1$.   **43.** Add $a - b$, $b + c$, $c - a$.

EXERCISE IV. b

1. What is the total length of a fence formed by 10 hurdles each r feet long and 12 hurdles each s feet long?

2. What is the total bill for c lb. of tea at 2s. per lb. and p lb. of sugar at 4d. per lb.? Answer (i) in pence, (ii) in shillings.

[3] What is the total weight of 5 jars each weighing P lb. and 7 jars each weighing Q lb.?

[4] What is the total cost of 18 bananas at x pence each and 6 peaches at y pence each? Answer (i) in pence, (ii) in shillings.

5. From a rod $(3l + 2m)$ inches long, a part $2l$ inches long is cut off. What is the length of the remainder?

[6] Subtract $7t$ pence from t shillings. Answer in pence.

7. Fig. 49 represents a skeleton box with base x inches square and y inches high. What length of wire is used in making it? Answer (i) in inches, (ii) in feet.

Fig. 49.

8. A box weighing $(6p + 4)$ lb. is put in one scale pan of a weighing machine and another box weighing $2p$ lb. is put in the other scale pan. What weight must be added to make them balance?

[9] A boy works for p hours on each Sunday, q hours on each Wednesday and on each Saturday, and r hours on each other day. How many hours does he work each week?

10. Fig. 50 represents a wire net; each small compartment is *h* inches high (*i.e.* up the page) and *l* inches long. What is the total length of wire required for the net?

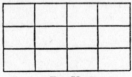

FIG. 50.

11. Fig. 51 shows the lengths of the sides of a triangle in inches.
    (i) What is the perimeter of the triangle?
    (ii) By how much does **AB** + **AC** exceed **BC**?
    (iii) By how much does **BA** + **BC** exceed **AC**?

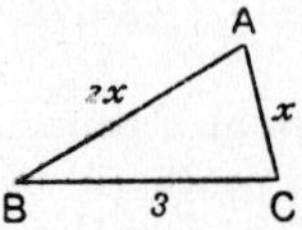

FIG. 51.

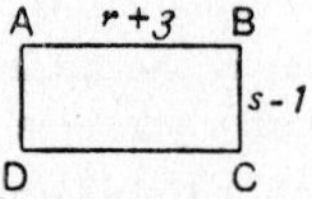

FIG. 52.

[12] Fig. 52 shows the lengths of two adjacent sides of a rectangle in inches.
    (i) What is the perimeter of the rectangle?
    (ii) What is the length of **AD** + **DC** + **CB**?
    (iii) What is the length of **AB** + **BC** + **CD**?

13. Fig. 52 shows the lengths of two adjacent sides of a rectangle in inches. If $r = 3s$, find in terms of *s* (i) the perimeter of the rectangle, (ii) the length of **AD** + **DC** + **CB**.

14. A man starts with £$(x + y)$. He pays *x* bills of 5 shillings each and *y* bills of 15 shillings each. How many shillings has he left?

15. Subtract *k* florins from £*g*. Answer in shillings.

Powers

The shorthand form of $x \times x \times x \times x$ is $\mathbf{x}^4$ and the shorthand form of $7 \times x \times x \times x \times x$ is $7\mathbf{x}^4$.

The numerical factor 7 in the term $7x^4$ is called the **coefficient** of the term $7x^4$ or more shortly the **coefficient of $\mathbf{x}^4$**.

The term $7x^4$ is said to be of **degree 4 in x** or of the **4th degree in x**. The symbol x^4 is read as "x to the power 4" and the 4 is called the **index** of x.

Thus, in the expression $2x^5 + 4x^3 + x^2 + 3$, the term of degree 3 is $4x^3$ and its coefficient is 4, the coefficient of x^2 is 1, and the coefficient of x is 0, since this term is missing. The *numerical* term 3 is called the **constant term** or the **term independent of x**, because its value does not depend on the value of x, since it does not contain x.

The expression $2x^5 + 4x^3 + x^2 + 3$ contains four *unlike* terms; it cannot be written more shortly unless we know the value of x.

Expressions should always be written in an orderly way. They are usually arranged *either* in **descending powers** of the unknown, *i.e.* beginning with the highest power, then the next highest, and so on, *or* in **ascending powers,** *i.e.* beginning with the constant term, then the term of first degree, then the term of second degree, and so on.

Thus $2x^5 + 4x^3 + x^2 + 3$ is arranged in *descending* powers of x.
And $3 + x^2 + 4x^3 + 2x^5$ is arranged in *ascending* powers of x.

Example 2. Simplify $2y^2 + 3y + 2 - y^2 + 2y + 1$ and arrange it in (i) descending powers of y, (ii) ascending powers of y.

Take the like terms together.

$$2y^2 - y^2 = y^2; \quad 3y + 2y = 5y; \quad 2 + 1 = 3;$$
$$\therefore \text{ the expression} = \mathbf{y^2 + 5y + 3}, \text{ descending powers}$$
$$= \mathbf{3 + 5y + y^2}, \text{ ascending powers.}$$

EXERCISE IV. c

Simplify:

1. $6a^2 + 2a^2 + a^2$.   2. $5b^3 + 3b^3 - 4b^3$.   3. $8c^4 - 4c^4 + c^4$.

[4] $9d^3 + 3d^3 - 6d^3$.   [5] $10e^5 - 5e^5 + 5e^5$.   [6] $9f^3 - 6f^3 - 3f^3$.

Simplify and arrange in *descending* powers:

7. $3g^2 - 4g + 2g^2$.   8. $1 + 9h^3 - 3h^3$.   9. $3k^2 + k^3 - k^2$.

[10] $7n^2 - 4n^2 + 3n$.   [11] $6 + 2p^3 - 4p$.   [12] $7r^2 - r^3 + 2r^3$.

13. $2s^2 + 6s - 3 - 3s + s^2$.   14. $5t^2 - 8 - 4t^2 + 2t - t^2 + 12$.

[15] $x^3 - 3x - x^2 + 4x^3 - x$.   [16] $2y - 1 + y^2 - 1 + 3y$.

17. $6z^2 - z^2 + 2z^2 - 3z - 5z^2$.   18. $9p^3 + 6 - 3p^3 - 3 + 2p^3$.

19] $8a^2 - 3a - 4a^2 + 2a^2 + 5a$. [20] $10 - 2b^2 + b^2 - 5 + 5b^2$.

21. $c - 1 + c^2 - 1 + c$. 22. $5 + 6d + 3d^2 - 5d + 4$.

[23] $1 + e + 2e^4 - e + 1$. [24] $f^3 + f^2 + f + 1 - f + f^2$.

25. $3 + 5g^2 - 2g - 1 + g^2$. 26. $4h - 2h^2 + 6h^3 - h + 2h^3$.

[27] $3k^2 - 5k + 7 - k^2 + 1$. [28] $6 + 6n^3 + 5n^2 - 4n^3 - 2n^3$.

Simplify and arrange in *ascending* powers:

29. $5a^2 + 3a - a^2$. 30. $4b^3 - b + 2b$. 31. $2c^2 - 3 + 6$.

[32] $9d^2 - 3d^2 + 3$. [33] $5e - 3e^2 + e$. [34] $8 + 2f - 2$.

35. $8g + 3 + g^2 - 2g + 1$. 36. $6h^2 - 3 + 2h^2 + 5 - 7h^2$.

[37] $5k^2 - k^3 + 7 - 2k^2 - 1$. [38] $5 - 2m^2 - m^2 + 1 - 3m^2$.

39. $7n - 4n^2 + 5n - n^2 + 6n^2$. 40. $5p + p^3 + 2 - p + 6p^3$.

[41] $8r^2 - 2 - 5r^2 + 6 - 3r^2$. [42] $2s^3 - 3s^2 + 4s - s^2 + s$.

Write down (i) the coefficient of x^2, (ii) the constant term, (iii) the term of degree 3, in the following:

43. $7x^4 + 2x^3 + x^2 + 5x + 2$. 44. $4x^6 + 1\frac{1}{2}x^3 + 2\frac{1}{2}x^2 + 7x$.

[45] $2\frac{1}{2}x^5 + 1\frac{1}{4}x^3 + 5x^2 + 7\frac{1}{2}$. [46] $7x^6 + 4x^3 + 2x + \frac{2}{3}$.

Write down (i) the coefficient of y, (ii) the constant term, (iii) the term of highest degree, in the following:

47. $5y^3 + 6y^2 + 4$. 48. $\frac{3}{4}y + 5y^2 + 2y^4$.

[49] $3y^3 + 9\frac{1}{2}y^2 + y + 5$. [50] $8 + \frac{1}{3}y + 6y^2 + 2y^3$.

Multiplication and Division

Example 3. Multiply x^2 by x^3.

$$x^2 = x \times x \quad \text{and} \quad x^3 = x \times x \times x.$$
$$\therefore \ x^2 \times x^3 = x \times x \times x \times x \times x = x^5.$$

Example 4. Multiply $12x^3$ by $\frac{2}{3} xy$.

$$12x^3 \times \tfrac{2}{3}xy = 12 \times x^3 \times \tfrac{2}{3} \times x \times y$$
$$= 12 \times \tfrac{2}{3} \times x^3 \times x \times y$$
$$= 8x^4 y.$$

Example 5. Divide a^6 by a^2.

$$a^6 \div a^2 = \frac{a \times a \times a \times a \times a \times a}{a \times a} = a \times a \times a \times a$$
$$= a^4.$$

Example 6. Simplify $\dfrac{12a^3bc}{9a^2c}$.

$$\frac{12a^3bc}{9a^2c} = \frac{12 \times a \times a \times a \times b \times c}{9 \times a \times a \times c} = \frac{4 \times a \times b}{3} = \frac{4ab}{3}.$$

Example 7. What is the square of a^4 ?

$$(a^4)^2 = a^4 \times a^4$$
$$= a^8.$$

Example 8. Find a square root of x^6.

$$x^3 \times x^3 = x^6,$$
$$\therefore \text{ a square root of } x^6 \text{ is } x^3.$$

This is often written, $\sqrt{x^6} = x^3$.

The methods used in Examples 3, 5 give the following results:

(i) If p, q are any whole numbers,

$$\mathbf{x}^p \times \mathbf{x}^q = \mathbf{x}^{p+q}.$$

This result is sometimes expressed in the form:

In multiplication, **add** *the indices ;*

but this applies only to **powers of the same number.**

(ii) If p, q are whole numbers such that p is greater than q,

$$\mathbf{x}^p \div \mathbf{x}^q = \mathbf{x}^{p-q}.$$

This result is sometimes expressed in the form:

In division, **subtract** *the indices ;*

but this applies only to **powers of the same number.**

EXERCISE IV. d

Simplify the expressions, Nos. 1–8, *giving the argument in full*:

1. $a^3 \times a^3$. 2. $b \times b^4$. 3. $(c^3)^2$. 4. $(d^2)^3$.

5. $e^4 \div e$. 6. $f^6 \div f^3$. 7. $5g \times 3gh$. 8. $(3k^4)^2$.

Simplify the following:

9. $a^3 \times a^2$. 10. $b^3 \times b$. 11. $c^4 \times c^3$. 12. $d^4 \times d^4$.

[13] $e \times e^5$. [14] $f^2 \times f^6$. [15] $2g^5 \times g^5$. [16] $6h^3 \times 2h^4$.

17. $3k^2 \times 4k^4$. 18. $2m^5 \times 4m$. 19. $3n^3 \times 3n^3$. 20. $5n \times 5np$.

21. $3r^2 \times 2s^4$. 22. $4t^2 \times 2t^3x$. 23. $4y^3 \times 4yz^2$.

24. $6x^3 \times 3x^3z^3$. [25] $4a^4 \times 4a^4$. [26] $3b^2 \times 3bc$.

[27] $6cd^3 \times 2cd$. [28] $5e^4 \times 2e^2f^2$. 29. $(3g^3)^2$.

30. $(2h^3)^3$. 31. $(2k^2m)^3$. 32. $(\frac{1}{2}m^2_{\_}p^3)^4$.

[33] $(5r^4)^2$. [34] $(3s^4)^3$. [35] $(4t^3x^4)^2$.

[36] $(\frac{1}{3}yz^5)^4$. 37. $\sqrt{(a^4b^2)}$. 38. $\sqrt{(9c^6)}$.

39. $\sqrt{(d^4e^8f^{10})}$. 40. $\sqrt{(16g^{16})}$. [41] $\sqrt{(h^6k^8)}$.

[42] $\sqrt{(25n^{12})}$. [43] $\sqrt{(p^6q^2r^8)}$. [44] $\sqrt{(36s^4t^{16})}$.

45. $a^6 \div a^2$. 46. $b^4 \div b$. 47. $c^5 \div c^5$.

48. $d^8 \div d^4$. [49] $e^9 \div e^3$. [50] $f^{12} \div f^6$.

[51] $4g^4 \div (2g)$. [52] $h^6k^3 \div (h^2k)$. 53. $2n^3 \div n^3$.

54. $6p^6 \div (3p^3)$. 55. $r^4s \div (rs)$. 56. $x^8y^4 \div (x^4y^2)$.

57. $6a^2b^4c \div (2abc)$. 58. $12de^6f^4 \div (9e^2f)$.

59. $4g^4h^8m^6 \div (6gh^2m^2)$. 60. $6n^3 \times \dfrac{n^3}{3}$. 61. $3p^2q^3 \times 3p^3q^2$.

62. $(4rs^3t)^2$. 63. $\dfrac{x}{y} \times \dfrac{y}{z} \times \dfrac{z}{x}$. 64. $2a^2 \times 3ab \times 4b^2$.

65. $(c^4)^2 \div c^2$. 66. $(6d)^3 \div (2d)^2$. 67. $(2ef)^3 \times 3f$.

68. $\frac{1}{2}g^2 \times \frac{1}{3}h^2 \div (\frac{1}{6}gh)$. [69] $6k \div (8k)$. [70] $2mn \times (3n)^2$.

[71] $3r^2s \div (2rs)$. [72] $t \times 2t^2 \times 3t^3$. [73] $(2x^2)^3 \div (2x^3)^2$.

[74] $\frac{2}{3}xy \times \frac{3}{4}yz$. 75. $\dfrac{a^9}{a^3 \times a^3}$. 76. $\dfrac{6b^2c^2d^2}{4bd}$.

77. $\dfrac{6f^2g \times 2fg^2}{8fg}$. 78. $\dfrac{h \times h^2 \times h^3}{h^4}$. 79. $\dfrac{9pq^3r}{15qr}$.

80. $\dfrac{3x^2y^2z^4}{9y^2z^3}$. *81. $(2a)^2 \times (3a)^3 \div (6a^2)$.

*82. $(3bc^3)^2 \div (3bc)$. *83. $d(2d)^3 \div d^2$. *84. $\dfrac{(4ef)^2}{4ef^2}$.

*85. $\dfrac{pq \times (pr)^2}{pqr \times p^2r}$. *86. $\dfrac{(3x^2y^3z^4)^2}{3x^2y^2z^2}$.

H.C.F. and L.C.M.

Factors and Multiples. Since $10ab^2c = 5ab \times 2bc$, we say that $2bc$ is a *factor* of $10ab^2c$, and that $10ab^2c$ is a *multiple* of $2bc$.

Consider the two expressions, $10ab^2c$, $12a^2b^2$.

$$10ab^2c = 2 \times 5 \times a \times b^2 \times c,$$
$$12a^2b^2 = 2^2 \times 3 \times a^2 \times b^2;$$

2, a, b^2 are factors of each expression and are called *common factors* of the two expressions.

Every common factor of $10ab^2c$, $12a^2b^2$ is itself a factor of $2ab^2$; we therefore call $2ab^2$ the *Highest Common Factor* or **H.C.F.** of $10ab^2c$, $12a^2b^2$.

Also every multiple of both the expressions $10ab^2c$, $12a^2b^2$ must have 2, 3, 5, a, b, c as factors, and each of these factors must occur to as high a power as it occurs in either of the expressions; therefore every *common multiple* of $10ab^2c$, $12a^2b^2$ must contain as factors 2^2, 3, 5, a^2, b^2, c; and we call $2^2.3.5a^2b^2c$ the *Least Common Multiple* or **L.C.M.** of $10ab^2c$, $12a^2b^2$ because every other common multiple is itself a multiple of $2^2.3.5a^2b^2c$.

These methods for finding the H.C.F. and L.C.M. are the same as the methods by prime factors used in Arithmetic.

EXERCISE IV. e

[Nos. 1–10 are intended for oral work.]

1. Is 12 a multiple of (i) 4, (ii) 48 ?
   Is $6ab$ a multiple of (i) $2a$, (ii) $6a^2b^2$?

2. Is 18 a multiple of (i) 180, (ii) 6 ?
   Is a^3 a multiple of (i) a^2, (ii) a^6 ?

3. Is 24 a factor of (i) 12, (ii) 48 ?
   Is $6xy$ a factor of (i) $3x$, (ii) $18xy^2$?

4. Is 24 a common multiple of (i) 2 and 3, (ii) 48 and 240 ?
   Is $6x^2y$ a common multiple of (i) $3x$, $2xy$, (ii) $6x^2y^2$, $12x^3y^3$?

5. Is 12 a common factor of (i) 3 and 4, (ii) 24 and 36 ?
   Is $6ab$ a common factor of (i) $2a$, $3b$; (ii) $12a^2b$, $18ab^2$?

6. Is $10x^4y^3$ a multiple of $5x^3y$?

7. Is $3b^2c$ a factor of $6bc^2$?

8. Is $2y^2z$ a common factor of $6y^3z$ and $4y^2z^3$?

9. Is $12x^2y^3$ a common multiple of any of the following pairs:
   (i) $3x^2y$, $4xy^2$; (ii) $12x^2$, y^3; (iii) $10x$, $4y$; (iv) $3x^2$, y^4?

10. Which of the pairs in No. 9 have a common factor, other than unity, and what is it?

Find the H.C.F. of the following expressions:

11. $4a$, $6b$.	12. $2cd$, c^2.	13. x, xyz.
[14] $15e^2$, $20f^2$.	[15] $3n$, $2mn$.	[16] $5p^2q$, $6p^3r$.
17. $3r^2$, $2rs^2$.	18. $9s^3$, $12s^2t$.	19. $2x^3y$, $4xyz^2$.
20. $2a^2$, $6ab$, $4ac$.	21. $9p^3q^2r$, $12p^2q^3s$, $15pq^4rs$.	
[22] $6x^2y$, $10xy^2$, $8xyz$.	[23] $8a^4c^2$, $16b^2c^3$, $4abc^4$.	

Find the L.C.M. of the following expressions:

24. $6a^2$, $3ab$.	25. cd^2, c^2d.	26. $5ef^2$, $2f^3$.
[27] $10g^2$, $15g^3$.	[28] p, qrp^2.	[29] $4xy$, $6y^2$.
30. p^2qr, pq^3r^2.	31. $4ax^2$, $6abx$.	32. $14ac^3y$, $21b^2y^2z$.
[33] $8a^4$, $6a^2b^2$.	[34] $6p^3r^3$, $15q^2rs$.	[35] $4yz^4$, $3x^2y^2z^2$.
36. $6x^2$, $3xy$, $6y^2$.	37. $4a^2b$, $5b^2c$, $6c^2a$.	
38. 24, $3x$, $3xy$, $6xz$.	39. $12a^3b$, $9abc$, $15a^2b^3$, $24ab^2x$.	

Find the H.C.F. and L.C.M. of the following expressions:

40. $6x$, $2xy$, $2y^3$, $4x^2$.	41. $2x^2yz$, $3xy^2z$, $4xyz^3$.
[42] 8, $10p$, $4p^3$, $3q^2$.	[43] $9x^3y$, $6y^3z$, $12x^2y^2z^2$.
44. $10x^3$, $15abx^2$, $20cxy$.	45. $(2ax)^2$, $(6bx)^2$, $(2cx)^2$.

Simplification of Fractions

Just as in Arithmetic, $\frac{21}{28}$ is reduced to $\frac{3}{4}$ by dividing numerator and denominator by the common factor 7, so in Algebra $\frac{6a^2}{15ab}$ is reduced to $\frac{2a}{5b}$ by dividing numerator and denominator by the common factor $3a$.

Example 9. Simplify (i) $\dfrac{2x}{4x^3}$; (ii) $\dfrac{6a^2b^2}{15ab^6}$.

(i) The H.C.F. of $2x$ and $4x^3$ is $2x$,

$$\therefore \frac{2x}{4x^3} = \frac{2x \cdot 1}{2x \cdot 2x^2} = \frac{1}{2x^2}.$$

(ii) The H.C.F. of $6a^2b^2$ and $15ab^6$ is $3ab^2$,

$$\therefore \frac{6a^2b^2}{15ab^6} = \frac{3ab^2 \cdot 2a}{3ab^2 \cdot 5b^4} = \frac{2a}{5b^4}.$$

The first step in this simplification may be omitted when the process is understood; and it is often easier to divide in succession by any obvious common factors: thus

$$\frac{6a^2b^2}{15ab^6} = \frac{2a^2b^2}{5ab^6} = \frac{2ab^2}{5b^6} = \frac{2a}{5b^4}.$$

EXERCISE IV. f

Simplify the following:

1. $\dfrac{3a}{3c}$.
2. $\dfrac{3b}{b}$.
3. $\dfrac{2c^2}{5c}$.
4. $\dfrac{2d}{2d}$.
5. $\dfrac{e^3}{e^2}$.

[6] $\dfrac{3f}{5f}$.
[7] $\dfrac{g^2}{g^2}$.
[8] $\dfrac{6h}{6}$.
[9] $\dfrac{k^4}{4k}$.
[10] $\dfrac{m^6}{m^3}$.

11. $\dfrac{3n^2}{6np}$.
12. $\dfrac{8rs}{6r^2s}$.
13. $\dfrac{s}{st}$.
14. $\dfrac{2x^2y^2}{xy}$.
15. $\dfrac{4z^4}{6z^6}$.

16. $\dfrac{ab^2}{b^2a}$.
17. $\dfrac{4c^4d^4}{4cd}$.
18. $\dfrac{e^6}{3e^2}$.
19. $\dfrac{6f^2g^2}{9g^2h^2}$.
20. $\dfrac{h^2}{h^2k^2}$.

[21] $\dfrac{3m^2}{6mn}$.
[22] $\dfrac{2pr}{r^2}$.
[23] $\dfrac{4rs}{6st}$.
[24] $\dfrac{xy}{yx}$.

[25] $\dfrac{12x}{12xz}$.
[26] $\dfrac{ab}{a^3b^3}$.
[27] $\dfrac{c^6d^8}{c^3d^4}$.
[28] $\dfrac{3ef}{6e^2f^2}$.

[29] $\dfrac{a^2gh}{ahk}$.
[30] $\dfrac{m^4}{m^8}$.
31. $\dfrac{4n^6p}{2n^3q}$.
32. $\dfrac{12r^2s^2}{8rst}$.

33. $\dfrac{x^6y^6}{x^3y^2}$.
34. $\left(\dfrac{3a}{2a}\right)^2$.
35. $\dfrac{b^3c}{(2bc)^2}$.
36. $\dfrac{3d^3e}{(d^2e)^2}$.

37. $\dfrac{f^2(2fg)^2}{(3fg)^3}$.
38. $\dfrac{4p^4q^2r^2}{(2pqr)^2}$.
39. $\dfrac{(3s^4t^2)^2}{3s^4t^4}$.
40. $\dfrac{(6xy^2)^3}{(4x^3y)^2}$.

[41] $\dfrac{3ab^2}{6b^2a^2}$.
[42] $\dfrac{c^3d^3}{(3cd^2)^2}$.
[43] $\dfrac{(2ef)^3}{2ef^3}$.
[44] $\dfrac{m^6n^6p^8}{m^2n^2p^2}$.

Addition and Subtraction of Fractions

Just as is done in Arithmetic, each fraction is replaced by an equivalent fraction so that all the denominators are equal.

Example 10. Simplify $b + \dfrac{2b}{3} - 1\frac{1}{6}b$.

$$1\tfrac{1}{6}b = \frac{7}{6} \times b = \frac{7b}{6},$$

$$\therefore \; b + \frac{2b}{3} - 1\tfrac{1}{6}b = \frac{b}{1} + \frac{2b}{3} - \frac{7b}{6}.$$

The L.C.M. of the denominators 1, 3, 6, is 6,

$$\therefore \; \text{expression} = \frac{6b}{6} + \frac{4b}{6} - \frac{7b}{6}$$

$$= \frac{6b + 4b - 7b}{6} = \frac{3b}{6}$$

$$= \frac{b}{2}.$$

As in Arithmetic, when the process is understood, the step, $\dfrac{6b}{6} + \dfrac{4b}{6} - \dfrac{7b}{6}$, may be omitted.

Example 11. Simplify $\dfrac{7}{10a} + \dfrac{2}{15a}$.

The L.C.M. of the denominators $10a$, $15a$, is $30a$.

$$\therefore \; \frac{7}{10a} + \frac{2}{15a} = \frac{21}{30a} + \frac{4}{30a}$$

$$= \frac{21 + 4}{30a} = \frac{25}{30a}$$

$$= \frac{5}{6a}.$$

Example 12. Simplify $\dfrac{b}{6c} - \dfrac{c}{4b}$.

The L.C.M. of the denominators $6c$, $4b$, is $12\,bc$.

$$\therefore \; \frac{b}{6c} - \frac{c}{4b} = \frac{b \times 2b}{6c \times 2b} - \frac{c \times 3c}{4b \times 3c}$$

$$= \frac{2b^2 - 3c^2}{12bc}.$$

Example 13. Express as a single fraction $\dfrac{r^2}{s} - t$.

$$\frac{r^2}{s} - t = \frac{r^2}{s} - \frac{t}{1} = \frac{r^2}{s} - \frac{ts}{s}$$

$$= \frac{r^2 - ts}{s}.$$

As soon as the process is understood, the intermediate steps in Examples 12 and 13 may be omitted.

EXERCISE IV. g

Copy and complete the following, Nos. 1–6:

1. (i) $\dfrac{3}{4} = \dfrac{\cdots}{12} = \dfrac{\cdots}{28} = \dfrac{\cdots}{100}$; (ii) $\dfrac{a}{b} = \dfrac{\cdots}{2b} = \dfrac{\cdots}{bc} = \dfrac{\cdots}{b^2}$.

2. (i) $\dfrac{8}{5} = \dfrac{16}{\cdots} = \dfrac{40}{\cdots} = \dfrac{64}{\cdots}$; (ii) $\dfrac{c}{d} = \dfrac{5c}{\cdots} = \dfrac{ac}{\cdots} = \dfrac{c^3}{\cdots}$.

[3] $\dfrac{3r}{4s} = \dfrac{\cdots}{8s} = \dfrac{\cdots}{12st} = \dfrac{3r^2}{\cdots}$. **[4]** $\dfrac{2l}{m} = \dfrac{\cdots}{6mn} = \dfrac{6l^3}{\cdots} = \dfrac{\cdots}{m^3}$.

5. $t = \dfrac{\cdots}{3} = \dfrac{\cdots}{2s} = \dfrac{\cdots}{t^3}$. **6.** $\dfrac{2t^2}{4tz} = \dfrac{\cdots}{2z} = \dfrac{3t}{\cdots} = \dfrac{t^3}{\cdots}$.

Simplify the following:

7. (i) $\dfrac{2}{3} + \dfrac{1}{7}$; (ii) $\dfrac{5a}{3} + \dfrac{2a}{7}$. **8.** (i) $\dfrac{3}{5} - \dfrac{2}{7}$; (ii) $\dfrac{4b}{5} - \dfrac{5b}{7}$.

9. (i) $\dfrac{3}{8} + \dfrac{4}{8}$; (ii) $\dfrac{1}{c} + \dfrac{5}{c}$. **10.** (i) $\dfrac{3}{4} - \dfrac{7}{10}$; (ii) $\dfrac{4}{5e} - \dfrac{1}{2e}$.

11. (i) $1 + \dfrac{4}{7}$; (ii) $1 + \dfrac{c}{d}$. **12.** (i) $2 - \dfrac{3}{5}$; (ii) $f - \dfrac{g}{h}$.

13. $\dfrac{a}{3} + \dfrac{a}{6}$. **14.** $\dfrac{2b}{15} - \dfrac{b}{30}$. **15.** $2\frac{1}{3}c + 1\frac{1}{6}c$. **16.** $2d - \dfrac{2d}{5}$.

[17] $\dfrac{e}{10} + \dfrac{e}{15}$. **[18]** $\frac{2}{3}f - \frac{1}{2}f$. **[19]** $g - \frac{1}{4}g$. **[20]** $1\frac{1}{2}h + 2\frac{1}{2}h$.

21. $\frac{2}{5}a + 1\frac{1}{2}a - \frac{1}{10}a - a$. **22.** $\dfrac{3b}{10} - \dfrac{2b}{15} + b + \dfrac{5b}{6}$.

[23] $3\frac{1}{2}c - 1\frac{3}{4}c + \frac{1}{4}c - c$. **[24]** $\dfrac{3d}{4} + d - \dfrac{2d}{3} + \dfrac{d}{6}$.

25. $\dfrac{1}{3a} + \dfrac{1}{6a}$.

26. $\dfrac{b}{2c} - \dfrac{b}{6c}$.

27. $\dfrac{d}{e} - 1$.

[28] $\dfrac{1}{f} - \dfrac{1}{4f}$.

[29] $\dfrac{1}{g} + \dfrac{1}{h}$.

[30] $1 - \dfrac{1}{mn}$.

31. $\dfrac{p}{q} - \dfrac{2p}{5q}$.

32. $\dfrac{1}{2q} + \dfrac{2}{3r}$.

33. $\dfrac{s}{t} + \dfrac{t}{2s}$.

34. $\dfrac{2x}{y} - z$.

35. $\dfrac{1}{a} - \dfrac{a}{2}$.

36. $b - \dfrac{b^2}{c}$.

37. $\dfrac{1}{2de} + \dfrac{3}{e^2}$.

38. $\dfrac{f}{g} - \dfrac{f^2}{g^2}$.

39. $\dfrac{1}{h} - \dfrac{n}{nh}$.

[40] $\dfrac{3}{5m} - \dfrac{1}{10m}$.

[41] $\dfrac{2n}{3p} - \dfrac{n}{6p}$.

[42] $\dfrac{r}{4s} + \dfrac{s}{6r}$.

[43] $t - \dfrac{1}{t}$.

[44] $1 + \dfrac{1}{x}$.

[45] $\dfrac{y}{yz} - \dfrac{1}{z}$.

46. $\dfrac{a}{4ab} + \dfrac{c}{6bc}$.

47. $\dfrac{c}{2d} + \dfrac{d}{2c} - 2$.

48. $\dfrac{f}{gh} + \dfrac{g}{fh} - \dfrac{h}{fg}$.

[49] $\dfrac{3a}{2b} + \dfrac{2a}{3b} + \dfrac{5a}{6b}$.

[50] $\dfrac{b}{c} - \dfrac{c}{d} + \dfrac{d}{b}$.

[51] $\dfrac{fg}{gh} - \dfrac{fg}{fh} - 1$.

52. Add $\dfrac{r}{4s}$ to $\dfrac{r}{12s}$.

53. Subtract $\dfrac{1}{15t}$ from $\dfrac{2}{5t}$.

[54] Add $\dfrac{u}{3v}$ to $\dfrac{u^2}{6uv}$.

[55] Subtract $\dfrac{y^2}{2z}$ from $\dfrac{2y^2}{3z}$.

Simplify the following:

56. (i) $\dfrac{7}{20} \times 60$; (ii) $\dfrac{a}{2b} \times 6b$.

57. (i) $1 \div \dfrac{3}{4}$; (ii) $1 \div \dfrac{c}{2d}$.

[58] (i) $\dfrac{5}{11} \times 2$; (ii) $\dfrac{e}{f} \times 2$.

[59] (i) $\dfrac{15}{14} \div 3$; (ii) $\dfrac{3g}{2h} \div 3$.

60. $p \times \dfrac{q}{r}$.

61. $r \div \dfrac{s}{t}$.

62. $2x \times \dfrac{y^2}{xz}$.

[63] $\dfrac{a}{b} \div \dfrac{c}{d}$.

[64] $\dfrac{e}{f} \times \dfrac{f}{e}$.

[65] $\dfrac{g^2}{h} \times \dfrac{h^2}{g}$.

66. $\dfrac{m}{n} \times \dfrac{n}{p} \div \dfrac{m}{p}$.

67. $x \div \dfrac{1}{y}$.

68. $\dfrac{1}{6r^2} \div \dfrac{1}{4rs}$.

[69] $x \div \dfrac{x^2}{y^2}$.

[70] $3y \times \dfrac{3z}{y^2}$.

[71] $ab^2 \times \dfrac{1}{b^2a}$.

72. $\dfrac{2ab}{15c^2} \times \dfrac{5bc}{4a^2}.$ **73.** $\dfrac{4f^2}{6gh} \div \dfrac{3fg}{5fh}.$ **74.** $\left(\dfrac{p}{3q}\right)^2 \times 3q.$

[75] $\dfrac{1}{r^3} \div r^3.$ **[76]** $\dfrac{s^6}{t^2} \times \dfrac{t^6}{s^2}.$ **[77]** $\dfrac{xy}{z} \div \dfrac{y}{zx}.$

Expressions involving Fractions

Example 14. In a mixed school of n pupils, there are b boys; what fraction of the school consists of girls?

Since there are b boys, there are $(n-b)$ girls;

$$\therefore \quad \frac{n-b}{n} \text{ of the school consists of girls;}$$

or $\dfrac{b}{n}$ of the school consists of boys,

$$\therefore \quad \left(1 - \frac{b}{n}\right) \text{ of the school consists of girls,}$$

$$\therefore \quad \frac{n-b}{n} \text{ of the school consists of girls.}$$

Note.—If a problem with letters presents any difficulty, invent a similar problem with special numbers and solve that first; *e.g.* In a school of 500 pupils, there are 200 boys; what fraction of the school consists of girls?

EXERCISE IV. h

1. Express in yards (i) $4\frac{1}{2}l$ feet, (ii) $8n$ inches.

2. What fraction is (i) 8 pence of 3 shillings, (ii) p pence of s shillings, (iii) r shillings of £t?

[3] What fraction is $2n$ inches of n feet?

[4] A rug is 6 feet long, m feet wide; find its area in sq. yards.

5. What must be added (i) to $\frac{2}{3}$ to make $\frac{3}{4}$,

$$\text{(ii) to } \frac{a}{b} \text{ to make } \frac{ap}{bq}?$$

6. (i) The product of two numbers is 8; one of them is 3, find the other.

   (ii) The product of two numbers is $6k$; one of them is $9n$, find the other.

[7] A jug contains p pints of water; how many pints remain after $\frac{q}{r}$ pints have been poured out?

8. 2 oz. of sweets cost 5 pence; find the cost of w oz.

[9] Taking 8 km. as equal to 5 miles, express d miles in km.

10. A man walks 4 miles an hour, how long does he take to walk $\frac{2p}{3}$ miles?

11. In a mixed school there are x boys and y girls; what fraction of the school consists of boys?

[12] A man buys n tons of fuel, of which k tons are coal and the rest is coke; what fraction of the total is coke?

13. From a stick l inches long a part p inches long is cut off; what fraction of the stick remains?

[14] A boy sleeps k hours each day; for what fraction of the day is he awake?

[15] After the nth day of January, what fraction of January remains?

16. A man buys a table for £($6n$) and sells it for £($8n$); what fraction of the cost price is his profit?

[17] A man buys a horse for £($12x$) and sells it for £($9y$); what fraction of the cost price is his profit?

18. What fraction of a cake remains when $\frac{c}{d}$ of it has been eaten?

[19] Three boys share a sum of money; the oldest gets $\frac{a}{3b}$ of the amount, the youngest gets $\frac{a}{6b}$ of the amount, what fraction of the amount does the third boy get?

20. (i) By what must 12 be multiplied to make 15?

(ii) By what must $\frac{r}{s}$ be multiplied to make $\frac{s}{r}$?

[21] A pencil costs $\frac{3p}{2}$ pence; how many pencils can be bought for half a crown?

22. A clerk addresses n letters an hour; how many minutes does he take to address $12p$ letters?

[23] A packet of paper 1 inch high contains k sheets; what is the thickness of 1 sheet?

24. In Fig. 53, what fraction is the shortest side of the perimeter of the triangle? If the perimeter of the triangle is $6s$ inches, find the length of the shortest side in terms of s.

FIG. 53.　　　　　　　FIG. 54.

[25] In Fig. 53, if the dimensions are given in inches and if $x = \dfrac{d}{10}$, express the perimeter of the triangle in terms of d.

26. A shed l feet long, b feet wide (see Fig. 54), is built in the corner of a rectangular enclosure x feet long, y feet wide. What fraction of the total area does the shed occupy? What is the value of this fraction if $x = 2l$, $y = 3b$?

[27] From a square sheet of cardboard of side $3t$ inches, a square of side $2t$ inches is cut away. What fraction of the original sheet remains?

[28] A man smokes $\frac{1}{4}$ lb. of tobacco a week; how long does **W** lb. of tobacco last him?

29. A man has to go from **A** to **B**; after travelling s miles he has gone $\frac{1}{5}$ of the total distance. How far is **A** from **B**?

*30. How many $\frac{3}{4}$-lb. packets of tea can be made up from w lb. of tea?

*31. I buy n oranges, but r per cent. of them are bad; how many of the oranges are fit to eat?

*32. After motoring d miles, I have gone $\dfrac{1}{n}$th of the total distance. What is the total distance? How much farther have I still to go?

*33. After $\frac{2}{3}$ of a chest of tea has been used, p lb. of tea remain; how many lb. of tea did the chest hold originally?

*34. Coal costs x shillings per ton; how many tons can be bought for £p? If the price rises to y shillings per ton, how many fewer tons can now be bought for £p?

*35. One tap can fill a bath in t minutes; what fraction of the bath is filled in 1 minute? A second tap can fill the bath in $2t$ minutes; what fraction of the bath is filled in 1 minute if both taps are turned on?

*36. After selling two-fifths of his sheep, a farmer has n sheep left. How many did he sell?

*37. The length of a rectangle is $\dfrac{1}{n}$th of the perimeter. What fraction is the breadth of the perimeter?

*38. A man starts from a boat-house B and rows downstream; he takes t minutes to row 4 miles; he then turns and takes $4t$ minutes to get back to B. How far from B is he (i) at a time $2t$ minutes after leaving B, (ii) at half-time?

Removal and Insertion of Brackets

Brackets show the order in which operations must be performed.

If brackets are absent, a different order may be necessary and this will often give a different answer.

$12 - (5 + 3)$ means "From 12 subtract $5 + 3$"; the result is the same as first subtracting 5 and then subtracting 3; thus $12 - (5 + 3) = 12 - 5 - 3$, as is easily checked:

$$12 - (5 + 3) = 12 - 8 = 4,$$
$$12 - 5 - 3 = 7 - 3 = 4.$$

In general $\qquad x - (y + z) = x - y - z.$

$12 - (5 - 3)$ means "From 12 subtract $5 - 3$." If we subtract 5 from 12 we have subtracted too much, namely 3 too much, we must therefore compensate by adding 3; thus

$$12 - (5 - 3) = 12 - 5 + 3,$$

as is easily checked:

$$12 - (5 - 3) = 12 - 2 = 10,$$
$$12 - 5 + 3 = 7 + 3 = 10.$$

In general $\qquad x - (y - z) = x - y + z.$

In the same way we see that $12 + (5 + 3) = 12 + 5 + 3$:

$$12 + (5 + 3) = 12 + 8 = 20,$$
$$12 + 5 + 3 = 17 + 3 = 20.$$

In general $x + (y + z) = x + y + z.$

Similarly we see that $12 + (5 - 3) = 12 + 5 - 3$:

$$12 + (5 - 3) = 12 + 2 = 14,$$
$$12 + 5 - 3 = 17 - 3 = 14.$$

In general $x + (y - z) = x + y - z.$

The rules for the removal of brackets are therefore as follows:

(i) If a bracket has a + sign in front of it, any sign connecting terms in the bracket remains the same when the bracket is removed.

(ii) If a bracket has a − sign in front of it, any sign connecting terms in the bracket is changed when the bracket is removed.

Thus $a + (b - c + d) = a + b - c + d$ and $a - (b - c + d) = a - b + c - d.$

Brackets may be inserted by reversing the process:

thus $x + y + z = x + (y + z)$ and $x + y - z = x + (y - z).$

But care is needed when a bracket is inserted after a **minus** *sign:*

thus $a - b - c - d = a - (b + c + d)$

and $p - q + r - s = p - (q - r + s).$

When a bracket is inserted after a **minus** *sign, all the signs connecting the terms which are put inside the bracket must be* **changed.**

Whenever a bracket is inserted after a minus sign, the work should be *checked* by removing the bracket *mentally* to make sure that the new expression is equal to the original expression.

Example 15.   Simplify $2a - 7b - 3b.$
$$2a - 7b - 3b = 2a - (7b + 3b)$$
$$= 2a - 10b.$$

Example 16.   Simplify $2c - 7d + 3d.$
$$2c - 7d + 3d = 2c - (7d - 3d)$$
$$= 2c - 4d.$$

Example 16 shows that the result of subtracting $7d$ and then adding $3d$ is equivalent to subtracting $4d$. Some oral work illustrating this process will be found useful:

Oral Work: Write down the results of the following operations:

1. Subtract $5d$ then add (i) $3d$, (ii) $8d$; $x - 5d + 3d$; $x - 5d + 8d$.

2. Subtract $8e$ then add (i) $2e$, (ii) $11e$; $x - 8e + 2e$; $x - 8e + 11e$.

3. Subtract $7f$ then add (i) $4f$, (ii) $9f$; $x - 7f + 4f$; $x - 7f + 9f$.

4. Subtract $9g$ then add (i) $3g$, (ii) $10g$; $x - 9g + 3g$; $x - 9g + 10g$.

EXERCISE IV. j

What are the values of the following:

1. $3 + (4 + 5)$; $3 + 4 + 5$. **2.** $10 + (6 - 2)$; $10 + 6 - 2$.

3. $9 - (2 + 3)$; $9 - 2 - 3$. **4.** $7 - (5 - 1)$; $7 - 5 + 1$.

State in words the meanings of the following:

5. $a + (b - c)$. **6.** $r - (s + t)$. **7.** $x - (y - z)$.

Remove the brackets from the following:

8. $a + (b - c)$. **9.** $d - (e + f)$. **10.** $(g - h) - k$.

11. $(a - b) + (c - d - e)$. **12.** $(p - q) - (r + s - t)$.

Simplify the following:

13. $a + (a + 2b)$. **14.** $3f + (2f - 2g)$. **15.** $(3 - k) + (3 + k)$.

[16] $c + (d - c)$. **[17]** $2e + (3 - e)$. **[18]** $(k - 4l) - 4l$.

19. $3m - (m + n)$. **20.** $2n - (p - n)$. **21.** $6x - (3x + 2y)$.

22. $r + 2s - (r + s)$. **23.** $1 - (t - 1)$. **24.** $4d - (c - 3d)$.

[25] $2y - (z - 5y)$. **[26]** $6a - (3a + 2b)$. **[27]** $9 - (3 + 6e)$.

28. $(g + 3) - (g - 1)$. **29.** $(m - 2n) + (2n - p)$.

[30] $(3r - 2s) - (5s - 4r)$. **[31]** $(1 + 2f) + (1 - 2f)$.

[32] $(2h + 3k) - (2h - 3k)$. **[33]** $(2 - 2t) - (t + 1)$.

34. $(a + b + c) + (a + b - c)$. **35.** $(d + 2e + 3f) - (d - 2e - 3f)$.

[36] $(f + g - h) - (f - g + h)$. **[37]** $(4p - 2q + 5r) + (r + 3q - p)$.

38. $(r - s) + (s - t) - (r - t)$. **39.** $x + 5y - 6z - (x - 5y + 6z)$.

40. $(2a - b) - (2b - c) - (c - a)$. **41.** $3d - 3 - (1 + d) + (1 - d)$.

[42] $(a + 2b - c) - (a - b - c)$. **[43]** $7 - (2 - k) - (4 - k)$.

Copy and complete the following:

44. $a+b-c=a+(...)$.

45. $x-y-z=x-(...)$.

46. $l-m+n=l-(...)$.

47. $r-s-t+x=r-(...)$.

[**48**] $f-g+h+k=f-(...)$.

[**49**] $a-b+c-d=a-(...)$.

Simplify the following:

50. $10a-2a-4a$.

51. $9b-b+4b$.

[**52**] $12c-8c+5c$.

53. $2d-3e-3e$.

54. $2f-2g+6g$.

[**55**] $5h-6k+7k$.

56. $4m-5n+3n$.

57. $3p-6r+2r$.

58. $4s-5t+t$.

59. $8r-10s+5s$.

60. $3t-7x+x$.

61. $4y-9z+3z$.

[**62**] $7a-8b+2b$.

[**63**] $5c-9d+d$.

[**64**] $2f+3g-6f$.

65. $5p-3q-6q+4q$.

66. $2r+9s-11s-3s$.

67. $3x-y+7y-10y$.

[**68**] $2a+5b-b-7a$.

[**69**] $c-7d-2d+5d$.

[**70**] $e+7f-4f-3e$.

Solve the following equations:

71. $x-(7-x)=5$.

72. $3y=7-(2+y)$.

[**73**] $4-(3t+1)=3$.

[**74**] $(3n-2)-(3-5n)=1$.

75. $(2z-1)-(z+1)=0$.

76. $1-(2r-4)-(r-5)=0$.

77. Subtract $(a-b+2c)$ from $(a+2b-c)$.

[**78**] Subtract $(d+e+f)$ from $(2d-e+f)$.

79. Subtract $(p-2q)$ from the sum of $(3q-p-r)$ and $(r+2p-q)$.

[**80**] Subtract $(r-s)$ from the sum of $(r+2s-t)$ and $(r-s+2t)$.

81. What must be added to $3m-2n+p$ to make $m+n-2p$?

82. By how much does $2x-y-z$ exceed $y-x+2z$?

Example 17. Simplify $2(4r+3s)-3(2r+3s)$.

$$2(4r+3s)-3(2r+3s)=(8r+6s)-(6r+9s)$$
$$=8r+6s-6r-9s$$
$$=2r-3s.$$

Mistakes are less likely to occur if the work is done in steps as in Example 17: multiply first and afterwards remove the bracket. *Do not try at first to do both operations in a single line.*

Example 18. Simplify $\frac{3}{4}(3x - 2) - \frac{2}{3}(2x - 1)$.

$$\frac{3}{4}(3x - 2) - \frac{2}{3}(2x - 1) = \frac{3(3x - 2)}{4} - \frac{2(2x - 1)}{3};$$

the L.C.M. of the denominators 4, 3, is 12,

$$\therefore \text{ expression} = \frac{9(3x - 2)}{12} - \frac{8(2x - 1)}{12}$$

$$= \frac{9(3x - 2) - 8(2x - 1)}{12}$$

$$= \frac{(27x - 18) - (16x - 8)}{12}$$

$$= \frac{27x - 18 - 16x + 8}{12}$$

$$= \frac{11x - 10}{12}.$$

Example 19. Simplify $\dfrac{a + b}{4a} - \dfrac{a - b}{6b} - 1$.

The L.C.M. of the denominators, $4a$ and $6b$, is $12ab$.

$$\frac{a + b}{4a} - \frac{a - b}{6b} - 1 = \frac{3b(a + b)}{12ab} - \frac{2a(a - b)}{12ab} - \frac{12ab}{12ab}$$

$$= \frac{(3ab + 3b^2) - (2a^2 - 2ab) - 12ab}{12ab}$$

$$= \frac{3ab + 3b^2 - 2a^2 + 2ab - 12ab}{12ab}$$

$$= \frac{3b^2 - 7ab - 2a^2}{12ab}.$$

Example 20. Solve the equation, $x - \dfrac{2x - 1}{5} - \dfrac{x + 2}{3} = 1$.

Multiply each side by 15,

$$15x - \frac{15(2x - 1)}{5} - \frac{15(x + 2)}{3} = 15,$$

$$\therefore \ 15x - 3(2x - 1) - 5(x + 2) = 15,$$

$$\therefore \ 15x - (6x - 3) - (5x + 10) = 15,$$

$$\therefore \ 15x - 6x + 3 - 5x - 10 = 15,$$

$$\therefore \ 15x - 6x - 5x = 15 - 3 + 10,$$

$$\therefore \ 4x = 22$$

$$\therefore \ x = \tfrac{22}{4}$$

$$= 5\tfrac{1}{2}.$$

EXERCISE IV. k

Remove the brackets from the following:

1. $2(3a - 4)$.   2. $b(x - y)$.   3. $3(p + q)p$.

[4] $a(b + 2c)$.   [5] $(c - d)k$.   [6] $2r(3r - s)$.

7. $x^2(x^2 - y^2)$.   8. $2ab(a + b)$.   9. $3c^2(1 - 3c)$.

10. $\frac{1}{2}(4n - 2)$.   11. $\frac{1}{x}(x^2 + 2xy)$.   12. $\frac{1}{3}(6b + 2c)$.

[13] $\frac{1}{5}(10x - 15y)$.   [14] $\frac{1}{a^2}(a^6 - a^3b^3)$.   [15] $\frac{1}{2}b(c + 6d)$.

Copy and complete the following:

16. $x + 2y - 2z = x + 2(...)$.   17. $a - 3b - 6c = a - 3(...)$.

18. $2r^2 - 8rs = 2r(...)$.   19. $p - 6q + 4r = p - 2(...)$.

[20] $2a - 8c - 3x - 9z = 2(...) - 3(...)$.

[21] $a^2 + 2ab - 3p^2 + 4pq = a(...) - p(...)$.

Simplify the following:

22. $5(t + 1) - 3(t - 1)$.   23. $4(r - s) + 3(s - r)$.

24. $3(a - b) - 2(a + b)$.   25. $7(c - d) - 2(c - 2d)$.

[26] $3(f + h) - 5(h - f)$.   [27] $4(u + v) - 3(u + 3v)$.

28. $a(a + 2b) - b(a - b)$.   29. $2x(4x - 5) - 5(x - 2)$.

30. $2p(p + 3q) - 3q(2p + q)$.   31. $y(x + 2y) - x(y - 3x)$.

[32] $a(a + 3b) - 3b(a + 3b)$.   [33] $3c(3c - 2d) - 2d(3c - 2d)$.

34. $\frac{t - 1}{3} + \frac{t + 1}{2}$.   35. $\frac{p - 2}{3} - \frac{p + 1}{4}$.

36. $\frac{1}{2}(x + 1) - \frac{1}{3}(x - 1)$.   37. $\frac{1}{5}(2a - 1) + \frac{1}{7}(1 - 2a)$.

[38] $\frac{r + s}{4} - \frac{r - s}{5}$.   [39] $\frac{2t - 3}{10} - \frac{2t + 3}{15}$.

40. $\frac{2}{3}(a + 2b) - \frac{1}{2}(a + b)$.   41. $\frac{3}{4}(c - d) - \frac{1}{6}(c + d)$.

[42] $\frac{4}{5}(p + 2q) + \frac{3}{5}(p - q)$.   [43] $\frac{1}{4}(x + 2y) - \frac{3}{10}(x - y)$.

44. $1 - \frac{a - b}{a}$.   45. $\frac{c}{2d} - \frac{c - d}{3d}$.   46. $\frac{3(d - e)}{4} + e$.

47. $\frac{s - 2}{4t} + \frac{s - 1}{6t}$.   48. $\frac{e - 2f}{12e} - \frac{e + 3f}{60e}$.

[49] $a - \dfrac{a-b}{2}.$

[50] $\dfrac{2c}{3d} - \dfrac{6-c}{12d}.$

[51] $1 - \dfrac{5p-3q}{5p}.$

[52] $\dfrac{a+x}{2ax} - \dfrac{a-x}{3ax}.$

53. $\dfrac{2y+z}{z} - \dfrac{y-z}{y}.$

54. $\dfrac{m}{n} - \dfrac{2n-m}{m}.$

55. $\dfrac{a}{2b} + \dfrac{b}{2a} - \dfrac{a^2+b^2}{6ab}.$

56. $\dfrac{x+y}{9x} - \dfrac{x-y}{6y} - 1.$

[57] $\dfrac{e-2f}{3f} - \dfrac{e-2f}{4e}.$

[58] $1 - \dfrac{c+d}{2c} - \dfrac{c-d}{3c}.$

[59] $\dfrac{a^3+2b^3}{b^3} - \dfrac{a^3-2b^3}{a^3}.$

[60] $\dfrac{r+2s}{3s} - \dfrac{2r-s}{2r} + 1.$

Solve the following equations:

61. $5(x+1) - 3(x-1) = 14.$

[62] $7(8-n) - 5(11-n) + 5 = 0.$

63. $t - \frac{1}{7}(2t-3) = 4.$

[64] $z - \frac{2}{5}(z+1) = 5.$

65. $\dfrac{r+1}{2} + \dfrac{r-1}{3} = 1.$

[66] $\dfrac{p+1}{2} - \dfrac{2(p-1)}{3} = 0.$

67. $\dfrac{2(y-1)}{3} - \dfrac{y+5}{4} = 6.$

[68] $6 - \dfrac{3(n-7)}{4} = \frac{1}{2}n.$

69. $10 - \dfrac{5(1+x)}{3} + \dfrac{3x+1}{5} = 0.$

[70] $\dfrac{2y+1}{5} - \dfrac{y-1}{3} = 1.$

Systems of Brackets

If one set of brackets is enclosed inside another set of brackets, the meaning of the expression is more easily understood if different shapes of brackets are used.

The ordinary forms of brackets employed are as follows:

$$a-(b+c); \quad a-\{b+c\}; \quad a-[b-c]; \quad a-\overline{b-c}.$$

The use of —— in the last expression is similar to its use in the fraction $\dfrac{b-c}{2}$ which means $\frac{1}{2}(b-c)$.

When simplifying expressions containing brackets enclosed in other brackets, remove the innermost bracket first, and collect like terms (if any) before removing the next inner bracket.

Example 21. Express in bracket form the result of subtracting $5a - (b + 3a)$ from $3b - (a - 2b)$, and simplify it.

The result of the subtraction may be written

$$\{3b - (a - 2b)\} - \{5a - (b + 3a)\}.$$

$$\text{The expression} = \{3b - a + 2b\} - \{5a - b - 3a\}$$
$$= \{5b - a\} - \{2a - b\}$$
$$= 5b - a - 2a + b$$
$$= 6b - 3a.$$

The answer may also be expressed in the form, $3(2b - a)$.

EXERCISE IV. m

Simplify the following:

1. $a - \{a - (b - c)\} - c$.

2. $p + q - [p - \{p - q\}]$.

3. $3\{(2a + b) - (a - b)\}$.

4. $2\{3(x + 1) - 2(x - 1)\}$.

[5] $c - \{c - (1 + c)\}$.

[6] $2d - 3\{4 - \overline{d - 1}\}$.

[7] $3f + g - \{4f - 3(f - g)\}$.

[8] $2\{n - (p - n)\} - 3(n + p)$.

9. $10r - 2\{r - 3(4 - r)\}$.

10. $t - 3\{t - 5(t - 1)\}$.

11. $2p[p - q - \overline{p - 2q}]$.

12. $5y(x - 2y) - 2x\{x - (x - y)\}$.

[13] $2\{a(a - b) - b(a + b)\}$.

[14] $2c^2 - [c(c + 2d) - d(c - d)]$.

15. $3\{e - [2 - 2(e - 1)] + e\}$.

16. $2f - \{2f - [f - 2(f - g) - g]\}$.

[17] $y^2 - 2y\{z - 4(y - z)\}$.

[18] $r\{r(r + s) - s(r - s)\}$.

Express the answers to Nos. 19–26 in bracket form, and simplify:

19. Subtract $4p - (p + 3q)$ from $5q - (2q - p)$.

[20] Subtract $a - (b - c)$ from $c - (b - a)$.

21. Subtract $xy - y(2x - z)$ from $3xy + x(2z - y)$.

22. By how much does $4l - 3(m - 2n)$ exceed $m - 2(l + 3n)$?

23. What must be added to $2f - 3\{u - v\}$ to make $3u - 4\{v - f\}$?

24. What must be subtracted from $5r(r - s) - s^2$ to leave $s^2 - 3r(s - r)$?

[25] By how much does $5x(x + y) - 2y^2$ exceed $2y(2x - y) - 3x^2$?

[26] What must be subtracted from $2(r - s) + t$ to leave $2(r - t)$?

27. Find the value of $\frac{n}{2}\{2a + (n - 1)d\}$ if $a = 1$, $d = 2$, $n = 10$.

28. If a wave h feet high travels across the sea where the depth is d feet, its velocity is $\sqrt{\{32(d+3h)\}}$ feet per second. What is the velocity of a wave 2 feet high moving across water 12 feet deep?

29. If a clothes-line, l feet long, is attached to the tops of two poles, d feet apart, the sag at the middle is approximately $\sqrt{\{\frac{3}{8}d(l-d)\}}$ feet. Find the sag if the poles are 24 feet apart and if the clothes-line is 25 feet long.

30. What sum of money is represented by £$\{\frac{1}{240}[12(20x+y)+z]\}$ if $x=3$, $y=5$, $z=7$? Give the answer as a compound quantity.

[31] What weight is represented by $\frac{1}{80}\{(20p+q)4+r\}$ tons, if $p=11$, $q=13$, $r=3$? Give the answer as a compound quantity.

REVISION EXERCISE R. 2. (Ch. III–IV)

Solve the equations:

1. $5-n=n-8$.　**[2]** $\frac{2}{5}p=9$.　　**3.** $2\cdot5r=3\cdot5$.

[4] $\dfrac{2t}{3}-\dfrac{4t}{9}=1$.　**5.** $\frac{1}{5}(x-2)=\frac{1}{4}$.　**[6]** $\dfrac{3}{2y}-\dfrac{4}{5y}=\dfrac{1}{4}$.

Simplify:

7. $b-\dfrac{b}{5}$.　**[8]** $3\frac{2}{3}c-1\frac{1}{6}c$.　**9.** $15d^2-5d^2-4d^2-6d^2$.

10. $6e^2\div3e^2$.　**[11]** $8f^6\div2f$.　**12.** $(3g^4)^3$.

13. $\dfrac{5a}{4b}\times\dfrac{4b}{5a}$.　**[14]** $1\div\dfrac{c}{d}$.　**15.** $8xy^6\div2\frac{2}{5}y^2$.

16. $3pq\times4qr$.　**[17]** $t^2\times2t^2\times4t^2$.　**[18]** $(2x)^3\times2x^3$.

19. $\dfrac{6r^6}{2r^2}$.　**20.** $\dfrac{3\frac{1}{2}x}{\frac{1}{4}y}$.　**[21]** $\dfrac{z^2}{(3z)^2}$.　**[22]** $1-\dfrac{4b}{6b}$.

23. $\dfrac{1}{15n}+\dfrac{1}{30n}$.　**[24]** $\dfrac{b^2}{c^2}-\dfrac{b^3}{c^3}$.　**25.** $\dfrac{1}{t}-t$.

26. $(x-y+z)-(z-x-y)$.　**[27]** $a(b+2c)-b(a-c)$.

28. $\frac{3}{4}(x-2)-\frac{1}{6}(x-1)$.　**[29]** $\frac{1}{4}(6y-12z)-(y-z)$.

30. $a-\frac{1}{2}(2a-3b)$.　**[31]** $x(y-2z)-y(z-2x)-z(x-2y)$.

32. $c-\{2c-(2-c)\}$.　**[33]** $3\{m-\overline{n-m}\}-2\{n-\overline{m-n}\}$.

34. Subtract $12n$ oz. from $2n$ lb. Answer (i) in oz., (ii) in lb.

[35] From a stick of length $\frac{3}{4}t$ feet a portion of length $6t$ inches is cut off. Find the length of the remainder in (i) inches, (ii) feet.

36. Find the total cost of p pears at 3 pence each and m melons at 1s. 6d. each, (i) in pence, (ii) in shillings.

[37] What fraction is $4k$ half-crowns of £$(3m)$?

38. A rectangular tank is $8l$ feet long, $3l$ feet wide; it contains $6l^3$ cu. ft. of water; find the depth of the water.

[39] A man bicycles 12 miles an hour; how many minutes does he take to go $\dfrac{4n}{5}$ miles?

40. A note-book costs $\dfrac{4t}{3}$ pence; how many can be bought for two shillings?

41. Simplify and arrange in *ascending* powers of x,

$$2x(x^2 + 4x + 5) - 3(x^2 + 4x - 5).$$

42. Find the H.C.F. and L.C.M. of $15p^2q^2r^2$, $10pqr^3$, $25q^3r$.

43. To an odd number I add twice the next larger odd number; the result is 55. Find the first odd number.

[44] The angles of a triangle are $2x$ degrees, $(3x + 5)$ degrees, $4(x + 10)$ degrees. Find the value of x and the angles.

45. A man is now 36 years old and his son is 4. In how many years' time will the man be just 3 times as old as his son?

[46] The frame for a picture costs three-quarters of the amount the picture costs; the two together cost £3, 3s. Find the cost of the picture.

47. For what value of p is $5(p - 3) - 5$ equal to $2(p + 3) + 1$?

[48] If $x = 5c - 17$ and $y = 12 - 3c$, find the value of c if $\frac{1}{3}x + \frac{1}{2}y$ is equal to 1.

49. A rectangle is $(3a - 2b)$ inches long and $(2a - b)$ inches wide. Find in *feet* the perimeter of the rectangle in terms of b, if $a = 3b$.

Write down by means of brackets expressions for the following:

50. The product of four consecutive whole numbers if the smallest is $n - 1$.

[51] The product of three consecutive odd numbers if the largest is $2m + 1$.

CHAPTER V

DIRECTED NUMBERS

Signless Numbers. In the previous chapters, the signs +
and − have been used solely as orders: "add," "subtract." The
expression, 5 − 3, means "From 5 subtract 3"; the numbers,
5 and 3, are signless. For many kinds of measurement, signless
numbers supply all that is needed, *e.g.* the number of days in a
week, the number of miles from London to Land's End, etc.
In quantities of this kind there is no idea of "up and down"
or "backwards and forwards" or "clockwise and counter-
clockwise." But when quantities which involve the idea of
direction occur, it saves time to give further meanings to the
symbols + and −.

Positive and Negative Numbers. Suppose I buy a number of
things and sell them again, the results of the transactions may be
recorded as follows:

	House	Car	Picture	Horse	Field	Carpet
Gain -	£80			0	£60	
Loss -		£40	£15	0		£12

But it is *shorter* to write:

	House	Car	Picture	Horse	Field	Carpet
Gain -	£(+80)	£(−40)	£(−15)	0	£(+60)	£(−12)

The symbols + and − in this table are not instructions to add or
subtract; they are called the signs of the numbers.

The number (+80) is called a **positive number**, the number
(−40) is called a **negative number**. My gain £(+80) is a short
way of saying that I am £80 better off, or that my capital *goes
up* £80; my gain £(−40) is a short way of saying that I am £40
worse off, or that my capital *comes down* £40. Thus this new
notation represents in a short form up-and-down movements,
backwards-and-forwards movements, etc., in fact, quantities
with which the idea of direction is associated; for this reason
positive and negative numbers are called **directed numbers**. The
symbol 0 means that there is no change either way, (+0) is the
same as (−0) and so each is simply denoted by 0.

EXERCISE V. a (Oral)

1. On a Centigrade thermometer (see Fig. 55) the freezing-point of water is indicated by 0°.

(i) Express in shorthand form the following temperatures: 4° below freezing-point; 20° above freezing-point; 15° of frost.

(ii) What is the meaning of (− 5) degrees, of (+ 100) degrees?

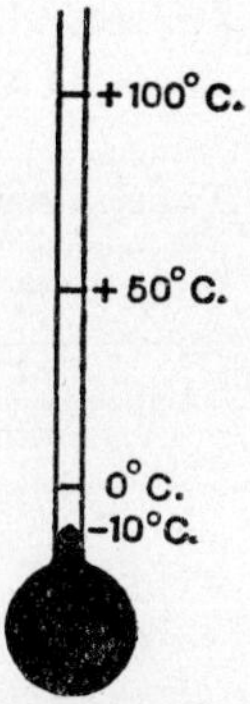

2. Explain the meaning of the following:

	Winchester	The Dead Sea
Height in feet above sea-level -	+ 128	− 1300

FIG. 55.

3. A gun is being ranged by an aeroplane on a target; the direction is correct; the distance of the fall of the shell from the target is signalled as follows:

Round	I	II	III	IV	V	VI
Distance in yards -	+ 260	− 180	+ 140	− 70	+ 35	O.K.

What do these signals mean?

4. Four clocks are being regulated; express in shorthand form the following records noted one day:

Clock	I	II	III	IV
Seconds fast -	17		8	
Seconds slow -		8		14

[5] Express in shorthand form a man's bank balance:

Date	Jan. 1	April 1	July 1	Oct. 1
Credit -		£70	£24	
Overdraft -	£55			£32

[6] A stone is thrown vertically upwards with velocity 40 feet per second. Explain the meaning of the following table, which shows its velocity at half-second intervals:

Time in seconds -	0	$\frac{1}{2}$	1	$1\frac{1}{2}$	2	$2\frac{1}{2}$
Velocity in ft. per sec.	+40	+24	+8	−8	−24	−40

7. Taking 12 noon as zero hour, and 1 hour as the unit, express by directed numbers the following times: 3 p.m.; 11 a.m.; 8 a.m.; 4.30 p.m.; 10.30 a.m.

8. Rewrite the following, using signless numbers:

(i) A temperature of (− 8) degrees Centigrade.

(ii) The surface of the Sea of Galilee is (− 680) feet above sea-level.

(iii) A is (− 5) miles east of B.

(iv) C is (− 8) miles north of D.

(v) My watch is (− 3) minutes fast.

(vi) This year I have gained (− 10) lb. in weight.

[9] Taking Greenwich time as the standard, the following variations occur in local time:

		Berne	Halifax	Petrograd	New York
Hours	-	+1	−4	+2	−5

What does this mean?

The Number-Scale

On the Centigrade scale, the temperature at which water freezes is marked 0 (zero); temperatures above zero are represented by positive numbers, temperatures below zero by negative numbers. This is an example of what is called the *number-scale* (see Fig. 56).

Addition and Subtraction

The number-scale can be used to perform addition and subtraction, moving up and down it, as on a ladder.

Thus, to add $(+2)$ to (-5), start at (-5) and move 2 steps up the ladder: $(-5)+(+2)=(-3)$.

We therefore also say that $(+2)+(-5)=(-3)$, and this means that to add (-5) to $(+2)$, we start at $(+2)$ and move 5 steps down the ladder.

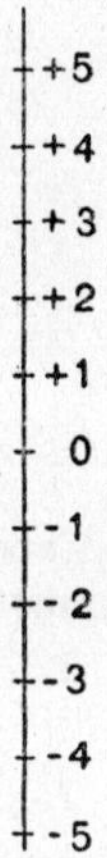

In general, $+(+N)$ means "add $(+N)$"; to do this, move N steps up the scale;

and $+(-N)$ means "add $(-N)$"; to do this, move N steps down the scale.

For *subtraction*,

since $\qquad (-3)=(-5)+(+2),$

we say that $\qquad (-3)-(+2)=(-5).$

But if we start at (-3), we arrive at (-5) by moving 2 steps down the scale; thus to subtract $(+2)$, we move 2 steps down the scale.

Also, since

$\qquad (-3)=(+2)+(-5),$ we say that $(-3)-(-5)=(+2).$

But if we start at (-3), we arrive at $(+2)$ by moving 5 steps up the scale; thus to subtract (-5), we move 5 steps up the scale.

In general, $-(+N)$ means "subtract $(+N)$"; to do this, move N steps down the scale;

and $-(-N)$ means "subtract $(-N)$"; to do this, move N steps up the scale.

The process of moving N steps up the scale may be represented more shortly by writing $+N$, and that of moving N steps down the scale by $-N$. We therefore make the following **rule of signs**:

$\qquad +(+N)=+N; \quad -(-N)=+N; \quad$ move up N steps.

$\qquad +(-N)=-N; \quad -(+N)=-N; \quad$ move down N steps.

+5
+4
+3
+2
+1
0
-1
-2
-3
-4
-5

Fig. 56.

Example 1. State how the following operations can be performed on the number-scale, and give the results:

(i) $(+3)-(+7)$; (ii) $(+2)+(-3)$; (iii) $(-4)-(-6)$.

(i) Start at $(+3)$ and move 7 steps down the scale, we arrive at (-4); $\therefore$ $(+3)-(+7)=(-4)$.

(ii) Start at $(+2)$ and move 3 steps down the scale, we arrive at (-1); $\therefore$ $(+2)+(-3)=(-1)$.

(iii) Start at (-4) and move 6 steps up the scale, we arrive at $(+2)$; $\therefore$ $(-4)-(-6)=(+2)$.

EXERCISE V. b (Oral)

State how the following operations can be performed on the number-scale and give the results:

1. $(+8)-(+5)$.   2. $(+7)+(-4)$.   3. $(+6)-(-2)$.
4. $(-2)-(+4)$.   5. $(-3)+(-6)$.   6. $(-4)-(-7)$.
7. $(-3)+(+3)$.   8. $0-(-4)$.   9. $(+2)+(-2)$.

Give in full expressions for the final temperatures on the Centigrade scale, and then simplify:

10. First temperature $(-3°)$; a rise of $(+5°)$.
11. First temperature $(+5°)$; a fall of $(+8°)$.
12. First temperature $(-4°)$; a rise of $(-3°)$.
13. First temperature $(-7°)$; a fall of $(-2°)$.

Give in full expressions for the *rise* in temperature on the Centigrade scale, and then simplify:

14. First temperature $(-4°)$; second temperature $(+3°)$.
15. First temperature $(+10°)$; second temperature $(+4°)$.
16. First temperature $(+5°)$; second temperature $(-3°)$.
17. First temperature $(-6°)$; second temperature $(-2°)$.

18. A is 100 feet above sea-level, B is 60 feet below sea-level. What is the height of A above B? What is the value of $(+100)-(-60)$?

19. A man starts the year £100 in debt and ends the year £30 in debt. How much has he gained during the year? Simplify $(-30)-(-100)$.

[20] The temperature of a freezing mixture is (– 12°) Centigrade. It is heated up to (+4°) Centigrade. What is the rise in temperature ?

[21] Which is the greater, (– 3) or (– 7), and by how much ?

22. What must be added to

    (i) (+5) to give (+2); (ii) (– 4) to give (– 1);
    (iii) (– 5) to give (– 9); (iv) (+3) to give 0 ?

[23] What must be added to

    (i) (+2) to give (– 3); (ii) (– 4) to give (+1);
    (iii) (– 5) to give 0;   (iv) 0 to give (– 2)?

Write down the values of:

24. $(+8) + (– 4)$.   25. $(– 7) + (– 3)$.   26. $(+2) – (+4)$.

27. $(– 2) – (– 3)$.   28. $(– 6) – (– 5)$.   29. $(– 9) + (+9)$.

30. $(– 2) – (+3)$.   31. $0 – (+2)$.   32. $(– 2) – (+2)$.

[33] $(– 9) + (+3)$.   [34] $(+2) – (– 3)$.   [35] $(– 5) + (– 5)$.

[36] $(– 6) – (– 6)$.   [37] $0 + (– 4)$.   [38] $– 4 – (+5)$.

Simplify the following:

39. $(+5t) + (– t)$.   40. $(– 3c) + (+c)$.   41. $(– 2e) + (– 4e)$.

[42] $(+r) + (– r)$.   [43] $(+5s) – (– 2s)$.   [44] $(+t) – (+2t)$.

45. $(– 4n) – (– 7n)$.   46. $0 – (– 3p)$.   47. $(– 3x) – (– 3x)$.

[48] $(– 6a) – (– 4a)$.   [49] $(+5b) + (– 10b)$.   [50] $(+c) – (+4c)$.

51. $d – 5d + 3d$.   52. $2e – 5e + 3e$.   53. $3f – 5f – 4f$.

Arrange in descending powers of x:

54. $6x – 2 – x^3 + 5x^2$.   [55] $5 – 2x^4 + 10x – x^3$.

Write down the term of degree 3, the coefficient of x, and the constant term in each of the following:

56. $5x^3 – 7x – 2$.   57. $x^4 – 2x^3 – x$.   58. $2x^4 – x^3 – 3x^2 + 4$.

Write down the term of highest degree, the coefficient of x^2, and the constant term in each of the following:

[59] $10x – x^3 – 2x^2 – 3$.   [60] $5 + 2x^4 – x^2 + 12x$.

Multiplication and Division

The temperature of the water in a boiler is being raised at a steady rate of 5° C. per hour throughout the day. If we regard mid-day as zero hour, the temperature at n o'clock is $(+5°) \times n$ above that at mid-day (zero hour).

Here n is a directed number: thus at 2 p.m. $n = (+2)$, and at 9 a.m. $n = (-3)$.

At 2 p.m. the temperature is evidently 10° *above* that at mid-day;

$$\therefore \ (+5) \times (+2) = (+10).$$

And at 9 a.m. the temperature is evidently 15° *below* that at mid-day;

$$\therefore \ (+5) \times (-3) = (-15).$$

Next, suppose that the temperature of the water in the boiler is *falling* at a steady rate of 5° C. per hour throughout the day. Then the *rise* per hour is $(-5°)$; $\therefore$ the temperature at n o'clock is $(-5°) \times n$ above that at mid-day (zero hour).

At 2 p.m. the temperature is evidently 10° *below* that at mid-day;

$$\therefore \ (-5) \times (+2) = (-10).$$

And at 9 a.m. the temperature is evidently 15° *above* that at mid-day;

$$\therefore \ (-5) \times (-3) = (+15).$$

This argument can be applied to any directed numbers; we therefore make the following rule of signs:

$$(+a) \times (+b) = (+ab) = ab; \quad (-a) \times (-b) = (+ab) = ab;$$
$$(+a) \times (-b) = (-ab) = -ab; \quad (-a) \times (+b) = (-ab) = -ab,$$

where, for simplicity, we write ab for $+ab$.

Oral Example. The temperature at mid-day is 60° C. What are the temperatures at 8 a.m. and at 5 p.m. if the temperature (i) is rising, (ii) is falling, at a steady rate of 3° C. per hour?

Division

Since　　$(+5) \times (+2) = (+10)$, 　$\therefore$ 　$(+10) \div (+2) = (+5)$.

Since　　$(+5) \times (-2) = (-10)$, 　$\therefore$ 　$(-10) \div (-2) = (+5)$.

Since　　$(-5) \times (+2) = (-10)$, 　$\therefore$ 　$(-10) \div (+2) = (-5)$.

Since　　$(-5) \times (-2) = (+10)$, 　$\therefore$ 　$(+10) \div (-2) = (-5)$.

We therefore make the following **rule of signs**:

$$(+a) \div (+b) = \left(+\frac{a}{b}\right) = \frac{a}{b}; \quad (-a) \div (-b) = \left(+\frac{a}{b}\right) = \frac{a}{b};$$

$$(+a) \div (-b) = \left(-\frac{a}{b}\right) = -\frac{a}{b}; \quad (-a) \div (+b) = \left(-\frac{a}{b}\right) = -\frac{a}{b},$$

provided that b is not zero.

Further, if any number is multiplied by 0, the product is 0. Also, if 0 is divided by any number which is itself not zero, the quotient is 0; but we shall never speak of dividing a number by 0.

The rules of sign given above may be stated as follows:

In multiplication and division of one directed number by another, like signs give a positive sign, and unlike signs give a negative sign.

Square Roots

From the rule of signs we see that

$$(+a) \times (+a) = (+a^2) = a^2 \text{ and } (-a) \times (-a) = (+a^2) = a^2.$$

This shows that a positive number, a^2, has two square roots, $(+a)$ and $(-a)$; these are usually written in the form $\pm a$. The symbol $\sqrt{(+a^2)}$ or $\sqrt{a^2}$ is used to represent the *positive* square root.

For example, if $x^2 = 9$, then $x = \pm 3$; but $\sqrt{9} = 3$.

There is no square root of a negative number.

EXERCISE V. c (Oral)

1. A man walking due north at v miles an hour (see Fig. 57) passes a milestone **A** at mid-day, zero hour, and therefore at

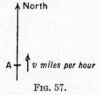

FIG. 57.

t hours after mid-day he is $(v \times t)$ miles *north* of **A**. Evaluate $v \times t$ and state the meanings of the data and the results if

(i) $v = +4$, $t = +3$;   (ii) $v = +4$, $t = -2$;
(iii) $v = -3$, $t = +3$;   (iv) $v = -3$, $t = -2$.

2. A train travelling due east at v yards per minute (see Fig. 58) passes a signal-box B at mid-day, zero hour, and therefore at

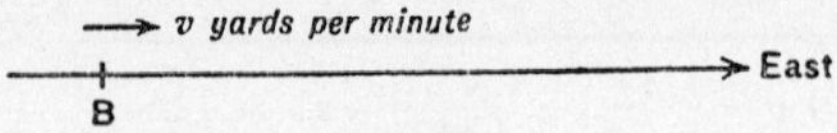

$\longrightarrow$ v yards per minute

B $\longrightarrow$ East

FIG. 58.

t minutes after mid-day it is $(v \times t)$ yards *east* of B. Evaluate $v \times t$ and state the meanings of the data and the results if

    (i) $v = +800$, $t = +10$;   (ii) $v = +900$, $t = -4$;

    (iii) $v = -1200$, $t = +5$;   (iv) $v = -1000$, $t = -7$.

3. A man, walking at a steady rate along a road which runs east and west, passes a milestone B at mid-day, zero hour, and is s miles *east* of B at t hours after mid-day, and therefore his speed is $\frac{s}{t}$ miles per hour *eastwards*. Evaluate $\frac{s}{t}$ and state the meanings of the data and the results if

    (i) $s = +12$, $t = +3$;   (ii) $s = -12$, $t = +4$;

    (iii) $s = +8$, $t = -2$;   (iv) $s = -12$, $t = -3$.

EXERCISE V. d

Find the values of the following:

  1. $(-2) \times (+3)$.   **2.** $(-3) \times (-4)$.   **3.** $(+5) \times (-2)$.

  [4] $(+5) \times (+1)$.   **[5]** $(-3) \times (+5)$.   **[6]** $(-2) \times (-1)$.

  7. $(-3)^2$.   **8.** $0 \times (-5)$.   **9.** $(-2)^3$.

 10. $(+6) \div (-2)$.   **11.** $(-12) \div (-1)$.   **12.** $(-8) \div (+8)$.

 [13] $(-6) \div (-3)$.   **[14]** $(-5) \div (+1)$.   **[15]** $(+4) \div (-1)$.

 16. $\frac{(-6)}{(+3)}$.   **17.** $\frac{(-10)}{(-1)}$.   **[18]** $\frac{(+12)}{(-3)}$.   **[19]** $\frac{(-2)}{(-2)}$.

If $a = (+2)$, $b = (-4)$, $p = (+1)$, $q = (-1)$, $r = 0$, evaluate:

 20. ab.   **21.** br.   **22.** q^2.   **23.** bpq.   **24.** b^2q.

 [25] pq.   **[26]** b^2.   **[27]** $3ab$.   **[28]** pqr.   **[29]** bq^2.

 30. $\frac{1}{b}$.   **31.** $\frac{b}{a}$.   **32.** $\frac{p}{q}$.   **33.** $\frac{r}{b}$.   **34.** $\frac{bp}{q^2}$.   **35.** $\frac{2pq}{b}$.

 [36] $\frac{q}{a}$.   **[37]** $\frac{r}{q}$.   **[38]** $\frac{bq}{a}$.   **[39]** $\frac{b^2}{q}$.   **[40]** $\frac{a^2q}{b}$.   **[41]** $\frac{b^3}{q^3}$.

Brackets

The object of using brackets in such cases as $(+3)$, (-4) is to distinguish between the positive number "plus three" and the order "add three," or between the negative number "minus three" and the order "subtract three." It is usually unnecessary to emphasise this distinction because the rules of sign have been chosen so that the rules for removing brackets containing directed numbers are precisely the same as the rules already given for signless numbers, and therefore for simplicity we write $(+3)$, (-4) as 3, -4. Also

$$+(-2a) \text{ may be written } -2a;$$
$$-(+3b) \text{ may be written } -3b;$$
$$-(-4c) \text{ may be written } +4c;$$
$$+(+5d) \text{ may be written } +5d.$$

Example 2. Simplify $(+3a) - 4\{(-2b) - (+3c)\}$.

The expression $= (+3a) - 4(-2b) + 4(+3c)$
$$= 3a + 8b + 12c.$$

Example 3. Simplify (i) $(-2xy) \times (+3y)$; (ii) $\dfrac{(-6a^2b)}{(-4ab^2)}$.

(i) $(-2xy) \times (+3y) = -2 \times 3 \times xy \times y$
$$= -6xy^2.$$

(ii) $\dfrac{(-6a^2b)}{(-4ab^2)} = \dfrac{(-6a^2b) \times (-1)}{(-4ab^2) \times (-1)} = \dfrac{6a^2b}{4ab^2}$
$$= \dfrac{3a}{2b}.$$

Example 4. Fill in the blanks in:

(i) $a - b = -(\ldots)$;   (ii) $\dfrac{b-a}{c-d} = \dfrac{a-b}{\ldots}$.

(i) $a - b = -(-a) - (+b)$
$$= -(-a + b).$$

(ii) $\dfrac{b-a}{c-d} = \dfrac{(b-a) \times (-1)}{(c-d) \times (-1)}$
$$= \dfrac{-b+a}{-c+d} = \dfrac{a-b}{d-c}.$$

It is customary to arrange an expression so that when possible it starts with a positive sign :

thus, instead of $-a + b$, we write $+b - a$, that is $b - a$.

EXERCISE V. e

Write more shortly:

1. $+(-2a)$.
2. $-(-b)$.
3. $(+2)(-5c)$.

4. $(-5)(-2d)$.
5. $(+2e)(-e)$.
6. $(-f)(+3f)$.

7. $(-3g)(-3h)$.
8. $(-km)(-1)$.
9. $(-4n^2)(+2)$.

[10] $(+3)(+4p)$.
[11] $(-4)(+2r)$.
[12] $(-3s)(-2s)$.

[13] $(-r)(+3t)$.
[14] $(+4x)(-8y)$.
[15] $(-2z^2)(0)$.

16. $(-6a^2) \div (+2a)$.
17. $(-12b^2) \div (-3b)$.

18. $(+10c^2) \div (-5c)$.
19. $(-4d^6) \div (-2d^3)$.

[20] $(+6ef) \div (-ef)$.
[21] $(-9g^3) \div (-3g)$.

22. $\dfrac{(-12mn)}{(-4)}$.
23. $\dfrac{(-6rs^2)}{(-2rs)}$.
[24] $\dfrac{(+5t^2)}{(-1)}$.
[25] $\dfrac{(-xy)}{(+xy)}$.

26. $a+(-3a)$.
27. $2b-(-b)$.
28. $c-(+c)+(-c)$.

[29] $(-d)+(-d)$.
[30] $e-(-e)+(+e)$.
[31] $f+(-f)-(-f)$.

32. $(g)+(-2g)-(-3g)-(+2g)$.
33. $-3(h-2k)+k$.

34. $2(m-n)-3(m+n)$.
35. $0-2(r-s)-(r+s)$.

[36] $q+(+4p)+(-3q)-(-2r)$.
[37] $2s-t-3(s+t)$.

38. $2x-3\{(-5)-(-2x)\}$.
39. $3y^2-5y-2(1-y+y^2)$.

[40] $3t+2\{(+3t)-(-t)\}$.
[41] $2(1-z)-3z(1-z)$.

42. $(a-b)(-1)-3(b-a)(-1)$.
43. $(c^2-3c+2)(-c)-(-2c)$.

[44] $(-2)(3f-2g-h)-(-1)(f-g+h)$.
[45] $r(s-t)+r(t-s)$.

46. $(-3a)^2$.
47. $(-2b)^3$.
48. $-(-cd)^2$.
49. $(-3ef^2)^3$.

[50] $g^2-(-g)^2$.
[51] $h^3+(-h)^3$.
[52] $(4k)^2 \div (-2k)$.

53. $\dfrac{3mn}{-m}$.
54. $\dfrac{-p^2}{-pq}$.
55. $\dfrac{8r^3}{-4rs}$.
56. $\dfrac{(-2t)^3}{2t}$.

[57] $\dfrac{x}{-xy}$.
[58] $\dfrac{y^2z^2}{-z}$.
[59] $\dfrac{-9ab}{3a^3}$.
[60] $\dfrac{(-cd)^2}{d}$.

61. $(-e) \div (ef)$.
62. $(-g) \div (-2g)$.
63. $(-2h) \times (-k)^2$.

64. $(-mn)^2 \times (-m)$.
65. $\dfrac{r}{s} \times (-s)$.
66. $\left(-\dfrac{s}{t}\right) \div (-s)$.

[67] $x \div (-x)^2$.
[68] $y \div \left(-\dfrac{1}{y}\right)$.
[69] $(x^2z^2) \div (-2xz)$.

Copy and complete the following:

70. $2a - 6b = 2(\dots) = -2(\dots).$ 71. $-c + 3d = -(\dots).$

[72] $e + f = -(\dots).$ 73. $\dfrac{-p}{-q} = \dfrac{p}{\dots}.$

[74] $\dfrac{r}{-s} = \dfrac{\dots}{s}.$ 75. $\dfrac{(-p)(-q)}{r(-s)} = \dots.$ [76] $\dfrac{a(-b)}{(-c)d} = \dots.$

*77. $x^2 = (-x)(\dots).$ *78. $r(y - z) = -r(\dots).$

*79. $\dfrac{r-t}{y-x} = \dfrac{\dots}{x-y}.$ *80. $\dfrac{(a-b)(c+d)}{(p-q)(r-s)} = \dfrac{(b-a)(d+c)}{\dots}.$

*81. What can you say about x if (i) $x^2 = 9$, (ii) $x^2 = 1$?

*82. What can you say about y if $2y^2 = 50$?

*83. What can you say about z if (i) $z = \dfrac{16}{z}$, (ii) $z = \dfrac{1}{z}$?

*84. Solve the equation, $3t^2 = 48.$

Simplify the following:

*85. $\dfrac{a-b}{b-a}.$ *86. $\dfrac{c+d}{-c-d}.$ *87. $\dfrac{(e-f)^2}{(f-e)^2}.$

In the previous examples, brackets have been used for performing addition, subtraction, multiplication and division. The working may, however, be arranged as in Arithmetic.

Example 5. Add $3y - x - 5z$ to $3x - 3y + z$.

Arrange the terms of the two expressions in similar orders.

$$
\begin{array}{r}
-x + 3y - 5z \\
3x - 3y + z \\
\hline
2x - 4z \\
\end{array}
$$

Example 6.   Subtract $3y - x - 5z$ from $3x - 3y + z$.

Arrange the terms of the two expressions in similar orders.

Subtracting $(-x)$ from $3x$ is the $3x - 3y + z$
same as adding $(+x)$ to $(+3x)$, $-x + 3y - 5z$
giving $(+4x)$ or $4x$, etc.

$$4x - 6y + 6z$$

Alternatively, if we use brackets, we write

$$(3x - 3y + z) - (3y - x - 5z) = 3x - 3y + z - 3y + x + 5z,$$

and this shows that if the expressions are set down as in Arithmetic the result is obtained by changing the sign of each term in the lower line (mentally) and then adding.

Example 7.   Divide $12a^3b - 6a^2b^2 + 18ab^3$ by $-6ab$

$$-6ab \overline{)12a^3b - 6a^2b^2 + 18ab^3}$$
$$-2a^2 \quad +ab \quad -3b^2$$

EXERCISE V. f

Add:

1. $3a - b$ and $3b - a$.   2. $2c + 3d - e$ and $2d - e - c$.

[3] $2f^2 - 1$ and $-f^2$.   [4] $g + h - k$ and $h + k - g$.

5. $2m^2 - 5m - 4$ and $1 + 3m - 3m^2$.

6. $1 - (n + p)$ and $p - (n - 1)$.   [7] $t - 3r + 2s$ and $s - r - 3t$.

[8] $2x(x - y)$ and $3y(y - x)$.

9. $2(3a - 1 - a^2)$ and $-3(2a - a^2)$.

10. $5(b^2 + 2b - 3)$ and $7(1 - 2b^2)$.

11. $3c - 2d - e$, $3d - 2e - c$, $3e - 2d - c$.

12. $1 - m - 3m^2$, $2m - 5 - m^2$, $2m^2 - m + 2$, $1 - m^2$.

[13] $3s - 2t - r$, $t - 3r - s$, $2r - 3t$.

[14] $-x + 2y$, $-y + 3z$, $-z + 4x$, $-(x + y + z)$.

Subtract:

15. $2c - d$ from $2d - c$.   16. $b^2 - 1$ from $2b^2$.

[17] $e^2 + f^2$ from $e^2 - f^2$.   [18] $2g$ from $1 + g$.

19. $3h$ from $3 - h$.   20. $2n - 1$ from n^2.

21. $r - s + t$ from $s + t - r$.   22. $3x + y + 1$ from $4x - y - 1$.

Subtract:

[23] $2a - 3b - c$ from $b - a + c$.   [24] $2c - d - e$ from $d - 2e$.

25. $3f + g + 1$ from $4f - g - 1$.   26. $3h^2 - 5h - 6$ from $h^3 + h^2$.

[27] $1 + m - m^2$ from 0.   [28] $x^3 - 2x^2 + 5x$ from $x^2 + 3x - 2$.

Multiply:

29. $x - b$ by $-z$.   30. $1 - t$ by $-2t$.

31. $-r + 2s$ by $-3s$.   [32] $-b - c$ by $-a$.

[33] $2d - 3d^2$ by $-2d$.   [34] $1 - 3h + h^2$ by -1.

Divide:

35. $a^2 - ab$ by $-a$.   36. $c + d$ by -1.

37. $6r^3 - 4r^2$ by $-2r$.   [38] $p^2 + pq$ by $-p$.

[39] $s^4 - s^2$ by $-s^2$.   [40] $12pq - 9q^2$ by $-3q$.

41. $6x^3 - 8x^2y - 4xy^2$ by $-2x$.

[42] $12y^2z^2 - 8y^3z + 16y^4$ by $-4y^2$.

Subtract:

	(i)	(ii)	(iii)	(iv)
43.	$4a + b$	$5c - 3d$	$7e + 4f$	$6g - 4h$
	$a + 3b$	$3c + 2d$	$3e - 5f$	$4g - 5h$
[44]	$2p - 6q$	$5r + 2s$	$4t + x$	$5y - 3z$
	$p - 2q$	$3r - 2s$	$t + 4x$	$y + z$
45.	$3b + 2c$	$4d + 3e$	$2f$	$m - n$
	$5b + 2c$	$6d - 3e$	$3f - g$	n
[46]	$2q - 5r$	$s - 3t$	$3x$	$5y + 2z$
	$2q - 3r$	$4s - 3t$	$k + 5x$	$6y$

47. $2a - b + 1$ from $a + 2b - 1$.   48. $3c - 4d - 3$ from $c + 4d + 1$.

[49] $p + q + 6$ from $3p - 2q + 4$.   [50] $2r + s - 4$ from $r - 3s - 3$.

51. $x + 3y + 2$ from $x - y - 1$.   52. $5 - 2y - z$ from $3 - y - 2z$.

Miscellaneous Operations with Negative Numbers

EXERCISE V. g

1. Subtract $-a-b-c$ from a.

2. Divide $x^2-3xy-x$ by $-x$.

3. Simplify $\dfrac{x}{-y}+\dfrac{-x}{-y}-\dfrac{-x}{y}$.

4. Copy and complete, $x-y=(-1)(\ldots\ldots)$.

Simplify:

5. $(-a)(-b)(-c)$.   6. $(-x^3)^2$.   7. $(-y)^2(-y^2)$.

8. $(-1)(d-e)+(-e)$.   9. $f+(-2)(f-g)$.

10. $(x^2-2xy)\div(-x)+y$.   11. $(-3)(p-q)+(-2)(q-p)$.

[12] $(r-s)\div(-1)+s$.   [13] $(2x)(-3y)\div(-1)^2$.

[14] $(a-b)-(b-a)$.   [15] $(6c^2+3cd)\div(-3c)-c$.

16. Subtract $4x^2+7$ from x^2-5x-2.

17. Add $-(1-2x)$ to $3(x+1)$.

[18] Divide $16x^4y^2-4x^2y^2$ by $-4xy$.

[19] Multiply $1-(2-z)$ by $-z$.

[20] Simplify $\dfrac{a^2}{-a}+\dfrac{a^2-a^4}{-a^2}+(-a)^2$.

21. If $(x-a)(y-a)=c^2$ and if $a=-1$, $c=-1$, $y=1$, find the value of x.

[22] If $r+s+4=0$ and $s=-1$, find the value of rs.

23. If $x=-\frac{1}{2}$ and $y=-\frac{1}{3}$, find the value of $\dfrac{1}{x}-\dfrac{1}{y}$.

[24] If $pq=p+q$ and $q=-1$, find the value of p.

25. Simplify $(a-2a^2)\div(-a)+(2b^2-b)\div(-b)$.

26. Multiply $\dfrac{1}{-a}+\dfrac{1}{-b}-\dfrac{1}{ab}$ by $-ab$.

27. Divide $x^3y^2z^2-x^2y^3z^2+x^2y^2z^3$ by $-xyz^2$.

28. What can you say about the value of x if $x^2=25$?

29. What can you say about the value of y if $(y-7)^2$ is equal to 16?

30. Simplify $\dfrac{y^2+2z^2}{yz}$ if $y+z=0$.

CHAPTER VI

SIMPLE EQUATIONS, PROBLEMS AND FORMULAE

In the following example, the steps marked * may be omitted when the process is understood.

Example 1. Solve the equation:

$$1 - \frac{1}{6}(t+5) = \frac{2t+7}{3} - \frac{t-10}{4}.$$

(The L.C.M. of the denominators 6, 3, 4 is 12.) *
Multiply each side by 12,

$$\therefore\ 12 - \frac{12}{6}(t+5) = \frac{12(2t+7)}{3} - \frac{12(t-10)}{4};\ *$$

$$\therefore\ 12 - 2(t+5) = 4(2t+7) - 3(t-10);$$

$$\therefore\ 12 - (2t+10) = 8t+28 - (3t-30);\ *$$

$$\therefore\ 12 - 2t - 10 = 8t + 28 - 3t + 30;$$

$$\therefore\ 2 - 2t = 5t + 58;$$

$$\therefore\ -2t - 5t = 58 - 2;$$

$$\therefore\ -7t = 56;$$

multiply each side by -1,

$$\therefore\ 7t = -56;$$

$$\therefore\ t = -8.$$

Check: If $t = -8$,

left side $= 1 - \frac{1}{6}(-8+5) = 1 - \frac{1}{6}(-3)$

$\qquad = 1 + \frac{3}{6} = 1\frac{1}{2};$

right side $= \dfrac{-16+7}{3} - \dfrac{-8-10}{4} = \dfrac{-9}{3} - \dfrac{-18}{4}$

$\qquad = -3 + 4\frac{1}{2} = 1\frac{1}{2}.$

$$\therefore\ \text{if } t = -8, \text{ left side } = \text{right side.}$$

Note.—If the root of an equation is an awkward fraction, it is better to look carefully through the working or to do it all over again than to check by substitution, because mistakes are as likely to occur in the check as in the original solution.

EXERCISE VI. a

Solve the following equations:

1. $5(x-2)-3(x-1)=-1.$ **2.** $y+1=2(y-3)-3(y-1).$

3. $2z-(1-2z)=5-3(1+z).$ **4.** $0=2(t+1)-5(t-5).$

[5] $3(6-m)-4(m+8)=0.$ **[6]** $2(n-1)-3(3+n)=5+n.$

[7] $4-4(r-5)=2(2-r)-6.$ **[8]** $4(s-1)-3(s-2)=4-5s.$

[9] $x(2+x)-3(1+x)=1+x^2.$

[10] $y^2-y(5-y)=6-2y(1-y).$

11. $z(2z-1)-3(5+z)=2z^2+2z+3.$

12. $0 \cdot 6x+0 \cdot 72=0.$ **13.** $1 \cdot 2y-0 \cdot 5y=4 \cdot 2.$

[14] $1 \cdot 8z+0 \cdot 63=0.$ **[15]** $1 \cdot 4t+0 \cdot 6t=0 \cdot 7.$

16. $0 \cdot 3(6-n)=0 \cdot 4(n+8).$

[17] $1 \cdot 4(m-3)-0 \cdot 4(2m-1)=-0 \cdot 2.$

18. $\frac{1}{2}(p-1)-\frac{1}{4}(3-p)=2.$ **[19]** $\frac{1}{5}(2r-1)=3-\frac{1}{4}(3r-1).$

20. $4t-\frac{1}{5}(t+4)=41.$ **[21]** $\frac{1}{2}(1+x)=\frac{1}{5}(2x-1)-1.$

22. $\frac{1}{3}(2y+4)=\frac{1}{4}y-2.$ **[23]** $\frac{1}{5}(z+3)=8-\frac{1}{4}(z-1).$

24. $\frac{1}{2y}-\frac{1}{3y}=\frac{1}{5}.$ **[25]** $\frac{7}{3z}-5=\frac{1}{2}-\frac{5}{z}.$

26. $\frac{1}{r}+\frac{1}{2r}-\frac{1}{3r}=2\frac{1}{3}.$ **[27]** $\frac{1}{2s}-\frac{1}{3s}=\frac{1}{4s}-1.$

28. $\frac{3}{2m}-4=3-\frac{9}{m}.$ **[29]** $\frac{5}{n}+\frac{1}{3}=\frac{3}{4}.$

30. $\frac{p+1}{3}-\frac{p-1}{2}=1+\frac{2p}{3}.$ **[31]** $\frac{4r-3}{5}-\frac{5r-3}{8}=1.$

32. $\frac{2x-1}{5}-\frac{3x+1}{2}=\frac{2}{5}.$ **[33]** $\frac{2y-1}{7}+12=\frac{7y-2}{5}.$

34. $\frac{2z+7}{4}-\frac{z+1}{3}=\frac{3}{4}.$ **35.** $\frac{t}{2}-\frac{5t+4}{3}=\frac{4t-9}{3}.$

36. $\frac{r+1}{2}-\frac{r-7}{5}=\frac{r+4}{3}.$ **37.** $\frac{3x+2}{5}-\frac{2x+5}{3}=x+3.$

[38] $\frac{1-y}{2}=\frac{3+y}{3}-\frac{9+y}{4}.$ **[39]** $z-1=\frac{z-2}{2}-\frac{z-3}{3}.$

[40] $\dfrac{t+1}{2} + \dfrac{t+2}{3} = 14 - \dfrac{t-5}{4}.$

[41] $\dfrac{3}{4}(k-3) - \dfrac{7k-2}{5} = 2 - k.$

[42] $\dfrac{2}{3}(x+5) = x - \dfrac{x-10}{4}.$

[43] $\dfrac{y+1}{2} + \dfrac{y+2}{3} + \dfrac{y+3}{4} + \dfrac{1}{4} = 0.$

*44. $\dfrac{x+1\cdot7}{2} - \dfrac{x-2\cdot3}{3} = 1.$

*45. $\dfrac{1+0\cdot2y}{3} - \dfrac{2-0\cdot3y}{7} = 0\cdot19.$

*46. $\dfrac{2z-1}{3} + \dfrac{4z+1}{5} = \dfrac{3(z-4)}{4}.$

*47. $\dfrac{3n+4}{5} - \dfrac{7n-3}{2} = \dfrac{n-16}{4}.$

*48. $\dfrac{p+5}{2\frac{1}{2}} - \dfrac{p-1}{3\frac{1}{3}} = 1.$

*49. $\dfrac{t-1}{0\cdot5} + \dfrac{2t+1}{0\cdot75} = 18.$

*50. $\dfrac{2}{5}(2w+1) - \dfrac{1-w}{4} - \dfrac{3(3w-1)}{10} = 0.$

Formulae and Equations

Example 2. If a man is photographed when standing u inches from the lens of a camera, focal length f inches, the plate should be v inches from the lens, where $\dfrac{1}{u} + \dfrac{1}{v} = \dfrac{1}{f}$.

Find the distance of the plate from a lens of focal length $4\frac{1}{2}$ inches, if the man is 6 feet from the lens.

Here $\qquad f = 4\frac{1}{2}$ and $u = 6 \times 12.$

$$\therefore \ \frac{1}{72} + \frac{1}{v} = \frac{1}{4\frac{1}{2}} = \frac{2}{9}.$$

Multiply each side by $72v$,

$$\therefore \ v + 72 = 16v;$$
$$\therefore \ 15v = 72$$
$$\therefore \ v = \frac{72}{15} = 4\cdot8.$$

$\therefore$ the distance of the plate from the lens is $4\cdot8$ inches.

EXERCISE VI. b

1. The area of a triangle is given by the formula, $\mathbf{A} = \frac{1}{2}\,hb$; find b if $\mathbf{A} = 6\frac{3}{4}$ and $h = 1\frac{4}{5}$.

2. The area of a trapezium is given by the formula, $\mathbf{A} = \frac{1}{2}h(a+b)$; find b if $\mathbf{A} = 5\cdot4$, $a = 1\cdot7$, $h = 3\cdot6$.

3. If $F°$ Fahrenheit is the same temperature as $C°$ Centigrade, then $F = 32 + \dfrac{9C}{5}$; find C if $F = 5$.

4. If A exceeds P by R per cent., then $A = P\left(1 + \dfrac{R}{100}\right)$; find R if $P = 96$, $A = 120$.

5. If the perimeter of a semicircular area of diameter d inches is p inches (see Fig. 59), then $p = d + \frac{1}{2}\pi d$, where π may be taken as $\frac{2 \cdot 2}{7}$; find d if $p = 4 \cdot 5$.

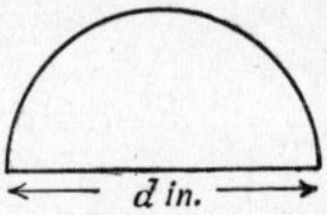

6. If $\frac{1}{2}x - 1$ is twice as large as $\frac{1}{3}x - 4$, find the value of each.

FIG. 59.

[7] If the velocity of a body sliding downhill increases steadily from u feet per second to v feet per second in t seconds, the distance, s feet, it moves in that time is given by $s = \dfrac{u + v}{2} \cdot t$.   Find v if $s = 84$, $u = 9$, $t = 3\frac{1}{2}$.

[8] A test showed that a load of W tons could be raised by means of a certain machine by using an effort of P tons, where $P = 0 \cdot 075W + 0 \cdot 05$. What load could be raised by an effort of 2 tons?

[9] From the formula, $\dfrac{pv}{273 + t} = c$, find t if $p = 16$, $v = 180$, $c = 9 \cdot 6$.

[10] From the formula, $d = t \cdot \dfrac{\mu - 1}{\mu}$, find μ if $d = 0 \cdot 25$, $t = 0 \cdot 8$.

11. After an examination the marks are scaled so that a boy who obtained n marks for the paper receives N marks, where $\dfrac{N}{100} = \dfrac{n - 17}{72 - 17}$. What is n, if N equals (i) 40, (ii) 100, (iii) 0?

12. The sum of the first n numbers of the set

$$a, \ a + d, \ a + 2d, \ a + 3d, \ \ldots\ldots$$

is s where $s = \dfrac{n}{2}[2a + (n - 1)d]$.

(i) Find d if $a = 9$, $n = 16$, $s = 48$.

(ii) Find the sum of the first 20 numbers of the set 1, 3, 5, 7, 9, ...

[13] From the formula, $n = \dfrac{2R}{R - r}$, find R if $n = 18$, $r = 2\frac{2}{3}$.

[14] The area of the total surface of a solid circular cylinder of height h inches, base-radius r inches, is **A** sq. in., where $A = 2\pi r(r + h)$ and π may be taken as $\frac{22}{7}$. If $A = 5 \cdot 5$ and $r = 0 \cdot 2$, find h.

15. If a bath can be filled by one tap in p minutes and by another tap in q minutes, it can be filled by both taps together in t minutes, where $\frac{1}{t} = \frac{1}{p} + \frac{1}{q}$. Find p if $t = 4\frac{1}{2}$ and $q = 7\frac{1}{2}$.

Problems

When *solving* a problem,

(i) If possible, make a rough diagram and show the data on it.

(ii) Choose a letter for some unknown number the problem involves, and state precisely what this letter represents.

(iii) Re-write the question, using the letter you have chosen for the unknown to make the statement of the problem more detailed.

When *checking* the answer to a problem,

Use the actual data of the problem. It is not sufficient to check by substituting in the equation, because your equation may be wrong.

Example 3. I walk at $3\frac{1}{2}$ miles an hour from my house to a town by a path through the fields. After waiting 40 minutes, I return in a bus travelling at $10\frac{1}{2}$ miles an hour. If the road adds another mile to the journey and if the total time taken is 4 hours, find the distance by road from my house to the town.

Let the distance *by road* from my house to the town be x miles; then the distance by the path is $(x - 1)$ miles.

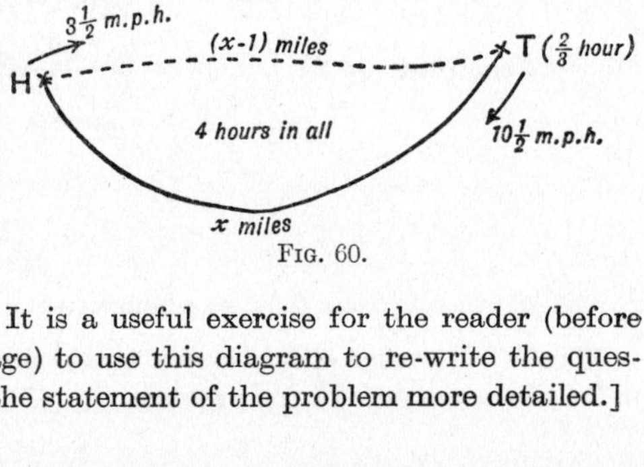

FIG. 60.

[All the data of the problem are shown in Fig. 60. It is a useful exercise for the reader (before turning over the page) to use this diagram to re-write the question so as to make the statement of the problem more detailed.]

I walk $(x - 1)$ miles at $3\frac{1}{2}$ miles an hour, then wait $\frac{2}{3}$ hour, and then ride back x miles at $10\frac{1}{2}$ miles an hour; the total time is 4 hours.   [See Fig. 60 repeated below.]

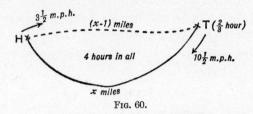

FIG. 60.

To walk $(x - 1)$ miles at $3\frac{1}{2}$ m.p.h. takes $\dfrac{x-1}{3\frac{1}{2}}$ hours; to ride x miles at $10\frac{1}{2}$ m.p.h. takes $\dfrac{x}{10\frac{1}{2}}$ hours; $\therefore$ the total time taken is

$$\frac{x-1}{3\frac{1}{2}} \text{ hours} + \frac{2}{3} \text{ hour} + \frac{x}{10\frac{1}{2}} \text{ hours};$$

but this is 4 hours,

$$\therefore \frac{x-1}{3\frac{1}{2}} \text{ hours} + \frac{2}{3} \text{ hour} + \frac{x}{10\frac{1}{2}} \text{ hours} = 4 \text{ hours},$$

$$\therefore \frac{x-1}{3\frac{1}{2}} + \frac{2}{3} + \frac{x}{10\frac{1}{2}} = 4;$$

but $\dfrac{x-1}{3\frac{1}{2}} = \dfrac{2(x-1)}{2 \times 3\frac{1}{2}} = \dfrac{2(x-1)}{7}$ and $\dfrac{x}{10\frac{1}{2}} = \dfrac{2x}{2 \times 10\frac{1}{2}} = \dfrac{2x}{21};$

$$\therefore \frac{2(x-1)}{7} + \frac{2}{3} + \frac{2x}{21} = 4;$$

multiply each side by 21, $\therefore 6(x - 1) + 14 + 2x = 84;$

$$\therefore 6x - 6 + 14 + 2x = 84,$$

$$\therefore 8x = 76$$

$$\therefore x = \frac{76}{8} = 9\frac{1}{2}.$$

$\therefore$ the distance *by road* from the house to the town is $9\frac{1}{2}$ miles.

Note.—The reader should check this answer by showing that it fits the *actual data* of the problem.

EXERCISE VI. c

1. Find a number such that if you add 7 and divide the sum by 5 you will get the same answer as if you had subtracted 1 and then divided by 3.

2. Fig. 61 gives the lengths of three sides of a rectangle in inches. Find the value of x and the perimeter of the rectangle.

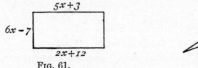

Fig. 61.   Fig. 62.

[3] Fig. 62 gives the lengths of the sides of a triangle in inches. If the triangle is isosceles, find the value of x and the perimeter of the triangle.

4. At a fair, a boy receives 8d. for a hit and pays 3d. for a miss. After 24 shots he has to pay 6d.; how many hits did he score?

[5] A boy counts 2 marks for each sum he gets right and (-1) mark for each he gets wrong. He does 18 sums and obtains 15 marks. How many sums did he get right?

6. Find a value of n for which the fraction $\dfrac{5n+2}{7n+1}$ reduces to $\dfrac{3}{4}$.

[7] What is the number which when added both to the numerator and denominator of the fraction $\frac{6}{13}$ makes a new fraction whose value is $\frac{2}{5}$?

8. What number must be added to both numerator and denominator of the fraction $\frac{11}{17}$ so that the new fraction may reduce to $\frac{2}{3}$?

9. Find six consecutive odd numbers whose sum is 12.

[10] A man gains x shillings on the sale of a chair and gains y shillings on the sale of a table. His total profit is 17 shillings. If $x = 20$, find y and interpret the answer.

11. Fig. 63 gives the lengths of the sides of a triangle in inches. Find the value of x if the triangle is isosceles, and find the perimeter of the triangle. *There is more than one answer.*

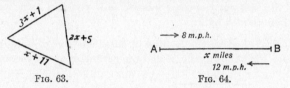

FIG. 63.   FIG. 64.

12. Fig. 64 represents a cyclist riding from **A** to **B** and back again; the double journey takes 5 hours.   Find x.

[13] A man rows upstream at 3 miles an hour and back to the same place at 5 miles an hour; he takes 48 minutes altogether. How far upstream did he go?

14. If $(5n - 2)$ inches and $\frac{1}{2}n$ feet together make up 3 yards, find the value of n.

15. If p half-crowns and $(2p - 1)$ florins together make up three guineas, find the value of p.

[16] If $(x - 1)$ cwt. and $1\frac{1}{2}x$ qr. together make up half a ton, find the value of x.

17. The present ages of **A** and **B** are 21 and 35 years.   In n years' time, **B** will be just twice as old as **A** will then be.   Find the value of n and interpret the answer.

18. In a factory, the men each get 7s. 6d. a day and the women each 6s. a day; 200 people are employed, and their wages amount to £69 a day.   How many men are there?

[19] A man buys one lot of eggs at 1s. 6d. a dozen, and a second lot, which is 3 dozen more than the first lot, at 2s. a dozen.   He sells them all at 2s. 6d. a dozen and makes 15s. profit.   How many eggs of each quality did he buy?

20. If **N** + (40 per cent. of **N**) equals 84, find **N**.

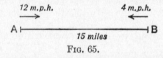

FIG. 65.

21. Fig. 65 represents a cyclist leaving **A** at the same moment as a pedestrian leaves **B**.   If they meet x miles from **A**, find x.

22. The total time for riding $2\frac{1}{2}n$ miles at 12 miles an hour and $5n$ miles at 30 miles an hour is 3 hours. Find n.

[23] The total time for walking n miles at $4\frac{1}{2}$ miles an hour and riding $(n+3)$ miles at $11\frac{1}{4}$ miles an hour is 2 hours 8 minutes. Find n.

[24] A man buys 800 bulbs for 42 shillings, some of them at 25 for a shilling and the rest at 6s. a hundred. How many of the first kind did he buy?

25. A first-class ticket costs *two-thirds as much again* as a third-class ticket for a certain journey. If the total cost of 8 first-class and 20 third-class tickets is £15, find the cost of a third-class ticket.

[26] A river flows at 3 miles an hour. What is the speed through the water of a steamer that can go downstream twice as fast as upstream?

27. A goods train travelling at 24 miles per hour passes a level-crossing at 2 p.m., and an express train, travelling at 60 miles per hour in the same direction, passes the crossing at 2.12 p.m. At what time will the first train be overtaken by the second?

[28] A messenger goes on an errand at 4 miles an hour; 20 minutes later a boy bicycles after him at 12 miles an hour. How far must the boy go to overtake the messenger?

29. My train starts in 12 minutes and the station is 1 mile away. I walk at 4 miles an hour and run at 8 miles an hour. How far must I run to reach the station in 12 minutes?

[30] A piece of wire 20 inches long is cut into two pieces, one of which is bent into a circle and the other forms the square enclosing it (see Fig. 66). Find the length of the diameter of the circle. Assume that the circumference of a circle is $\frac{22}{7}$ times its diameter.

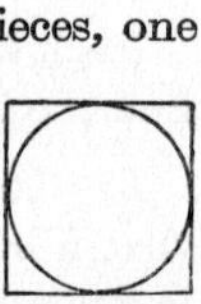

Fig. 66.

31. A rectangle is l feet long and its perimeter is 5 feet; find its breadth in terms of l. Another rectangle is twice as long and half as broad as the first and its perimeter is 7 feet. Find l.

32. If C° Centigrade is the same temperature as F° Fahrenheit, $C = \frac{5}{9}(F - 32)$. (i) Find x if $x°$ Centigrade is the same temperature as $2x°$ Fahrenheit. (ii) Find the temperature which is measured by the same number on both scales.

[33] Use the data of No. 32 to find the temperature which is measured by a number five times as large on the Fahrenheit scale as on the Centigrade scale.

[34] The "rise" AB, R inches, and the "tread" BC, T inches, of a staircase (see Fig. 67) are connected by the formula, $R = \frac{1}{2}(24 - T)$. Find the rise if it equals $\frac{5}{6}$ of the tread.

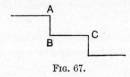

Fig. 67.

[35] A kettle of water is placed on a stove. After t minutes the temperature of the water is $(16 + 5t)$ degrees Centigrade. Use this formula to *write down* the temperature after 10 minutes and to find how long the water takes to boil. [Water boils at 100° Centigrade.]

36. Two large kettles are being heated, A on a gas stove and B on a primus. At t minutes past eleven, the temperatures in degrees Centigrade of the water in A and B are $30 + 2t$ and $48 + 5t$. Use these formulae to *write down* the temperatures at 3 minutes past eleven and to find the time when the water is at the same temperature in the two kettles.

Each kettle was filled originally with water at 14° Centigrade, find the times at which A and B were put on the stoves.

[37] The marks obtained in an examination were scaled so that a boy who had scored n marks received p marks, where p is given by the formula, $p = \frac{5}{3}(n - 24)$.

    (i) What marks were given to boys who scored 84 and 24 marks?

    (ii) What marks did a boy score if he received the same number as he scored?

*38. Use Fig. 68 to find two consecutive whole numbers whose squares differ by 37.

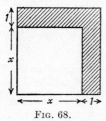

Fig. 68.

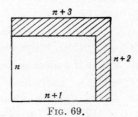

Fig. 69.

*39. Use Fig. 69 to find four consecutive whole numbers such that the product of the two largest exceeds the product of the others by 70.

*40. A table is marked at £P, but there is a discount of 5s. in the £ for cash.   The cash price is £12; find P.

*41. 5 lb. of tea at a certain price is mixed with 4 lb. of tea costing 9d. per lb. *more*.   The value of the mixture is 2s. 7d. per lb.   Find the price per lb. of the cheaper kind.

*42. How much tea at 2s. 6d. per lb. must be mixed with 12 lb. of tea at 1s. 10d. per lb. so that the mixture may be worth 2s. 3d. per lb. ?

*43. Two express trains **A** and **B** are travelling northwards at 48 miles an hour and 40 miles an hour respectively.   When **A** is 16 miles north of a station **S**, **B** is 12 miles north of **S**.   If **A** passed **B** at a place x miles north of **S**, find the value of x and interpret the answer.

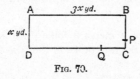

Fig. 70.

*44. Fig. 70 represents a rectangular enclosure; $CP = \frac{1}{4}CB$; $CQ = \frac{1}{4}CD$; the path **ABP** is 12 yards longer than the path **ADQ**. Find the length of **AD**.

*45. If I walk to the station at 4 miles an hour to catch a train, I shall have 3 minutes to spare; but if I walk at 3 miles an hour, I shall miss the train by 1 minute. How far off is the station?

*46. The nth number in the set of numbers 3, 7, 11, 15, 19, ... is $4n - 1$. Verify this statement when $n = 5$. Does 299 belong to the set? If so, where does it come?

*47. Find v if v miles an hour is the same speed as $(v + 3\frac{1}{2})$ feet per second.

*48. A man, who died some time ago, lived twice as long before the War (1914–1918) as after it. If the War had taken place 15 years earlier and lasted the same time, he would have lived three times as long after the War as before it, assuming he attained the same age. When did he die?

*49. A man has £a in one bank and £b in another. He has £c more to deposit. How must he share this money to make the two accounts equal? What can you say about the value of c, if this is impossible?

*50. A certain sum of money is sufficient to pay A's wages for 20 days or B's wages for 30 days. For how long will it suffice to pay A and B if both are at work?

*51. What integral value of N makes $3N - 1$ greater than $N + 5$, and also makes $4N - 7$ less than $N + 7$?

*52. Fig. 62 (see p. 101) gives the lengths of the sides of a triangle in inches. What is the least possible value of x? [Any two sides of a triangle are together greater than the third side.] What is the greatest possible value of x?

*53. What can you say about the value of p if $\dfrac{p-3}{p+5}$ lies between $\frac{2}{3}$ and $\frac{3}{4}$?

*54. What must be a man's income if he has £450 a year left after paying tax at the rate of 4s. in the £ on the part of it above £150?

*55. I pay no tax on the first £135 of my income, I pay a tax of 2s. in the £ on the next £225, and a tax of 4s. in the £ on the rest. My income after the tax has been deducted is £577. 10s. What is my gross income?

Transformation of Formulae

Most formulae are given or remembered in some standard form; but for the purposes of a particular problem it may be convenient to express the formula differently.

For example, the volume, V cu. inches, of a rectangular block l inches long, b inches broad, h inches high, is given by the formula

$$V = lbh.$$

Here V is called the **subject** of the formula.

Suppose, however, we are given the volume of the block and also its length and breadth and are asked to find the height. With the same notation as before,

$$lbh = V.$$

Divide each side by lb,

$$\therefore \ h = \frac{V}{lb}.$$

This is a formula whose subject is h. It has been obtained from the first formula *by using precisely the same methods as are employed in solving equations.* The process is called **changing the subject of the formula**.

EXERCISE VI. d

1. If $x°$, $y°$, $z°$ are the angles of a triangle, $x + y + z = 180$. Make z the subject of this formula.

2. If P pints of water weigh W lb., then $W = 1\frac{1}{4}P$. Make P the subject of this formula.

[3] If the sum of the angles of an n-sided polygon is r right angles, then $r = 2n - 4$. Make n the subject.

4. The rise R inches and the tread T inches of a staircase are connected by the formula $R = \frac{1}{2}(24 - T)$. Make T the subject.

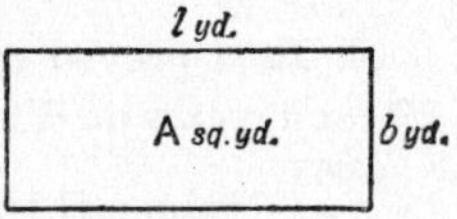

5. With the data of Fig. 71, $A = lb$. Make b the subject.

FIG. 71.

6. If the perimeter of the rectangle in Fig. 71 is p yards, express p in terms of l and b, and then make l the subject of the formula.

[7] What relation connects x and y in Fig. 72 ?   Make x the subject of the formula.

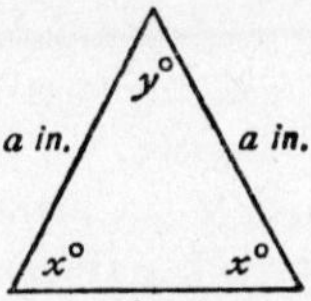

FIG. 72.

[8] If the perimeter of the triangle in Fig. 72 is p inches, express p in terms of a and b, and then make a the subject of the formula.

9. What relation connects a and b in Fig. 73 ?   (i) Make a the subject; (ii) make b the subject.

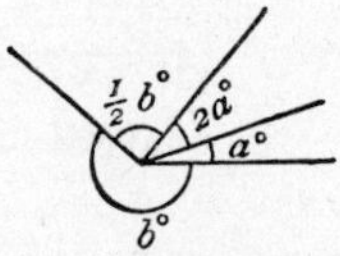

FIG. 73.

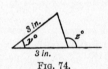

FIG. 74.

[10] What relation connects y and z in Fig. 74 ?   (i) Make y the subject; (ii) make z the subject.

[11] If $C°$ Centigrade is the same temperature as $F°$ Fahrenheit, $C = \frac{5}{9}(F - 32)$.   Make F the subject.

12. If the circumference of a circle of radius r inches is C inches, then $C = 2\pi r$.   Make r the subject.

[13] The area A sq. in. of a triangle whose base is b inches and height is h inches is given by the formula $A = \frac{1}{2}bh$.   Make h the subject.

14. It is proved in arithmetic that the simple interest £I on £P for T years at R per cent. per annum is given by the formula $I = \dfrac{PRT}{100}$.   Make R the subject.

15. Make t the subject of the formula $s = (u + v)t$.

[16] Make P the subject of the formula $A = P(1 + R)$.

17. Fig. 75 represents the four walls of a room l feet long, b feet wide, h feet high. The total area of the four walls is A sq. ft. Express A in terms of l, b, h, in factors. Then make h the subject of the formula.

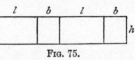

FIG. 75.

[18] The area of a trapezium is given by the formula $A = \frac{1}{2}h(x+y)$. Make h the subject.

19. Find x if $x^2 = 9$ and make l the subject of the formula $A = l^2$.

[20] The edge of a cube is l inches long and the total area of its surface is A sq. inches. Express A in terms of l and then make l the subject. What is l if $A = 96$?

21. If the area of a circle of radius r inches is A sq. inches, then $A = \pi r^2$. Make r the subject.

*22. Make r the subject of the formula $V = \pi r^2 h$.

*23. Make d the subject of the horse-power formula $H = \frac{2}{5}nd^2$.

*24. If the perimeter of a semicircular plate of radius r inches is p inches, then $p = \pi r + 2r$. Make r the subject.

*25. Make R the subject of the formula $n(R - r) = 2R$.

*26. If the perimeter of the rectangle in Fig. 71, p. 107, is p yards, then $p = 2(l + b)$ and $A = lb$.

    (i) Express p in terms of A and b only.

    (ii) Express A in terms of l and p only.

*27. (i) What is N if $\sqrt{N} = 5$?

    (ii) What is A if $\sqrt{A} = d$?

*28. Make n the subject of the formula $(n-1)^2 = t$.

REVISION EXERCISE R. 3. (Ch. V–VI)

Simplify:

1. $2(x^2 - 7x + 3) - 5(x^2 - x + 1)$.   2. $6d - 3[b - 2(d - c)]$.

[3] $a(b + c) - a(a - b + c)$.   [4] $\frac{1}{3}(1 + x) - \frac{2}{5}(1 - x)$.

5. $\dfrac{2n - 3}{6n} - \dfrac{n - 2}{4n} + 1$.   [6] $\frac{1}{3}p\left(\dfrac{1}{6p} - \dfrac{1}{2p}\right)$.

If $x = -3$, $y = -2$, $z = 0$, $t = 4$, evaluate:

7. $\frac{1}{2}xy$.   8. $3xyz$.   9. $x^2 + y^3$.   10. $x(y - t)$.

[11] $2x^3$.   [12] $\frac{3}{4}ty$.   [13] $y^2 - 2tz$.   [14] $(x - y)(z - t)$.

If $a = -2$, $b = -1$, $c = 0$, $d = 3$, evaluate:

15. $\dfrac{a - b}{a + d}$.   16. $\dfrac{2bc}{3ad}$.   [17] $\dfrac{a^2 - d^2}{b - c}$.   [18] $\dfrac{a}{b} - \dfrac{b}{d}$.

Simplify:

19. $(-3)(-a)$.   20. $-(-b) + (+b)$.   [21] $(-2c)^3$.

22. $\dfrac{-12r^3}{-3r}$.   23. $\dfrac{-x}{y} \times \dfrac{-y}{-x}$.   [24] $\dfrac{st}{-t}$.

25. $2r(3 - t) - 3t(2 - r) - r + 7(t - 2r)$.

[26] $2y + 3[z - (y + z)] - y[3 - 2(y + 1)]$.

27. $[3x + y - (8y - 11x)] \div 7$.   [28] $[a - \frac{1}{3}(a - 4b)] \div 2$.

29. Add: $2x(3y - z + x)$; $x^2 - 7xy + 5xz$; $3xy - x(2x + z)$.

30. Subtract $3a^2 - a + 1$ from a.

31. Divide $x^4 - x^2 y^2$ by $-x^2$.

[32] Subtract $1 - 3x - x^2 + 2x^3$ from $4x^2 - x + 3$.

[33] Multiply $4 - 6x + 2x^2 - 4x^3$ by $-\frac{1}{2}x$.

34. What must be added to $m + n - p$ to make $m - n - p$?

[35] By how much does $a - 3b + 4c$ exceed $b + 2c - a$?

Solve:

[36] $(x + 1) + (x + 2) + (x + 3) = 0$.   37 $\frac{3}{4}(1 - y) = 1\frac{1}{2}$.

38. $1 \cdot 2n - 3 \cdot 4 = 0 \cdot 05n + 1 \cdot 2$.   [39] $\dfrac{1}{t} + \dfrac{0 \cdot 2}{5t} = 0 \cdot 1$.

40. $\dfrac{z + 2}{5} = 8 - \dfrac{z - 2}{4}$.   [41] $\dfrac{2p - 1}{5} = 3 + \dfrac{1 - 3p}{4}$.

42. $\dfrac{3x + 5}{5} - \dfrac{4x - 6}{7} = x - 3$.   [43] $\dfrac{2(x - 3)}{3} + \dfrac{3}{4}\left(x + \dfrac{7}{3}\right) = \dfrac{5}{8}$.

44. For what value of p is $x = -1$ a root of the equation $x^3 = 5x - 2x^2 + p$?

45. If $y = 3(2x + 1)$, express x in terms of y.

[46] Make r the subject of the formula $S = 2\pi rh$.

47. Make h the subject of the formula $V = \frac{1}{3}\pi r^2 h$.

[48] Make h the subject of the formula $A = 2\pi r(r + h)$.

49. If $x = 3(y + z)$ and if $A = yz$, express (i) x in terms of A, y only, (ii) A in terms of x, z only.

[50] A man is y years older than his son whose present age is x years. In 5 years' time the father will be just twice as old as his son. Find y in terms of x.

51. If $(\frac{1}{5}n - 1)$ is two-thirds of $(\frac{1}{3}n - 1)$, find the value of n, and the value of each expression.

[52] From the formula $F = 32 + \dfrac{9C}{5}$, find the value of C if $7C = 4F$.

53. I walk for $2\frac{1}{2}$ hours in the morning at x miles an hour and for $\frac{1}{2}x$ hours in the afternoon at $3\frac{1}{2}$ miles an hour; this makes 17 miles altogether. Find the value of x. Find also the total number of hours walking.

[54] For what value of k does the fraction $\dfrac{3(k + 1)}{4k + 1}$ reduce to $\dfrac{4}{5}$?

55. If $2p$ half-crowns and $(3p + 4)$ shillings are together worth £3, find the value of p.

56. A has £a, B has £b. A owes £p to B, and B owes 10 guineas to A. How many pounds will A have when both debts have been paid?

[57] A man takes 15 minutes to go $1\frac{1}{4}$ miles, running part of the way at 6 miles an hour and walking the rest at $4\frac{1}{2}$ miles an hour. How far does he walk?

58. A man bought some tea of one kind at 1s. 10d. per lb. and mixed it with 3 times as much tea of another kind at 1s. 6d. per lb. One-eighth of the total amount was damaged and the remainder was sold at 2s. per lb. If the total gain was 4 shillings, find how many lb. of each kind of tea were bought.

[59] A dealer buys 144 articles. He sells some at a profit of 1s. 6d. each, but has to sell the rest at a loss of 9d. each. If he makes £4, 10s. profit on the whole sale, how many articles did he sell at a profit?

60. If p is a whole number, find the least value of p for which $8(p - 2)$ exceeds $5p + 7$.

CHAPTER VII

SIMULTANEOUS EQUATIONS AND PROBLEMS

Example 1. Two tanks, A and B, contain respectively 120 gallons and 300 gallons of water. If water is allowed to run into A at the rate of 10 gallons per minute, and to run out of B at the rate of 20 gallons a minute, find a formula for the number of gallons n in tank A after t minutes, and a similar formula for tank B.

Water runs into A at 10 gallons per minute;

∴ in t minutes, $10t$ gallons run into A;

∴ after t minutes, there are $(120 + 10t)$ gallons in A.

$$\text{∴ for tank A, } n = 120 + 10t.$$

Water runs out of B at 20 gallons per minute;

∴ in t minutes, $20t$ gallons run out of B.

∴ after t minutes, there are $(300 - 20t)$ gallons in B.

$$\text{∴ for tank B, } n = 300 - 20t.$$

Since the amount of water in A steadily increases, and that in B steadily decreases, there must come a single moment when A and B contain equal amounts of water. This means that there is one value of t which makes the value of n for tank A the same as the value of n for tank B.

At this moment, *and only at this moment*, the equations

$$n = 120 + 10t; \quad n = 300 - 20t$$

are true for each tank, and we call them **simultaneous equations.**

If the equations $\begin{cases} n = 120 + 10t \\ n = 300 - 20t \end{cases}$ are simultaneous,

then $\qquad 120 + 10t = 300 - 20t; \quad ∴ \ 10t + 20t = 300 - 120;$

$$∴ \ 30t = 180; \quad ∴ \ t = 6.$$

Also $n = 120 + 10t = 120 + 60 = 180.$

Check: Take the other equation,

$$n = 300 - 20t = 300 - 20 \times 6 = 300 - 120 = 180, \text{ as before.}$$

This shows that in 6 minutes' time there will be equal amounts of water, namely 180 gallons, in the two tanks. At no other time will this be true.

EXERCISE VII. a (Oral)

1. A and B have £110 and £600 respectively in the bank. If A increases his bank balance by £30 every year and if his balance is £P after n years, find P in terms of n. If B decreases his bank balance by £40 every year and if his balance is £P after n years, find P in terms of n.

Find also the time at which their balances are equal and the amount of the balance at this time.

2. A joins a club for which he has to pay an entrance fee of £10 and a subscription of £9 a year. If the total cost for t years is £n, find n in terms of t. B joins another club for which he has to pay an entrance fee of £25 and a subscription of £6 a year. If the total cost for t years is £n, find n in terms of t.

Find also the number of years for which the total costs of the two clubs are the same and what this cost is.

3. Find the formula for the tax £T on an income of £P, calculated by each of the following rules:

Rule I. No tax on the first £200 of a man's income, and 5s. in the £ on the rest. [Assume P is greater than 200.]

Rule II. No tax on the first £160 of a man's income, and 4s. in the £ on the rest.

For what income do the two rules give the same tax, and how much is this tax?

4. When a load is attached to the hook of the spring A (see Fig. 76), the spring stretches $\frac{1}{2}$ inch for each 1 oz. weight attached. If the *total* length of spring A, when a load of weight W oz. is attached, is l inches, find l in terms of W.

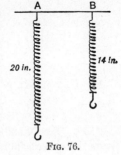

When a load is attached to the spring B, the spring stretches $1\frac{1}{4}$ inches for each 1 oz. weight attached. If the *total* length of spring B, when a load of weight W oz. is attached, is l inches, find l in terms of W.

FIG. 76.

Find also what load makes the total lengths equal, and what this length is.

5. Write down three pairs of numbers, x and y, such that $y = 2x + 1$, and three pairs of numbers, x and y, such that $y = 16 - x$.

Find the values of x and y for which $y = 2x + 1$ and $y = 16 - x$ are simultaneous equations.

Find pairs of values which satisfy the following simultaneous equations:

6. $a = 7 - 2b.$ 7. $n = 2t - 3.$ 8. $y = 5 - 3z.$
   $a = b - 2.$ $n = 7t - 13.$ $y = 13 + z.$

9. $r = 3 + s.$ 10. $u = v - 3.$ 11. $P = 3Q.$
   $r = 12 - s.$ $u = 5v - 19.$ $P = 20 - 2Q.$

There are two methods for solving simultaneous equations.

Method I. Solution by Substitution

Example 2.   Solve the simultaneous equations:

$$3x + 2y = 21 \dots\dots\dots\dots\dots\dots\text{(i)}$$

$$2x + 5y = \ 3 \dots\dots\dots\dots\dots\dots\text{(ii)}$$

From (i), $2y = 21 - 3x,$

$$\therefore \ y = \frac{21 - 3x}{2} \dots\dots\dots\dots\dots\dots\text{(iii)}$$

Substitute this value of y in (ii), then

$$2x + \frac{5(21 - 3x)}{2} = 3,$$

$$\therefore \ 4x + 105 - 15x = 6,$$

$$\therefore \ -11x = -99$$

$$\therefore \ x = 9.$$

Put $x = 9$ in (iii), $\therefore \ y = \dfrac{21 - 27}{2} = -3,$

$$\therefore \ x = 9, \quad y = -3.$$

Check: If $x = 9$ and $y = -3$, $2x + 5y = 18 - 15 = 3$, as in (ii). The value of y was found by substituting $x = 9$ in (iii), which is equivalent to (i). We therefore use (ii) for the check, *not* (i).

If this method is employed, the following oral work is desirable.

EXERCISE VII. b (Oral)

Find y in terms of x in Nos. 1–6:

1. $3x - y = 11$.   2. $5x + 2y = 12$.   3. $\frac{1}{3}x - 4y = 16$.

[4] $2x + y = 7$.   [5] $9x - 7y = 3$.   [6] $7x + 3y = 0$.

Find x in terms of y in Nos. 7–12:

7. $x + 5y = 3$.   8. $4x + 9y = 0$.   9. $\frac{1}{3}x = \frac{1}{6}(y - 1)$.

[10] $3x - 7y = 1$.   [11] $\frac{1}{3}x + 7y = 8$.   [12] $\frac{1}{2}x - \frac{1}{3}y = 0$.

Is it better to find x in terms of y or to find y in terms of x when solving the following? *Do not solve them.*

13. $7y - 2x = 4$.   14. $2x - 5y + 3 = 0$.   15. $\dfrac{y}{2} + x = 1$.

     $3y - x = 1$. $3x + 4y - 1 = 0$. $\dfrac{y}{3} - 7x = 4$.

Method II.   Solution by Addition or Subtraction

If the method by substitution involves awkward fractions, it is easier to use the method by addition or subtraction.

Example 3.   Solve the simultaneous equations:

$$3x - 2y = 11 \dots\dots\dots\dots\dots\dots\dots\dots \text{(i)}$$

$$5x + 2y = 29 \dots\dots\dots\dots\dots\dots\dots\dots \text{(ii)}$$

The result of adding the left side of (i) to the left side of (ii) equals the result of adding the right sides; but if we do this, the term in y disappears, leaving a simple equation in x.

Thus, $3x + 5x = 11 + 29$; $\therefore 8x = 40$;

$$\therefore x = 5.$$

Put $x = 5$ in (i), then $15 - 2y = 11$; $\therefore -2y = -4$;

$$\therefore y = 2.$$

$$\therefore \text{ the solution is } x = 5, \ y = 2.$$

Check: If $x = 5$ and $y = 2$, $5x + 2y = 25 + 4 = 29$, as in (ii).

Example 4.   Solve the simultaneous equations:

$$2x - 5y = 27 \dots\dots\dots\dots\dots\dots\dots \text{(i)}$$
$$2x + 3y = 3 \dots\dots\dots\dots\dots\dots\dots \text{(ii)}$$

If we subtract, the term in x disappears.

Subtracting, $-5y - 3y = 27 - 3;$ $\therefore$ $-8y = 24;$

$$\therefore \ y = -3.$$

Put $y = -3$ in (ii), then $2x - 9 = 3;$ $\therefore$ $2x = 12;$

$$\therefore \ x = 6.$$

$\therefore$ the solution is $x = 6,\ y = -3.$

Check: If $x = 6$ and $y = -3,\ 2x - 5y = 12 + 15 = 27,$ as in (i).

The process of getting rid of one of the unknowns is called elimination.   In Example 3 we eliminated y; and in Example 4 we eliminated x.   It does not matter which unknown is eliminated, always do whichever is easier.

Example 5.   Solve the simultaneous equations:

$$7x - 6y = 20 \dots\dots\dots\dots\dots\dots\dots \text{(i)}$$
$$3x + 4y = 2 \dots\dots\dots\dots\dots\dots\dots \text{(ii)}$$

The L.C.M. of 6 and 4 is 12; therefore if we multiply each side of (i) by 2, and each side of (ii) by 3, we shall obtain equations in which the coefficients of y are *numerically* equal.

It is easier to do this than to make the coefficients of x equal, because in this case we should have to multiply by 3 and 7 respectively.

Multiply each side of (i) by 2, $\therefore$ $14x - 12y = 40 \dots\dots\dots\dots \text{(iii)}$
Multiply each side of (ii) by 3, $\therefore$ $9x + 12y = 6. \dots\dots\dots\dots \text{(iv)}$
From (iii) and (iv) by adding, $23x = 46$

$$\therefore \ x = 2.$$

Put $x = 2$ in (ii) $\therefore$ $6 + 4y = 2$

$$\therefore \ 4y = -4$$
$$\therefore \ y = -1$$

$\therefore$ the solution is $x = 2,\ y = -1.$

Check: If $x = 2$ and $y = -1,\ 7x - 6y = 14 + 6 = 20,$ as in (i); we must use (i) for the check because the value of y was found by substituting in (ii).

General Instructions

(i) First decide which unknown it is easier to eliminate.

(ii) When one unknown has been found, obtain the other by substituting in the EASIEST equation you have containing it.

(iii) When checking, use that one of the ORIGINAL equations which is not equivalent to the equation used for substitution.

(iv) If the answers involve awkward fractions or decimals, it is often better to look over your working again or solve by an independent method, instead of checking by substitution.

(v) Number the chief equations, and use the numbering to explain your method. A way of abbreviating the explanation is indicated on p. 125.

EXERCISE VII. c

Solve the following pairs of simultaneous equations and check the answers. In each case state *at the start* which unknown can be eliminated the more easily, or whether it makes no difference.

1. $x + y = 13.$
   $x - y = 1.$

2. $u = 3v.$
   $u = 15 - 2v.$

3. $3p + q = 11.$
   $p + q = 7.$

4. $2r - s = 3.$
   $r + s = 9.$

5. $2y - 3z = 13.$
   $2y - 4z = 10.$

6. $b = 2a - 1.$
   $b = 9 - 2a.$

[7] $c - 5d = 4.$
   $c - 2d = 16.$

[8] $x + y = 11.$
   $x - y = 5.$

[9] $r + 3s = 8.$
   $r - 2s = 3.$

[10] $x - 5y = 1.$
   $x + 4y = 28.$

[11] $p = 2 + q.$
   $q = 8 - p.$

[12] $y - 2z = 5.$
   $2z + y = 1.$

13. $2a = 3b - 6.$
   $a = 2b - 5.$

14. $5c - d = 3.$
   $3d - 8c = 5.$

15. $c - 3d = 0.$
   $2c - d = 20.$

[16] $l + 2m = 8.$
   $2l + m = 7.$

[17] $3s - t = 1.$
   $5s + 2t = 20.$

[18] $a - 2b = 3.$
   $3a + b = 72.$

19. $x + 2y = 11.$
   $2x - y = 2.$

20. $3y - z = 11.$
   $2y - 3z = 5.$

21. $3r + 5s = 21.$
   $r + 2s = 7.$

[22] $3a + 2b = 4.$
   $a + 3b = 13.$

[23] $4c + 3d = 1.$
   $5c + 4d = 2.$

[24] $l = 2m + 1.$
   $3l = 5(m + 1).$

25. $2m + 5n = 8.$
   $3m + 4n = 5.$

26. $7p - q = 2.$
   $6p = q.$

27. $4s = 3r + 2.$
   $3s + r + 1 = 0.$

[28] $x - 2y = 27.$
$7x + y = 9.$

[29] $b = 3a - 2.$
$a = 1 - 2b.$

[30] $2c + d = 10.$
$3c - 2d = 1.$

[31] $2r = 6s + 1.$
$2s = 3 - 2r.$

[32] $6x - 5y = 24.$
$9x - 4y = 22.$

[33] $3a - 5b = 4.$
$2(3 - a) = 3 + a.$

34. $3x + 4y + 11 = 0.$
$5x + 6y + 7 = 0.$

35. $2(r - 2s) = 3s.$
$3s - 2r = 1.$

36. $2(y + 2) = 6(z + 1).$
$2y - 5z = 4.$

[37] $P + 13Q = 19.$
$P - 11Q = 67.$

[38] $6a - 5b = 21.$
$5a + 4b = 17\frac{1}{2}.$

[39] $10c + 10d = 7.$
$3d - c = 0 \cdot 1.$

40. $0 \cdot 2x + 0 \cdot 2y = 1.$
$0 \cdot 3x + 0 \cdot 5y = 2 \cdot 1.$

41. $1 \cdot 2x + y = 0 \cdot 6.$
$0 \cdot 7x + 0 \cdot 8y = 1.$

[42] $0 \cdot 2x + 0 \cdot 9y = 3.$
$0 \cdot 3x + 0 \cdot 6y = 1 \cdot 5.$

[43] $4a - 2b = 4b - 5a = a + b - 3.$

[44] $3l - 8 = l - 2m - 1 = 40.$

45. $3p - 1 = 10p + q = 1\frac{1}{2}p.$

46. $2y - 3z = 6y + 5z = 70.$

[47] $5a - 3b = 7a - 6b = 9.$

[48] $x - y = y - x + 2 = 3y.$

49. $2c - d - 3 = 3d - c + 4 = 5c - 8d - 4.$

[50] $4x - 6y - 3 = 7x + 2y - 4 = 3y - 2x + 24.$

51. $\dfrac{4}{x} - \dfrac{1}{y} = 17.$
$\dfrac{2}{x} + \dfrac{3}{y} = 19.$

52. $\dfrac{2}{a} + \dfrac{5}{b} = 5.$
$\dfrac{1}{a} - \dfrac{7}{b} = 12.$

53. $\dfrac{3}{x} + \dfrac{5}{y} = 5.$
$\dfrac{15}{y} - \dfrac{12}{x} = 1.$

[54] $\dfrac{3}{r} + \dfrac{4}{s} = 5.$
$\dfrac{5}{r} - \dfrac{1}{s} = 16.$

[55] $\dfrac{3}{c} + \dfrac{2}{d} = 12.$
$\dfrac{4}{c} + \dfrac{3}{d} = 17.$

[56] $\dfrac{5}{y} + \dfrac{3}{z} = 9.$
$\dfrac{2}{y} - \dfrac{5}{z} = 16.$

57. If $y = mx + b$ is satisfied by $x = 2$, $y = 3$, and also by $x = -4$, $y = 1$, find the values of m and b.

58. If $x = 3$, $y = -2$ satisfy simultaneously the equations $x + ay = 5$, $bx + y = 7$, find the values of a and b.

*59. Find *two pairs* of numbers satisfying $7x - 2y = 38$, and such that one number is three times the other.

*60. If $2a + 3b = 9$ and $3a + 2b = 16$, find the value of $3a - 2b$.

*61. If $3p + 4q = -119$ and $5p - 11q = 102$, prove that $p = q$.

*62. If $x = my + a$ is satisfied by $x = 2$, $y = 3$ and also by $x = -5$, $y = 4$, find the value of y when $x = 9$.

*63. If $y = ax(x + 1) + b$ is satisfied by $x = -2$, $y = 1$ and also by $x = 3$, $y = 21$, find the value of y when $x = 2$.

Problems

Example 6. A certain number is formed of two digits; its value equals four times the sum of its digits. If 27 is added to it, the sum is the number obtained by interchanging the digits. What is the number?

Let x be the tens-digit and y the unit-digit. Then the value of the number is $10x + y$, and the sum of the digits is $x + y$.

$$\therefore 10x + y = 4(x + y);$$
$$\therefore 10x + y = 4x + 4y; \quad \therefore 6x - 3y = 0;$$
$$\therefore 2x - y = 0 \quad \dots\dots\dots\dots\dots\dots\dots\dots\dots(i)$$

The value of the number formed by interchanging the digits is $10y + x$.

$$\therefore 10x + y + 27 = 10y + x; \quad \therefore 9x - 9y = -27;$$
$$\therefore x - y = -3 \dots\dots\dots\dots\dots\dots\dots\dots\dots(ii)$$

From (i) and (ii) by subtracting, $\quad x = 3.$

$$\therefore \text{ from (i), } 6 - y = 0; \quad \therefore y = 6.$$
$$\therefore \text{ the original number is } 36.$$

Check by using the data of the problem:

$4 \times (\text{sum of digits}) = 4 \times (3 + 6) = 4 \times 9 = 36 = \text{the number.}$

$36 + 27 = 63 = \text{number obtained by interchanging the digits.}$

EXERCISE VII. d

Use **simultaneous** *equations to solve the following problems:*

1. Find a pair of numbers whose sum is 39 and whose difference is 11.

2. A jug and basin cost 6 shillings; the jug costs 6 pence more than the basin. Find the cost of each.

3. 2 knives and 4 forks cost 24 shillings; 5 knives and 6 forks of the same kind cost £2. Find the cost of a knife and of a fork.

4. A farmer can buy 3 cows and 5 sheep for £90, and he can buy 4 cows and 10 sheep for £140. Find the price of a cow and of a sheep.

[5] 5 lb. of apples and 2 lb. of pears cost 4s.; 1 lb. of apples and 2 lb. of pears cost 2s. Find the cost of 1 lb. of pears.

[6] 3 lb. of jam and 2 lb. of butter cost 8s.; also 6 lb. of jam and 3 lb. of butter cost 14s. Find the cost of 1 lb. of jam.

7. Fig. 77 shows the lengths of the sides of a triangle in inches. If the triangle is equilateral, find the values of x and y and the perimeter of the triangle.

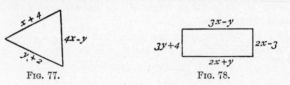

FIG. 77.   FIG. 78.

8. Fig. 78 shows the lengths of the sides of a rectangle in inches. Find the values of x and y and the area of the rectangle.

9. I am thinking of a pair of numbers. If I add 11 to the first, I obtain twice the second; and if I add 20 to the second, I obtain twice the first. What are the numbers?

10. Find two numbers whose sum is 90 and such that one-third of the smaller is equal to one-seventh of the larger.

[11] Find two numbers such that three times the smaller exceeds twice the larger by 3, and seven times the smaller exceeds five times the larger by 2.

[12] A gramophone with 20 records costs £8, 10s.; the same gramophone with 50 similar records costs £12, 5s. Find the cost of the gramophone by itself.

[13] A builder requires 3 lorry-loads and 8 cart-loads to fetch 15 tons of gravel. He would require 2 lorry-loads and 20 cart-loads for 21 tons. How much is a lorry-load and a cart-load?

14. In 4 years' time a father will be 3 times as old as his son will be; 4 years ago he was 5 times as old as his son was. Find their present ages.

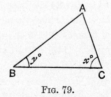

FIG. 79.

15. In Fig. 79, $\angle A = 2 \angle B$ and $\angle C - \angle B = 36°$. Find the angles of the triangle.

[16] In Fig. 79, $\angle$ **A** can be expressed either as $(2x - y)$ degrees or as $(2y + x)$ degrees. Find the angles of the triangle.

[17] If **A** gives **B** 3 shillings, **B** will have twice as much as **A** will have. If **B** gives **A** 5 shillings, **A** will have twice as much as **B** will have. How much has each?

18. **A** owes £4, **B** owes £5; **A** could just pay his debt if he borrowed from **B** one-eighth of what **B** has; **B** could just pay his debt if he borrowed from **A** two-sevenths of what **A** has. How much has each?

19. I have to pay for 500 cigarettes two shillings more than for 3 lb. of tobacco; and I have to pay for 4 lb. of tobacco four shillings more than for 600 cigarettes. What do I pay for 1 lb. of tobacco and for 100 cigarettes?

20. A number of two digits is equal to 7 times the sum of the digits and exceeds by 36 the number formed by interchanging the digits. What is the original number?

[21] A number of two digits is equal to 6 times the sum of the digits, and the number formed by reversing the digits exceeds four times the sum of the digits by 9. What is the original number?

[22] A number of 3 digits is such that the tens digit exceeds the units digit by 2. If this number exceeds the number formed by reversing the digits by 297 and if the sum of its digits is 14, find the number.

23. Some oranges are distributed amongst some children. If each receives 10 oranges, there are 3 left over; but there are 4 oranges too few for each to receive 11. Find the number of oranges.

[24] If the larger of two numbers is divided by the smaller the quotient and remainder are each 2. If 5 times the smaller is divided by the larger, the quotient and remainder are again each 2. Find the two numbers.

25. A man travels 12 miles in $2\frac{1}{4}$ hours, part of the time at 9 miles an hour and the rest at $3\frac{1}{2}$ miles an hour. How far did he go at the faster speed?

[26] A bench 18 feet long holds either 3 men and 8 boys or 6 men and 4 boys. What length of bench is required for 10 men and 10 boys?

27. The external perimeter of the wire network in Fig. 80 is 20 inches, and the total length of wire used for the network is 3 feet. Find the total area of the network.

FIG. 80.

28. Find a fraction which reduces to $\frac{2}{3}$ if the numerator and denominator are each increased by 1, and reduces to $\frac{2}{5}$ if the numerator and denominator are each diminished by 2.

[29] Find a fraction which reduces to $\frac{3}{4}$ either if 1 is added to the numerator or if 11 is subtracted from the numerator and the denominator is halved.

[30] If A gives B two pence, B has four times as much as A then has. If C gives A and B ten pence each, B will have twice as much as A. How much have A and B?

31. A heap of florins and half-crowns is worth £2. If there were 3 times as many florins and half the number of half-crowns, it would be worth 5 shillings more. How many coins of each kind are there?

32. A delivers 12 gallons of milk, some of it in quart bottles and the rest in pint bottles. B delivers one-third of the number of quart bottles but three times as many pint bottles as A, and this amounts to 16 gallons. How many quart bottles did A deliver?

[33] The coins in a bag containing £5 are half-crowns and shillings. A second bag contains one-third of the number of half-crowns but 40 per cent. more shillings than are in the first bag. The contents of the second bag amount to £3. Find the numbers of coins of each kind in the first bag.

[34] A shilling weighs $\frac{1}{5}$ oz. and a penny weighs $\frac{1}{3}$ oz.; 11 coins, some shillings, the rest pence, weigh 2·6 oz. What is the value of the coins?

*35. A man's age in A.D. 1887 was equal to the sum of the digits of the year A.D. "18xy" in which he was born; and he was $8x + y$ years old in A.D. 1920. In what year was he born?

*36. In Fig. 81, **AB** = **AC** and $\angle$ **ABC** = $\frac{1}{5}(x + 2y)$ degrees; find x and y.

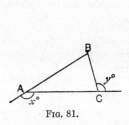

FIG. 81.

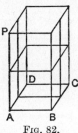

FIG. 82.

*37. A skeleton cuboid (see Fig. 82) has a square base **ABCD**; the wire composing the cuboid is 11 feet long, and of this 7 feet is used for the outside edges, *i.e.* all the rims. Find the dimensions of the cuboid.

*38. A piece of wire $6\frac{1}{2}$ feet long can be bent into either of the shapes in Fig. 83, the units of the data being inches and all the corners right-angled. Find the values of x and y, and the area of each figure.

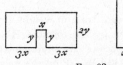

FIG. 83.

*39. The incomes of two men are in the ratio 5 : 3; their expenditures are in the ratio 9 : 5. Each saves £30 a year. Find their incomes.

*40. If **A** gives two-thirds of the money he has to **B**, then **B** will have $3\frac{1}{2}$ times as much as **A** will have. If **B** gives 9 shillings to **A**, then **A** will have $2\frac{1}{2}$ times as much as **B** will have. How much have they between them?

*41. **APQB** is a straight line and **PQ** = 2 inches. If **AQ** = $1\frac{1}{2}$**QB** and **AP** = $\frac{1}{2}$**PB**, find the lengths of **AP** and **QB**.

*42. p shillings and q half-crowns have the same value as $(q-1)$ shillings and $(p-2)$ half-crowns. If this value is £3, find the value of $(p-q)$ half-crowns.

*43. The area of Fig. 84 is 72 sq. inches, and the perimeter is 4 feet. Find the values of x and y.

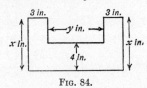

FIG. 84.

*44. If in Fig. 85 **AC** = **AB** = **BD**, find one equation connecting x and y. If, further, **BC** = **CD**, find x and y.

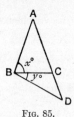

FIG. 85.

*45. The resistance **R** lb. to a train of weight 100 tons running at **V** miles an hour is given by the formula $R = a + bV^2$, where a, b are independent of the speed. At 20 m.p.h. the resistance is 960 lb.; at 50 m.p.h. it is 2850 lb. Find the values of a, b, and the resistance at 30 m.p.h.

*46. A number of two digits is equal to 7 times the sum of its digits. Prove that the number formed by reversing the digits is equal to 4 times the sum of its digits.

Fractional Equations. When x or y have fractional (or decimal) coefficients, it is usually best to start by clearing these terms of fractions; *it is not necessary to clear of fractions the terms which do not contain* x *or* y.

Number the chief equations: a short method of indicating that each side of equation (i) is to be multiplied by 15, say, is to write "(i) × 15," (see Example 7).

Example 7. Solve the simultaneous equations:

$$\frac{2x-1}{3} - \frac{3(y+1)}{5} = 1\tfrac{1}{2} \quad \dots\dots\dots\dots\dots(i)$$

$$\frac{2x-y}{2} - \frac{y-1}{3} = 4\tfrac{1}{12} \quad \dots\dots\dots\dots\dots(ii)$$

(i) × 15 gives

$$5(2x-1) - 9(y+1) = 1\tfrac{1}{2} \times 15;$$
$$\therefore\ 10x - 5 - 9y - 9 = 22\tfrac{1}{2};$$
$$\therefore\ 10x - 9y = 36\tfrac{1}{2} \quad \dots\dots\dots\dots\dots(iii)$$

(ii) × 6 gives

$$3(2x-y) - 2(y-1) = 4\tfrac{1}{12} \times 6;$$
$$\therefore\ 6x - 3y - 2y + 2 = 24\tfrac{1}{2};$$
$$\therefore\ 6x - 5y = 22\tfrac{1}{2} \quad \dots\dots\dots\dots\dots(iv)$$

(iii) × 3 gives $\quad 30x - 27y = 36\tfrac{1}{2} \times 3 = 109\tfrac{1}{2} \dots\dots\dots\dots\dots(v)$

(iv) × 5 gives $\quad 30x - 25y = 22\tfrac{1}{2} \times 5 = 112\tfrac{1}{2} \dots\dots\dots\dots\dots(vi)$

(v) − (vi) gives

$$-2y = -3;$$
$$\therefore\ y = 1\tfrac{1}{2}.$$

Substituting in (iv) for y, $6x - 5 \times 1\tfrac{1}{2} = 22\tfrac{1}{2}$;

$$\therefore\ 6x = 22\tfrac{1}{2} + 7\tfrac{1}{2} = 30; \quad \therefore\ x = 5.$$
$$\therefore\ \text{the solution is } x = 5,\ y = 1\tfrac{1}{2}.$$

The reader should now consider which of the equations, (i) or (ii), should be used for checking.

EXERCISE VII. e

Solve the following pairs of simultaneous equations:

1. $x + \tfrac{1}{2}y = 13.$
$\tfrac{1}{3}x - y = 2.$

2. $\tfrac{3}{4}p - \tfrac{1}{3}q = 9.$
$2q - p = 2.$

3. $\tfrac{1}{3}r + \tfrac{1}{5}t = 8.$
$\tfrac{1}{9}r - \tfrac{1}{10}t = 1.$

[4] $\frac{1}{2}a - 2b = 5.$
$\quad\ \frac{1}{3}a + b = 1.$

[5] $y - \frac{2}{7}x = \frac{1}{3}.$
$\quad\ x - y = 2\frac{1}{6}.$

[6] $2c + 5d = 1\frac{1}{2}.$
$\quad\ 9c - 7d = 1\frac{7}{20}.$

7. $Q + 2 = \frac{1}{3}P.$
$\quad \frac{1}{5}P - 1 = \frac{2}{3}Q.$

[8] $\frac{1}{2}u + 2v = 5.$
$\quad 2u - \frac{1}{7}v = -8\frac{1}{2}.$

[9] $\dfrac{2y}{5} - \dfrac{z}{3} = 2\frac{2}{3}.$
$\quad y = 2(z + 1).$

10. $3a + \frac{1}{2}b = 8a + 7b - 9 = 2.$

[11] $\dfrac{5p}{3} + \dfrac{2q}{3} = 3p + 3q = 6p + 9q + 3.$

12. $0 \cdot 5t - 0 \cdot 7v = 2.$
$\quad 1 \cdot 8t - 2 \cdot 2v = 8 \cdot 8.$

13. $1 \cdot 2x - 0 \cdot 8y = 0 \cdot 4.$
$\quad y = 0 \cdot 3 - 0 \cdot 1x.$

[14] $h + 5 \cdot 2n = 12 \cdot 1.$
$\quad\ h + 3 \cdot 8n = 10.$

[15] $1\frac{1}{4}a - \frac{1}{2}b = \frac{1}{4}.$
$\quad\ 0 \cdot 2a + 0 \cdot 1b = 1 \cdot 3.$

16. $\frac{1}{3}(r + 2) - \frac{1}{4}(t - 1) = 1,\ t = 1\frac{1}{4}r.$

17. $l - 5 = \dfrac{n - 2}{7}.$
$\quad 4n - 3 = \dfrac{l + 10}{3}.$

18. $\dfrac{x + 1}{2} = 8 - \dfrac{y - 7}{3}.$
$\quad \dfrac{y + 1}{2} = 9 - \dfrac{x - 1}{3}.$

[19] $p = \frac{1}{2} - 3(q - \frac{3}{4}).$
$\quad\ p = \frac{1}{3}q + \frac{1}{4}.$

[20] $\dfrac{y + 1}{3} + \dfrac{z - 1}{2} = 5.$
$\quad\ \dfrac{2y + 5}{3} - \dfrac{z + 1}{4} = 3.$

21. $\dfrac{r}{10} + \dfrac{s}{8} = r - s.$
$\quad \dfrac{2r - s}{3} + 2s = \frac{1}{2}.$

22. $\dfrac{a - 1}{2} + \dfrac{b + 1}{5} = 4\frac{1}{5}.$
$\quad \dfrac{a + b}{3} = b - 1.$

[23] $2l - \dfrac{m - 3}{5} = 9.$
$\quad\ 3m + \dfrac{l - 2}{3} = 25.$

[24] $\dfrac{y + 1}{3} - \dfrac{3z - 1}{2} = 1.$
$\quad\ \dfrac{3 - 8z}{5} - \dfrac{7 - 3y}{4} = 1.$

25. $\dfrac{x}{2} - \dfrac{y}{3} = \dfrac{2x}{5} - \dfrac{y}{4} = 3x - 2y - 5.$

[26] $\frac{1}{2}(c - 3) + \frac{1}{3}(d - 7) = c - d = \frac{1}{3}(5c + d).$

27. $\frac{1}{5}(4y + 5z - 9) = 5y - 5z.\ \ \frac{1}{3}(2y - z - 1) = 2\frac{1}{2} - 2z.$

28. $\frac{1}{3}(b + 1) - \frac{1}{2}(c + 1) = 2b + c + 1,\ \frac{1}{3}(b - 2) = \frac{1}{2}(c + 3).$

[29] $r + s - 8 = \frac{1}{2}(r - s) + \frac{2}{3}(r - \frac{1}{3}s + 2) = 0.$

[30] $\frac{1}{5}(x - 2) - \frac{1}{4}(y - 3) = 2\frac{3}{4},\ \frac{1}{4}(3 - x) = \frac{1}{5}(y - 1).$

Miscellaneous Equations

EXERCISE VII. f

Solve the following:

1. $3x + 5 = 8y + 4 = 7x - 7y - 1$.

[2] $0 = 3x - 7y - 5 = y - x + 3$.

[3] $u + 3v = 2u + 5v = 2v - 2$.

4. $2(a + b + 2) = 3(2a - 3b + 3) = 6(a - b)$.

5. If $p = 2q$ and $q + r = 1$, find the value of pq when $r = 2$.

[6] If $2r + 3s = 9$ and $3r + 2s = 16$, find the value of $3r - 2s$.

[7] If $3y + 4z = -154$ and $5y - 11z = 132$, prove that $y = z$.

8. If $a + b = 9$ and $x = 3a + 7b$, express x in terms of a only.

Solve the following:

9. $\dfrac{1}{x} + y = 15$.

$\dfrac{1}{x} - y = 7$.

10. $\dfrac{1}{x} + \dfrac{1}{y} = 20$.

$\dfrac{1}{x} - \dfrac{1}{y} = 8$.

[11] $\dfrac{2}{u} + \dfrac{1}{v} = 5$.

$\dfrac{1}{u} + \dfrac{2}{v} = 7$.

12. $\dfrac{x+y}{5} = \dfrac{x-y}{3}$.

$\dfrac{x+y}{15} - \dfrac{x-y}{12} = \dfrac{1}{4}$.

[13] $\dfrac{x+y}{3} - \dfrac{x-y}{5} = 1$.

$\dfrac{x-y}{3} - \dfrac{x+y}{4} = 2$.

*14. $2xy - 3y = 10$.

$3xy - 8y = -6$.

*15. $pq + 13p = 19$.

$pq - 11p = 67$.

*16. $x^2 + 2y = 10$.

$2x^2 + 7y = 11$.

*17. $\mathsf{W}(x - 2) = 10$, $\mathsf{W}(x - 1\frac{1}{2}) = 13\frac{1}{2}$.

*18. $\mathsf{P}(1 - 2c) = 27$, $\mathsf{P}(7 + c) = 9$.

19. $x + 2y = 8$, $y + 2z = 13$, $z + 2x = 9$.

20. $x + y + z = 5$, $2x - y + z = 0$, $4x + y + 2z = 6$.

21. $2x + y + z = 2$, $3x + 2y + 3z = 3$, $6x + 3y - 2z = 1$.

*22. If $\dfrac{1}{a} = a + \dfrac{1}{b} = b + \dfrac{1}{c} = c + \dfrac{1}{d} = 2$, find the value of $abcd$.

23. $3x + 2y + z = -4$, $2x - y + 2z = 11$, $y + z = 2$.

24. $2a + 3b - c = 19$, $3a + 4c = 3$, $5a - b + c = 20$.

25. $2x - y = 7$, $3y - z = -5$, $4z - x = 5$.

26. $3x + y + z = x - y - z = y - 3z + 1 = 2(x + y) - z$.

CHAPTER VIII

GRAPHS

GRAPHICAL representation of tables of statistics forms part of the arithmetic course; the object of the present chapter is to revise and extend that work.

Facts are represented graphically in order to convey information rapidly; for example, the points marked in Fig. 86 represent the temperatures at selected times during the day of a boy with a feverish cold, and show at a glance how his temperature went up and down. If his temperature had been taken more frequently, it would have been possible to mark more points on the chart; but there are sufficient to give a good idea of how the temperature changed during the day.

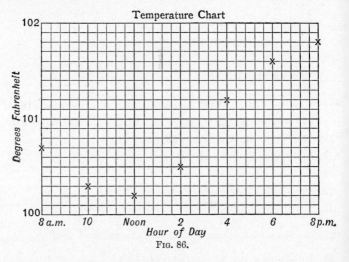

FIG. 86.

Make a copy of this diagram and draw a smooth curve through the marked points; then the other points on this curve probably represent with fair accuracy the boy's temperature at intermediate times.

Oral work on Fig. 86.

Use *your copy* of Fig. 86 for the following examples:

(i) Estimate his temperature at 9 a.m., at 5 p.m.

(ii) Estimate the time when his temperature is 101°, 101·7°.

(iii) Estimate the times when his temperature is 100·4°.

In Fig. 86, the line across the page along which the time-graduations are marked is called the **time-axis,** and the line up the page along which the temperature graduations are marked is called the **temperature-axis.** A graph always records how one quantity varies in size when another quantity on which it depends varies. We *select* values of the latter quantity and then find by *measurement or calculation* the corresponding values of the former quantity. The axis for the quantity whose values we *select* should always be drawn **across the page,** and the axis for the quantity whose values we *measure or calculate* should be drawn **up the page.** Thus in the temperature chart we *select* special times for taking the temperature and then *measure* the temperatures at these times; therefore the time-axis is drawn *across* the page. The quantity whose values we select is called the **independent variable,** the quantity whose values we measure or calculate is called the **dependent variable.**

Oral Examples.

State which quantity should be measured along the axis drawn across the page for the following graphs:

1. Postage on parcels of various weights.

2. A boy's age and height.

3. A travel graph: distance from home and time of day.

4. Record times for races of various lengths.

5. The horse-power of a motor-car and the tax on it.

6. Stretch of a spiral spring under various loads.

7. A man's age and his expectation of life.

8. Rainfall in London and time of year.

Scales. *Great care is needed in the choice of scales* : a bad scale may make the graph worthless. First see what range of values is to be represented; then see what length of axis is available for graduation. For example in the barograph, Fig. 87, all the readings lie between 29 inches and 30 inches; the lowest graduation on the upright axis is therefore taken as 29 inches. If the upright axis had been graduated from 0 to 30, the scale would have been inconveniently small.

Choose a scale which makes plotting and reading easy. 1 inch may be taken to represent 1, 10, 100, etc., or 0·1, 0·01, etc., or 2, 20, etc., or 5, 50, etc. Occasionally 1 inch may be taken to represent 4, 40, etc., but this is not an easy scale to work with; 1 inch should not be taken to represent 3 or 7, etc.

Oral Examples.

What scales would you choose, and what would be the smallest and largest graduations, to represent the following ranges of values, for the given lengths of axes?

1. 45 to 100; 6 inches.
2. 100 to 250; 8 inches.
3. 5·6 to 23·8; 10 inches.
4. 7 to 53; 10 inches.
5. 135 to 1050; 10 inches.
6. 65 to 295; 5 inches.
7. 0 to 1; 5 inches.
8. 21 to 78; 4 inches.

To make a graph easy to understand, the following instructions must always be carried out:

(i) Write above the graph a title or a brief explanatory heading.

(ii) The quantity whose values are selected must be measured along the axis across the page: the quantity whose values are observed, or calculated, along the axis up the page.

(iii) Write along each axis what that axis represents.

(iv) Choose as large a scale as the paper will allow, but it must be a scale which makes plotting and reading easy.

(v) Graduate each axis so as to show clearly the scale for that axis.

The two following examples are intended for oral work:

An automatic recording machine shows how the height of the barometer changes during part of a day, by tracing out the barograph in Fig. 87.

Barograph

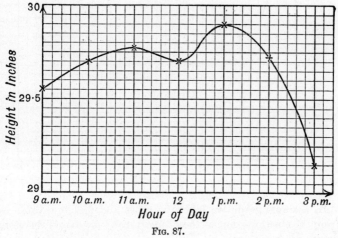

FIG. 87.

Oral work on Fig. 87.

1. What was the height of the barometer at 10 a.m., 11 a.m., 12.24 p.m., 2.48 p.m.?

2. At what times was the height of the barometer 29·15 inches, 29·55 inches, 29·70 inches, 29·65 inches?

3. At what time was the barometer highest, and what was the height at this time?

4. Between what times was the height of the barometer more than 29·65 inches?

5. How much did the barometer rise from 9 a.m. to 10 a.m.?

6. How much did the barometer fall from 2.12 p.m. to 3 p.m.?

7. Between what times was the barometer rising?

8. The graph *slopes downwards more rapidly* between 2 p.m. and 3 p.m. than between 11 a.m. and 12 noon. What does this mean?

Fig. 88 shows some points on the travel graph of a steamer:

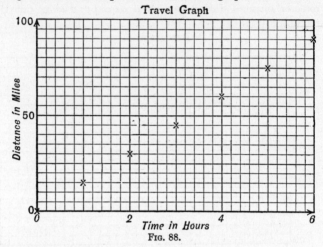

FIG. 88.

In a travel graph we *select* the times and find the distances from the starting-point at these times; the time-axis is therefore drawn *across the page*.

Oral work on Fig. 88.

1. How far did the steamer travel in (i) 2 hours, (ii) 4 hours, (iii) 6 hours?

2. Use a ruler to see whether the marked points lie on a *straight* line. What does this mean? What is the speed of the steamer?

3. *Make a copy of the diagram* and draw on it travel graphs for speeds of 50 m.p.h., 25 m.p.h., 5 m.p.h.

4. Draw on your copy a travel graph of a man, travelling eastwards, who goes at 10 m.p.h. for 1 hour, then at 20 m.p.h. for 3 hours, then at 15 m.p.h. for 2 hours.

5. Draw on your copy of the diagram a travel graph of a man, travelling eastwards, who goes 55 miles in the first 3 hours at a uniform speed, then halts for 1 hour, and then goes 35 miles in the next 2 hours at a uniform speed.

6. What is the meaning of the statement that one part of a travel graph is steeper than another part?

Example 1. X and Y are two towns 50 miles apart; a man A leaves X at 8 a.m. and travels at a uniform speed of 16 m.p.h. to Y; another man B leaves Y at 8.30 a.m. and walks at 4 m.p.h. along the road to X; after 1 hour he waits for half an hour and then continues along the same road by bus at 12 m.p.h. At what time and at what distance from X does A pass B?

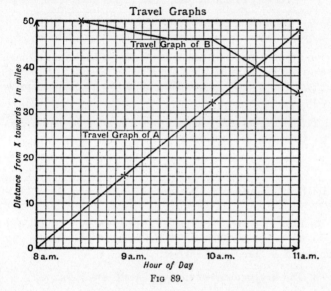

Fig 89.

Since A travels at a uniform speed, his travel graph is a *straight* line.

To draw B's travel graph, first mark the point which represents the fact that B is 50 miles from X at 8.30 a.m., and then the point which represents the fact that B is 46 miles, (50 − 4), from X at 9.30 a.m. For the next half-hour B remains the same distance from X, and therefore the graph runs parallel to the time-axis. The remainder of B's travel graph is obtained by using the fact that he travels 12 miles towards X in the next hour.

The point where the graphs cut shows that at 10.30 a.m. A and B are both 40 miles from X, thus giving the time and place at which A passes B.

EXERCISE VIII. a

1. The following table gives the distances in which a train can be stopped for various velocities:

Velocity in m.p.h.	30	40	45	50	60
Distance in yards	100	176	223	276	400

Find from a graph (i) how much farther a train runs after the brakes are put hard on when the speed is 35 m.p.h., 55 m.p.h.; (ii) how fast a train is travelling if it can be stopped in 200 yards.

[2] The heights of a shell fired from a howitzer at various times after projection are as follows:

Time in seconds - -	5	10	20	30	35	40	50	60
Height in hundreds of ft.	15	28	45	52	52	49	35	10

Find from a graph (i) the height after 15 seconds, (ii) the times when the height is 4300 feet, (iii) the length of the time for which the height is more than 3000 feet.

3. The British amateur running records are as follows:

Distance in yards -	150	200	440	600	880	1000
Time in seconds - -	14·6	19·4	47·0	70·8	112·2	132·4

(i) What would be the probable record for 500 yards, 750 yards?

(ii) The American record for 300 metres (1 metre = 1·09 yard) is 33·2 seconds; how does this compare with British records?

(iii) How far should it be possible for an amateur to run in 1 minute, 2 minutes?

[4] Expectation of life of a man at different ages:

Age in years - - -	30	40	50	60	70	80
Expectation in years -	33·2	26·5	19·9	13·6	8·6	5·2

Find from a graph (i) how much longer a man may expect to live at the age of 34, 53, 66; (ii) at what age the expectation of life is 22, 16, 11 years.

5. If £100 is allowed to accumulate at 4 per cent. per annum compound interest, the amount is as follows:

Number of years	0	5	10	20	30	35
Amount in £ -	100	122	148	219	324	395

Find from a graph the amount after (i) 15 years, (ii) 25 years, (iii) 33 years.

After what time will £100 amount to £350?

At 4 per cent. simple interest, the amounts of £100 after 10, 20, 30 years are £140, £180, £220 respectively; draw the corresponding simple interest graph on the same figure. After what time does the amount of £100 at compound interest exceed that at simple interest, at 4 per cent. per annum, by £50?

[6] The time of a complete oscillation of a pendulum depends on its length; the following results hold in London:

Length in feet -	1	2	3	4	5	6
Time in seconds	1·11	1·57	1·92	2·21	2·48	2·71

Find from a graph (i) the time for lengths 2 feet 6 inches, 4 feet 9 inches; (ii) the length to give a time, 2 seconds.

The pendulum of a clock should make complete oscillations every 2 seconds if the clock is keeping time. How should the length be corrected if a complete oscillation takes 2·1 seconds? What alteration in length is required to reduce the time of a complete oscillation from 1·3 seconds to 1·2 seconds?

7. Interpret the given travel graph, stating the different speeds in miles per hour. What is the average speed for the whole journey? How can you tell without any calculation which part of the graph corresponds to the greatest speed?

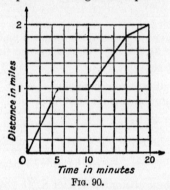

FIG. 90.

[8] Draw the travel graph of a man, travelling due north, who starts at 11 a.m. and walks at 4 m.p.h. for half an hour, then bicycles at 12 m.p.h. for 1¾ hours, then stops for ¾ hour, then motors at 32 m.p.h. for 1¼ hours. How far has he gone at 2.30 p.m.? What is the time when he has travelled 10 miles, 28 miles? Find his total average speed.

[9] A spiral spring is suspended from one end, and its length is measured when different weights are attached to the other end:

Weight in gm.	10	15	30	50	75
Length in cm.	22	24	30	38	48

Draw a graph to show the relation between the length and the load, and use it to find:

(i) the length if the load is 20 gm., 40 gm., 65 gm.;

(ii) the load if the length is 23 cm., 28 cm., 42 cm.;

(iii) the natural length, *i.e.* the length when there is no load.

Is the graph a straight line? If so, what does this mean? The corresponding graph for another spiral spring is a steeper straight line; what does this mean?

10. The diagram shows the travel graphs **OCG, OQS** of two men, **X** and **Y** respectively, who start from the same house at 10 a.m. and proceed on the same road.

(i) Describe the journey represented by **OCG** in detail, giving the various speeds. Can you tell at a glance when the man is moving fastest, when he is resting? How far does he go altogether? When does he start to come home?

(ii) Repeat (i) for the graph **OQS**.

(iii) When does **X** overtake **Y**?

(iv) When and where do **X** and **Y** pass one another?

(v) How far is **X** ahead of **Y** when he turns back?

(vi) How far does **X** go while **Y** is resting?

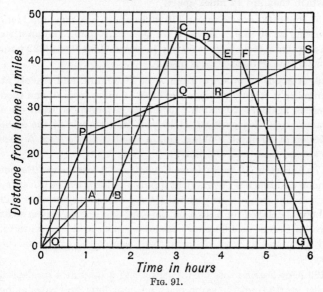

Fig. 91.

11. Draw a graph for converting miles to kilometres, for distances up to 5 miles, given that 1 mile ≏ 1·6 km. Use the graph to express 2·3 miles in km., and 6·2 km. in miles.

12. Draw a graph for converting degrees Centigrade to degrees Fahrenheit, given that 0° Centigrade, 100° Centigrade are equivalent to 32° Fahrenheit, 212° Fahrenheit respectively. Use the graph to express in degrees Fahrenheit, 35° Centigrade, 70° Centigrade, and to express in degrees Centigrade, 140° Fahrenheit.

[13] Draw a graph for converting speeds in miles per hour to speeds in feet per second up to 60 m.p.h., given that 30 m.p.h. is the same speed as 44 ft. per second. Use the graph to express in feet per second, 22 m.p.h., 46 m.p.h., and to express in miles per hour, 20 ft. per second, 75 ft. per second.

14. A cyclist starts from A at noon and rides steadily at 12 m.p.h. towards B, 60 miles away. At 2 p.m. a motorist leaves B for A and travels at 36 m.p.h. Find from a graph when the two meet and their distance from A at this time. Find also the times at which they are 12 miles apart.

[15] P and Q are two towns 116 miles apart. A non-stop train travelling at 40 m.p.h. leaves P for Q at 12.10 p.m., and another non-stop train travelling at 50 m.p.h. leaves Q for P at 12.22 p.m. How far from P do the trains meet?

16. A goods train starts from A at 10.30 a.m. and travels at 20 m.p.h.; it stops for 15 minutes at B, 10 miles from A, and then proceeds again at 20 m.p.h.; a non-stop passenger train on a separate track leaves A at 11.10 a.m. and travels in the same direction at 40 m.p.h. When and at what distance from A does the second train pass the first?

[17] Barnet is 80 miles from Coventry. A car leaves Barnet at noon and reaches Coventry at 3 p.m. A lorry leaves Coventry at noon and would have reached Barnet at 4 p.m., but after half an hour is delayed for 1 hour on the road and is then driven so as to reach Barnet at 4.30 p.m. Assuming the speeds are uniform, find when and at what distance from Barnet the car meets the lorry.

18. A pedestrian sets off to walk along a road at 4 m.p.h.; a cyclist starts from the same place an hour later and rides along the same road to a town 18 miles away at 10 m.p.h., waits there for half an hour and then returns at the same speed. When and where does he meet the pedestrian on his return journey?

[19] A man starts from A at 10 a.m. to walk to B, 12 miles off, at 4 m.p.h. After 45 minutes he meets a bus coming from B to A, where it waits 10 minutes and then returns to B. The bus travels at 10 m.p.h. Find when and at what distance from A the man is overtaken by the returning bus.

20. A cyclist leaves P at 10 a.m. and rides at 12 m.p.h. to Q, 45 miles away. A motorist leaves P at 10.30 a.m. and drives by the same road at 36 m.p.h. to Q where he waits 10 minutes and then returns to P. At what times and at what distances from P does he pass the cyclist ?

[21] A and B bicycle from the same place in the same direction at the same rate of 12 m.p.h., B starting 5 minutes after A. A meets C who is walking in the opposite direction at 4 m.p.h. after riding 1 mile. How far will B have ridden before he meets C ?

22. A train P leaves A at 10 a.m., stops for 5 minutes at B, 18 miles from A, and again for 5 minutes at C, 30 miles from A, and arrives at D, 60 miles from A, at 11.30 a.m. A non-stop train Q leaves D at 10.30 a.m. and arrives at A at 11.40 a.m. At what time does Q pass P, assuming that P travels at the same uniform speeds between the stops, and that Q's speed is also uniform.

*23. A cyclist starts at 10 a.m. to ride to a place 8 miles away, riding at 12 m.p.h. till he has a puncture; he waits 10 minutes and then walks on at 4 m.p.h. and reaches his destination at 11.15 a.m. How far had he ridden when the puncture occurred ?

*24. X, Y are two places 32 miles apart. A leaves Y at 1.10 p.m. and drives at a rate which would bring him to X at 2.30 p.m. for a meeting. On the way he meets B, who left X at 1 p.m. and has driven at 30 m.p.h. They talk for 10 minutes and A hears that the meeting is at 2.15 p.m. At what rate must A drive for the rest of the journey to be in time ? Solve graphically.

*25. A man wishes to catch a train 6 miles away and has 40 minutes in which to do it. He can cycle at 12 m.p.h., but if his bicycle breaks down he will have to continue on foot at 4 m.p.h. How far must he have gone on his bicycle before he can feel sure he will catch the train?

*26. Three men A, B, C travel from X to Y by the same road. A walks the distance in 5 hours. B cycles, starting $1\frac{1}{2}$ hours after A and arriving 1 hour before him. C motors, starting $\frac{3}{4}$ hour after B and arriving $\frac{1}{2}$ hour before him. Show by a graph that B and C pass A at the same place.

Graphs of Functions

Example 2. Draw a graph representing the squares of numbers from 0 to 5.

Make a table showing the values of x^2 for selected values of x.

x	0	1	2	3	4	5
x^2	0	1	4	9	16	25

We choose scales as follows:

For the scale of numbers (values of x), 2 units to 1 inch; for the scale of squares (values of x^2), 10 units to 1 inch. Plot the points which represent the values in the above table. The last three points are rather far apart; we therefore take additional values to make the drawing of the graph easier;

x	3·5	4·5
x^2	12·25	20·25

add these to the table and plot the corresponding points. Now draw a smooth curve through the plotted points. This gives Fig. 92 (see p. 141).

The graph may now be used to read off (approximately) squares of numbers between 0 and 5; *e.g.* $2 \cdot 6^2 \simeq 6 \cdot 8$.

Since this graph represents the relation between a number x and its square x^2, it is called the **graph of the function x^2**

Any expression, containing x, whose value can be found when the value of x is given, is called a **function** of x. Thus $7x$, $\frac{3}{4}x - 5$, $x^3 - 5x$, $\frac{2x - 1}{x + 3}$, etc., are all functions of x. The letter y is generally used to represent the function of x. Fig. 92 represents the graph of y, where $y = x^2$ for values of x from 0 to 5.

The point which represents $x = 0$, $y = 0$ is called the **origin** and is usually denoted by O. The line *across* the page through O, along which values of x are measured, is called the **x-axis,** and the line *up* the page through O, along which values of y are measured, is called the **y-axis.**

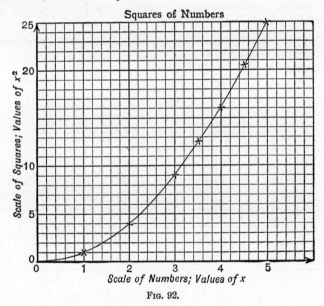

Fig. 92.

Oral work on Fig. 92.

(i) Read off from the graph the squares of 3·8, 2·4, 4·4.

(ii) Use the graph to find approximately a value of x such that $x^2 = 10$.

(iii) Read off the square roots of 23, 5, 14.

Example 3. Draw the graph of y, where $y = x^2$ for values of x from -4 to $+4$.

Make a table of values.

x	-4	-3	-2	-1	0	1	2	3	4
$y \equiv x^2$	16	9	4	1	0	1	4	9	16

Regard the x-axis as a number-scale, points to the right of O representing positive numbers; then points to the left of O represent negative numbers.

Using the same scales as before, plot the points which represent the table of values, and draw the graph (see Fig. 93, slightly reduced).

Graph of y, where y = x²

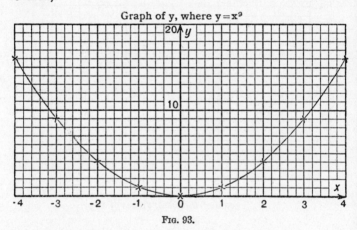

Fig. 93.

Oral work on Fig. 93.

(i) Read off from the graph the squares of -1.8, -3.4.

(ii) Read off from the graph the two square roots of 7, and the two square roots of 13.

(iii) Between what values does x lie if x^2 is less than 8?

Example 4. A marble is projected up a sloping groove **QAP** and moves so that it passes at zero hour $(t=0)$ a marked point **A**. and t seconds later is s feet *up* the groove from **A**, where $s = 20t - 5t^2$.

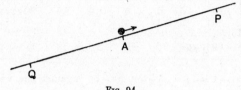

FIG. 94.

Draw a graph showing the distances of the marble from **A** for the period 2 seconds before zero hour $(t = -2)$ to 6 seconds after zero hour $(t = +6)$.

In making a table of values, proceed as follows: *Write down the whole of a row,* before beginning the next row.

First write down the row of selected values of t, then the row of values of $20t$. *Before* writing down the row of values of $-5t^2$, put down the row of values of t^2 *above* the table to help you to find $-5t^2$.

t^2	4	1	0	1	4	9	16	25	36
t	-2	-1	0	1	2	3	4	5	6
20t	-40	-20	0	20	40	60	80	100	120
$-5t^2$	-20	-5	0	-5	-20	-45	-80	-125	-180
$20t - 5t^2$	-60	-25	0	15	20	15	0	-25	-60

As before, points to the right of the origin on the t-axis represent positive numbers, those to the left of it, negative numbers. Similarly on the s-axis, points above the origin represent positive numbers, and points below the origin, negative numbers.

We choose scales as follows: for the t-axis, 1 inch represents 2 seconds; for the s-axis, 1 inch represents 40 feet.

Since $20t - 5t^2 = 5t(4 - t)$, the table of values can be made by the following *alternative method*:

t	-2	-1	0	1	2	3	4	5	6
$5t$	-10	-5	0	5	10	15	20	25	30
$4-t$	6	5	4	3	2	1	0	-1	-2
$5t(4-t)$	-60	-25	0	15	20	15	0	-25	-60

Plotting the values of s or $20t - 5t^2$ against the values of t, we obtain Fig. 95.

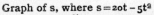

Graph of s, where $s = 20t - 5t^2$

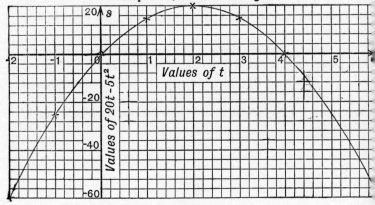

Fig. 95.

EXERCISE VIII. b

Use Fig. 95 to answer the following questions:

1. What is the value of s when $t = 3 \cdot 8$, $4 \cdot 4$, $-0 \cdot 6$?

2. How far above or below **A** is the marble when $t = 0 \cdot 6$, $4 \cdot 8$, $-1 \cdot 4$, $3 \cdot 5$, $2 \cdot 6$, $1 \cdot 4$, $-1 \cdot 8$? What do these values of t mean?

3. What is the highest point the marble reaches and at what time?

4. What can you say about the value of t if $s = 8$, -12, -36?

5. When is the marble at **P** (see Fig. 94, p. 143) if AP is
(i) 4 feet, (ii) 14 feet, (iii) 20 feet?

6. When is the marble at **Q** (see Fig. 94, p. 143) if AQ is
(i) 16 feet, (ii) 32 feet, (iii) 52 feet, (iv) 60 feet?

7. At what time does the marble pass **A**, coming down?

8. (i) For what values of t is $20t - 5t^2$ equal to 14?

(ii) Solve the equation $20t - 5t^2 = 10$.

9. Solve the equations: (i) $20t - 5t^2 = 4$; (ii) $20t - 5t^2 = -14$;
(iii) $20t - 5t^2 = -40$; (iv) $5t^2 - 20t + 8 = 0$.

10. Is there a value of t for which $20t - 5t^2 = 25$? What is
the connection between your answer and the movement of
the marble?

11. If, in Fig. 94, p. 143, **AQ** is 60 feet, how long is it between the
times when the marble passes **Q** going up and coming down?

12. For what values of t is s positive? For what values of t
is s greater than -20?

13. How far does the marble move between the times, $t = 0.6$
and $t = 1$? What is its average velocity in this interval?

14. Interpret the fact that the graph is (i) steeper at $t = -2$
than at $t = 1$; (ii) flat at $t = 2$.

EXERCISE VIII. c

1. Draw the graph of y, where $y = x^2 - 4x$ for values of x
from -2 to $+6$, with the following scales: along the x-axis
1 inch represents 1 unit; along the y-axis 1 inch represents
2 units.

Use your graph to answer the following:

(i) What is y when $x = 5.5$, 2.6, -1.4?

(ii) For what values of x is $y = 10$, $y = -2$?

(iii) What is the least value of $x^2 - 4x$?

(iv) For what values of x is $x^2 - 4x$ equal to 8?

(v) Solve the equations, $x^2 - 4x = 3$; $x^2 - 4x = -3.6$.

(vi) For what values of x is $x^2 - 4x$ less than 6?

2. A stone projected vertically upwards with velocity 40 feet per second is s feet above its starting-point after t seconds where $s = 8t(5 - 2t)$.

Represent $8t(5 - 2t)$ by a graph for values of t from 0 to 3. For scales, along the t-axis let 1 inch represent $\frac{1}{2}$ unit; along the s-axis let 1 inch represent 10 units. Start by making a table of values for $t = 0$, $\frac{1}{2}$, 1, $1\frac{1}{2}$, etc. After plotting these values, you will see that the graph can be drawn more accurately if you add to the table $t = 1\frac{1}{4}$, $2\frac{3}{4}$, and two other values.

Use your graph to answer the following questions:

   (i) What is s when $t = 0.8$, 1.9, 2.6?

  (ii) For what values of t is $s = 11$, 20, 22?

 (iii) What is the greatest height the stone reaches and after what time?

 (iv) How long is the stone in the air?

  (v) At what times is the stone 15 feet above the ground?

 (vi) For how long is the stone more than 12 feet above the ground?

(vii) What meaning can you give to the part of the graph for which $t > 2.5$?

(viii) For what values of t is $8t(5 - 2t)$ equal to 5? Solve the equation $40t - 16t^2 = 7$.

 (ix) Solve the equations: (a) $8t(5 - 2t) = 21$; (b) $40t - 16t^2 = 15$.

  (x) Find one value of t for which $8t(5 - 2t) = -15$.

 (xi) Is there a value of t for which $8t(5 - 2t) = 27$?

3. Draw the graph of y, where $y = (x + 1)(x - 2)$ for values of x from -3 to $+4$. Use it to answer the following:

   (i) What is y when $x = 2.4$, 1.6, -2.6?

  (ii) For what values of x is $y = 6$, -1.5?

 (iii) What is the least value of $(x + 1)(x - 2)$? For what value of x is it least?

 (iv) For what values of x is $(x + 1)(x - 2)$ equal to 8? Solve the equation $(x + 1)(x - 2) = 5$.

  (v) Solve the equations, (a) $(x + 1)(x - 2) = 3$;

                        (b) $(x + 1)(x - 2) = -1$.

 (vi) Is there a value of x for which $(x + 1)(x - 2) = -3$?

(vii) For what values of x is $(x + 1)(x - 2)$ less than 7?

[4] Draw the graph of y, where $y=(x+3)(2-x)$ for values of x from -5 to $+4$.

What is the greatest value of $(x+3)(2-x)$?

Solve the equations:

    (i) $(x+3)(2-x)=5$;   (ii) $(x+3)(2-x)=2$;

    (iii) $(x+3)(2-x)=-10$;   (iv) $(x+3)(2-x)=0$.

5. The manager of a shop finds that the profits per week depend on how he divides his time between the shop and the office. If he spends n hours per day in the shop, the weekly profits £p are given by the relation, $p=11+24n-3n^2$.

Represent $11+24n-3n^2$ by a graph for values of n from 0 to 8, and use it to answer the following:

  (i) Is it more profitable for the manager to be in the shop $2\frac{1}{2}$ hours or $3\frac{1}{2}$ hours? $2\frac{1}{2}$ hours or 6 hours?

  (ii) What is the most profitable length of time for him to be in the shop?

  (iii) What is the profit if he stays in the shop $1\frac{1}{2}$ hours, $5\frac{1}{2}$ hours?

  (iv) How long is he in the shop if the profit is £20, £40, £50?

  (v) Solve the equation, $11+24n-3n^2=36$.

  (vi) What is the greatest value of $24n-3n^2$?

[6] A leaden sheet, 30 inches wide, is bent to form an open gutter of rectangular section (see Fig. 96).

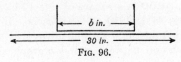

Fig. 96.

If the area of the cross-section is **A** sq. in., when the width of the gutter is b in., prove that $A=\frac{1}{2}b(30-b)$.

Represent the relation between **A** and b by a graph, for values of b from 3 to 27; hence answer the following:

  (i) What is the maximum area of the cross-section?

  (ii) For what values of b is the area of the cross-section 90 sq. in., 100 sq. in.?

  (iii) For what values of b is the area of the cross-section greater than 80 sq. in.?

  (iv) Solve the equations, (a) $\frac{1}{2}x(30-x)=60$; (b) $x(30-x)=190$.

7. Draw the graph of y, where $y = 4x^2 + 6x - 7$ for values of x from -3 to $+2$.

(i) Has it a greatest or a least value? How much is it?

(ii) For what values of x is $4x^2 + 6x - 7$ less than 5?

(iii) For what values of x is $4x^2 + 6x - 7$ equal to -5?

(iv) Solve the equation, $4x^2 + 6x - 7 = 0$.

[8] The length of a degree of longitude in latitude $x°$ is y miles, where $y = 69 - \dfrac{x^2}{100}$ approximately. Draw the corresponding graph of y for values of x from 0 to 60. What is the length of a degree of longitude through London (latitude $51\frac{1}{2}°$) and through Rome (latitude $42°$)? In what latitude is a degree of longitude 63 miles long?

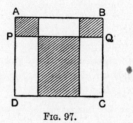

Fig. 97.

9. In Fig. 97, ABCD is a square of side 10 inches; there are equal squares, sides AP and BQ, at the corners. If AP $= x$ inches, and if the unshaded area is y sq. in., prove that $y = 2x(15 - 2x)$. Represent the relation between y and x graphically for values of x from 0 to 5, and find the value of x for which y is greatest and the maximum value of the unshaded area.

*10. In Fig. 98, ABCD is a rectangle; AB $= 10$ in., BC $= 8$ in.; if AP $=$ AS $=$ CQ $=$ CR $= x$ inches, find in terms of x the area of each of the four triangles at the corners, and prove that the area of PQRS is $[80 - x^2 - (10 - x)(8 - x)]$ sq. in.

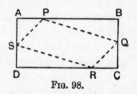

Fig. 98.

Find graphically the maximum area of PQRS.

*11. Draw the graph of y, where $y = x^3$ for values of x from 0 to 5.

Read off from the graph (i) the cubes of 2·3, 3·8, 4·7; (ii) the cube roots of 20, 36, 74.

For what range of values of x is x^3 less than 50? Find a few values of x^3 when x is negative, then draw freehand on plain paper a rough *sketch* of the graph of $y = x^3$ between $x = -5$ and $x = +5$.

*12. Draw the graph of y, where $y = \dfrac{1}{x}$ for values of x from 0·2 to 10. $\dfrac{1}{x}$ is called the *reciprocal* of x.

Find from the graph the reciprocals of 1·3, 4·8, 6·7.

Calculate the value of y when $x = 0·1$, when $x = 0·01$, when $x = 0·001$. How does the graph behave when x approaches 0? Calculate the value of y when $x = 50$ and when $x = 500$. How does the graph behave when x is large and positive?

Find a few values of $\dfrac{1}{x}$ when x is negative, then draw freehand on plain paper a rough *sketch* of the graph of $y = \dfrac{1}{x}$ from $x = -10$ to $x = -0·2$ and from $x = 0·2$ to $x = 10$.

*13. If a man is h feet above sea-level, the distance of the horizon is about $\sqrt{\left(\dfrac{3h}{2}\right)}$ miles. Represent this function by a graph. Make a table of values by taking $h = 0, 6, 24, 54, 96, 121·5, 150$. What is the object in selecting these special values of h? Find from the graph the height at which the distance of the horizon is 10 miles.

*14. From a sheet of cardboard (see Fig. 99) equal squares, side x inches, are cut away at each corner. A box is then formed by folding along the dotted lines. If the volume of the box is V cu. in., prove that $V = 4x(10 - x)(8 - x)$, and represent the relation between V and x graphically for values of x from 0 to 8.

For what value of x is the volume of the box greatest?

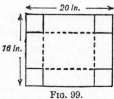

FIG. 99.

Functions of the First Degree

The graph of y, where y = 3x − 2.

Consider the following table of values:

x	− 2	− 1	0	1	2	3	4
$3x − 2$	− 8	− 5	− 2	1	4	7	10

We have selected values of x which increase by 1, and we find that the corresponding values of $3x − 2$ increase by equal amounts, namely 3. This means that *the graph has the same slope throughout and must therefore be a straight line.* It corresponds to the fact that if you slide down a straight staircase on a tea-tray, and if all the steps have the same width and the same height, you will move in a straight line. The values in the table are plotted in Fig. 100; they lie on the straight line **AB**.

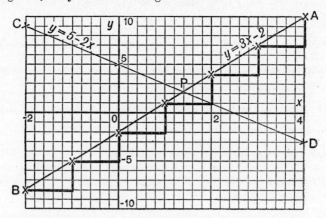

Fig. 100.

The same argument applies to every first-degree function of x; since its graph is a straight line, it is called a linear function of x.

Thus, any function of the form $bx + c$, where b, c are constants, is called a *linear function* of x, and its graph can be drawn by plotting two points only, and drawing the straight line which joins them; *it is, however, advisable to plot a third point as a check.*

Example 5. Find from the graph the value of x for which the functions $5 - 2x$ and $3x - 2$ are equal.

x	-2	0	2	4
$5 - 2x$	9	5	1	-3

We have selected values of x which increase by 2, and we find that the corresponding values of $5 - 2x$ decrease by equal amounts, namely 4. This means that *the graph has the same slope throughout (here a downward slope) and must therefore be a straight line.*

The graph is the straight line **CD** in Fig. 100.

From the figure, we see that the two functions have the same value when $x = 1 \cdot 4$, and this value is $2 \cdot 2$.

The reader should check this result by calculation.

Co-ordinates. The position of a point in a plane is described most easily as follows:

If Ox, Oy are two perpendicular lines (see Fig. 100) called the x-axis and the y-axis, the position of the point **A** is fixed by saying that if we start from **O** and move 4 units x-wards and 10 units y-wards, we arrive at **A**; we call 4 the x *co-ordinate* of **A** and 10 the y *co-ordinate* of **A**, and we speak of **A** as the point (4, 10). **The x co-ordinate is always named first.** Similarly, to arrive at **C**, we start from **O** and move (-2) units x-wards and then $(+9)$ units y-wards; $\therefore$ **C** is the point $(-2, 9)$. Similarly **B** is the point $(-2, -8)$ and **D** is the point $(4, -3)$.

Graphs and Equations. The graph of y, where $y = 3x - 2$, was obtained (see Fig. 100) by plotting the points $(-2, -8)$, $(-1, -5)$, $(0, -2)$, $(1, 1)$, $(2, 4)$, $(3, 7)$, $(4, 10)$ and drawing the straight line **AB** which passed through them. We call $y = 3x - 2$ the *equation of this straight line*, because each pair of values of x and y which satisfy the equation, $y = 3x - 2$, are the co-ordinates of a point on the line **AB**. Similarly, $y = 5 - 2x$ is the equation of the line **CD** in Fig. 100. The co-ordinates of the point of intersection **P** of the lines **AB** and **CD** therefore satisfy both equations, $y = 3x - 2$ and $y = 5 - 2x$. Hence if we read off from the graph the co-ordinates of **P**, $x = 1 \cdot 4$, $y = 2 \cdot 2$, we obtain the solution of the *simultaneous* equations, $y = 3x - 2$; $y = 5 - 2x$.

The equation of the curve in Fig. 93 is $y = x^2$ and the equation of the curve in Fig. 95 is $y = 20x - 5x^2$; these curves are called parabolas. Any function of the second degree in x is of the form $ax^2 + bx + c$, where a, b, c are constants, and is called a **quadratic function** of x; and the graph of $y = ax^2 + bx + c$ is shaped as in Fig. 93 if a is positive and as in Fig. 95 if a is negative.

EXERCISE VIII. d

1. Draw the graphs of $y = 2x + 3$ and $y = 9 - 3x$ for values of x from -2 to $+3$. For what value of x are the functions $2x + 3$ and $9 - 3x$ equal?

Solve the simultaneous equations $y = 2x + 3$, $y = 9 - 3x$ graphically and compare by solving algebraically.

2. Draw on the same figure the graphs of y, where

(i) $y = 2x$; (ii) $y = 3x$; (iii) $y = 4x$; (iv) $y = -2x$.

What do you notice about all of them? What can you say about the graph of $y = bx$, where b is a constant? What also if b is positive, if b is negative?

3. The values of $5x - 7$ are calculated for values of x which increase by 3, e.g. $x = 1$, 4, 7, 10, etc.; how do the corresponding values of $5x - 7$ change? How is this shown in the graph of $5x - 7$?

[4] The values of $21 - 3x$ are calculated for values of x which increase by 4, e.g. $x = 1$, 5, 9, 13, etc.; how do the corresponding values of $21 - 3x$ change? How is this shown in the graph of $21 - 3x$?

Solve graphically the following simultaneous equations, and compare by solving algebraically:

5. $y = 2x - 1$.   **6.** $y = 3x$.   **7.** $y = \frac{1}{3}(x - 2)$.

    $y = 9 - 2x$. $y = 7 - 2x$. $y = \frac{1}{4}(3 - x)$.

[8] $y = 5x + 4$.   **[9]** $y = \frac{1}{4}(3 - 5x)$.   **[10]** $y = \frac{1}{3}(2x + 6)$.

    $y = 2x + 9$. $y = \frac{1}{4}x + 3$. $y = -\frac{1}{2}(x + 5)$.

11. (i) If $3x + 2y = 6$, prove that $y = 3 - \dfrac{3x}{2}$;

    (ii) If $4y - 4x = 7$, express y in terms of x.

    (iii) Solve graphically the equations, $3x + 2y = 6$, $4y - 4x = 7$.

Solve graphically the following simultaneous equations and compare by solving algebraically:

12. $2y - x = 4$.　　　　[13] $x + 2y = 5$.　　　　[14] $3x = 5y$.

$\quad\;\; x + 2y = 3$.　　　　　　$2x - 3y = 6$.　　　　　$\frac{1}{2}x + \frac{1}{3}y = 1$.

15. For a certain journey the charge for W lb. of luggage is P pence, where $P = 2(\frac{1}{5}W - 12)$. Draw a graph showing the scale of charges for weights from 75 lb. to 150 lb. Find from the graph (i) the charge for 110 lb.; (ii) the weight for which the charge is half a crown. How can you use the graph to find what luggage is allowed free? How much is it?

16. The freezing-point of water is 0° Centigrade and 32° Fahrenheit; its boiling-point is 100° Centigrade and 212° Fahrenheit. Draw a graph for converting degrees Centigrade to degrees Fahrenheit and explain why it is a straight line. From the graph, (i) express in Fahrenheit, 35° C., 60° C., −10° C., −30° C.; (ii) express in Centigrade, 98° F., 150° F., 180° F., 5° F.

If F° Fahrenheit is the same temperature as C° Centigrade, prove that $F = \dfrac{9C}{5} + 32$.

*17. Draw the graph of $y = x^2 - 3x$ from $x = -2$ to $x = +5$. With the same scale and axes draw the graph of $y = \frac{1}{2}x$. Solve graphically the simultaneous equations, $y = x^2 - 3x$, $y = \frac{1}{2}x$.

*18. Draw with the same scale and axes the graphs of $y = 2x + 1$ and $y = x^2 - 1$ from $x = -1$ to $x = +3$. Solve graphically the simultaneous equations, $y = 2x + 1$, $y = x^2 - 1$.

*19. Draw with the same scale and axes the graphs of $y = \frac{1}{10}(4x + 1)$ and $y = \frac{1}{10}x^3$ from $x = -2$ to $x = +3$. For what values of x are the functions $\frac{1}{10}(4x + 1)$ and $\frac{1}{10}x^3$ equal? What equation in x can be solved in this way?

REVISION EXERCISE R. 4 (Ch. VII–VIII)

Solve the following simultaneous equations:

1. $x - y = 11$.　　　　　[2] $x = 5y$.　　　　　3. $y = \frac{1}{3}(5x + 1)$.

$\quad x + y = 8$.　　　　　　$2x - 7y = 15$.　　　　　$x = \frac{2}{5}(y + 3)$.

4. $0 \cdot 5x + 1 \cdot 2y = 1 \cdot 4$.　　　　　　[5] $5x + 3y = \frac{2}{3}(3x - 5y)$.

$\quad 0 \cdot 6x - 7y = 5 \cdot 9$.　　　　　　$13x - 57y = 190$.

[6] $2x + y = 5 - 7x - 3y = \frac{1}{4}y$.

7. $\frac{1}{2}(2x + y) = \frac{1}{9}(4x - 3y) = \frac{1}{5}(x - 2y + 2)$.

[8] $\dfrac{2x + 3y}{2x - 3y} = 1\frac{2}{11}$; $x - 10y = 1\frac{1}{5}$.

[9] If $2a - b = 1$ and $3a + 2b = 3$, find the value of $a + 2b$.

10. If $5x = \frac{1}{2}(15 - 3y)$ and $3y = \frac{1}{3}(15 - 20x)$, find the numerical value of $5x^2 - 3y^2$.

[11] For 30 shillings I can hire for 1 hour either 18 men and 20 boys or 12 men and 40 boys. How much do I pay per hour for a man and how much for a boy?

[12] If A gives B 5 shillings, B will have 3 times as much as A. If B gives A 7 shillings, A will have 3 times as much as B. How much has each?

13. A fraction is such that if 1 is added to the numerator and 5 to the denominator, it reduces to $\frac{1}{3}$. If the numerator of the original fraction is doubled and if the denominator is increased by 13, it reduces to $\frac{1}{2}$. Find the fraction.

14. Find a number of 2 digits which exceeds four times the sum of its digits by 3 and which is increased by 18 when the digits are interchanged.

15. The relation between the effort P lb. required to raise a load W lb. by a machine is $P = a + bW$, where a, b are constants. For loads of 130 lb. and 200 lb. the necessary efforts are 30 lb. and 40 lb. Find the values of a, b, and the effort required to raise a load of 80 lb. Solve (i) algebraically, (ii) graphically.

[16] Tests for the breaking strain of a wire rope gave the following results:

Circumference in inches	1·5	2	2·5	3	3·5	4
Breaking strain in tons	4·0	7·5	12	18	26	37

Find from a graph (i) the breaking strain if the circumference is 2·8 inches, 3·7 inches; (ii) the girth if the breaking strain is 9 tons, 20 tons.

17. Interpret the given graphs *in detail*. When and where do A and B pass one another?

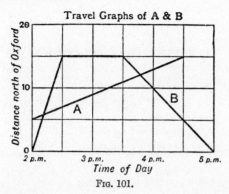

Travel Graphs of A & B

FIG. 101.

18. Use Fig. 95, p. 144, to find approximately the values of t for which (i) $20t - 5t^2 = 16$; (ii) $20t - 5t^2 = -52$; (iii) $5t^2 - 20t - 44 = 0$.

19. Draw the graph of y, where $y = (x+1)(4-x)$ for values of x from -3 to $+6$. Use the graph to answer the following:

(i) What is the greatest value of $(x+1)(4-x)$?

(ii) For what values of x is $(x+1)(4-x)$ equal to 3?

(iii) Solve $(x+1)(4-x) = 5$.

(iv) Solve $(x+1)(4-x) + 4 = 0$.

(v) For what values of x is $(x+1)(4-x)$ positive?

[20] Draw the graph of y, where $y = (x+2)(2-3x)$ for values of x from -4 to $+2$. Use it to find

(i) the range of values of x for which y exceeds 1;

(ii) the range of negative values of x for which y is positive;

(iii) the roots of $3x^2 + 4x = 9$.

21. Draw the graph of y, where $y = x(x-3)$ for values of x from -2 to $+5$. Use it to find (i) the roots of $x^2 - 3x = 2 \cdot 6$; (ii) the value of c if the roots of $x^2 - 3x = c$ differ by 2.

[22] Solve graphically the simultaneous equations, $2y + x = 12$; $3y - 2x = 6$. Solve them also algebraically.

TESTS IN MANIPULATION

TESTS 1–6 (Ch. I–IV)

Test 1

1. If $a = 3$, $b = 7$, evaluate $2ab$; $3a - b$; ba^2.
2. If $cd + d = 48$ and if $d = 6$, find c.

Simplify:

3. $6ab - 3ba + 2ba - 4ab$. 4. $\dfrac{6xy}{9y^2}$. 5. $2pq \times p^2 \times 4qr$.

6. $a(b - c) + b(c - a) + c(a - b)$. 7. $\frac{5}{6}(2x + 1) - \frac{3}{4}(2x + 3)$.

8. $3x(2x - 3y) + 2y(2x - 3y) - 3(x^2 + y^2)$.

Solve the equations:

9. $\frac{2}{5}t = 7$. 10. $10 - 5(r + 2) = 7r$.

Test 2

1. If $x = 2$, $y = 7$, $z = 0$, evaluate $3xy$; $7xz$; $3x^3$.
2. Subtract $3a$ from $6ab$.
3. Find the L.C.M. of 18, $4x^2$, $15xy^4$, $6x^3z$.

Simplify:

4. $3d - \frac{3}{4}d$. 5. $\dfrac{5c}{2} \times 4c^2$.

6. $\dfrac{6x^6y^6}{2x^2y^2}$. 7. $\dfrac{a^2}{b} - b$.

8. $7x - 2\{x + 2y - (y - 2x)\}$.

Solve the equations:

9. $4p + 3 = 17$. 10. $\dfrac{n}{4} - \dfrac{n - 1}{5} = 1$.

Test 3

1. If $a = 1$, $b = \frac{1}{3}$, evaluate a^3; b^2; $a + b - 3ab$.

2. Add $2xy$ to $4xz$ and divide the sum by x.

Simplify:

3. $a^2 \times 2a^2 \times 4a^2$.

4. $2\frac{1}{2}b - 1\frac{3}{4}b + \frac{1}{4}b$.

5. $(6c)^3 \div (3c)^2$.

6. $x(x + y) - y(x + y) - x^2 + y^2$.

7. $\dfrac{r^3}{s^3} - \dfrac{r^2}{s^2}$.

8. $\dfrac{3p + q}{q} - \dfrac{p - 2q}{p}$.

Solve the equations:

9. $0.7r = 4.2$.

10. $\dfrac{1}{4n} + \dfrac{1}{6n} = 1$.

Test 4

1. If $c = \frac{1}{2}$, $d = \frac{1}{3}$, evaluate $1 - d$; $12cd^2$; $\dfrac{c}{d}$.

2. Subtract $\dfrac{1}{2t}$ from $\frac{1}{2}t$.

Simplify:

3. $\dfrac{n^3 \times n^4}{n^6}$.

4. $\dfrac{2}{5y} + \dfrac{1}{10y}$.

5. $\frac{3}{4}(2p - 2)$.

6. $15x^2y \times 1\frac{1}{3}xz$.

7. $1 - 3x + x(1 - 3x) - 1 + x^2$.

8. $\{3a(a + b) - 2b^2\} - 3\{b(a - b) - a^2\}$.

Solve the equations:

9. $5 = \frac{2}{3}(2x - 1)$.

10. $\dfrac{3(1 + 2y)}{5} - \dfrac{7 - 2y}{3} = 2$.

Test 5

1. If $y = 2x^2 - 3x + 1$, find y when $x = 0, 1, 2, \frac{1}{4}$.

2. What must be added to $2a + b$ to make $a + 2b$?

Simplify:

3. $a^2 \div \dfrac{a}{b}$.

4. $\dfrac{r}{2r} + \dfrac{s}{2s}$.

5. $\sqrt{(16n^8)}$.

6. $\dfrac{c}{a}(a^2 - ab)$.

7. $\dfrac{4rs}{15t^2} \times \dfrac{5st}{6r^2}$.

8. $x(x + 2y) + x(x - 2y) - (x - 2y)$.

Solve the equations:

9. $\dfrac{3n}{4} = 1\frac{1}{2}$.

10. $z - \dfrac{2z - 3}{5} = \frac{1}{3}z + 1$.

Test 6

1. If $y = (5 - x)(x - 1)$, find y when $x = 1, 2, 3$.

2. If $h = \dfrac{12}{b}$ and if $b = \frac{3}{4}$, find h.

Simplify:

3. $(3t)^2 \times (2t)^3$.

4. $\dfrac{2n}{3n^2} - \dfrac{n^2}{6n^3}$.

5. $\dfrac{b}{x} \div \dfrac{b}{x^2}$.

6. $\dfrac{a + 2b}{6b} - \dfrac{3a - 2b}{9a}$.

7. $6(x + y) - 3\{y - 2(y - x)\}$.

Solve the equations:

8. $\dfrac{1}{y} = 3 - \dfrac{1}{y}$.

9. $\dfrac{x - 1}{5} = 8 - \dfrac{x - 5}{4}$.

10. Express $\frac{1}{9}(n - 1)(2n + 1)$ in terms of k if $n = 3k - 2$. Leave the answer in factors.

TESTS 7–12 (Ch. I.–VI)

Test 7

1. If $a=2$, $b=1$, $c=-3$, evaluate $3a^2b$; $a-2c$; $(b+c)^3$.

2. Subtract $r-s$ from r.

Simplify:

3. $4-6p-1+2\frac{1}{2}p$.

4. $\dfrac{ab}{bc} \times \dfrac{cd}{da}$.

5. $\dfrac{x}{2xy}+\dfrac{1}{6y}$.

6. $\dfrac{2n}{-6n}$.

7. $2a(a-b)-b(3b-2a)$.

8. $6r-\{5r-3(r-2)-8\}$.

Solve:

9. $\frac{2}{3}(t+1)=8$.

10. $\dfrac{y}{2}-\dfrac{y}{5}=1+1\frac{1}{2}y$.

Test 8

1. If $x=3$, $y=-2$, $z=0$, evaluate $x-2y+3z$; $2xz+3y$; $\sqrt{(x^2+y^4)}$.

2. Divide $ab-b^2$ by $-b$.

Simplify:

3. $1\frac{2}{3}a-\dfrac{a}{6}$.

4. $b^4 \times b^4 \div b^2$.

5. $x-2\{3x-2(1+x)\}$.

6. $\dfrac{c+d}{6}-\dfrac{c-d}{4}$.

7. $\frac{3}{4}(3x+2)-\frac{2}{5}(4x+5)$.

Solve:

8. $1\cdot4p=21$.

9. $\frac{1}{3}(z+1)=\frac{2}{5}(z-1)$.

10. Make t the subject of the formula, $p(s-t)=3t$.

Test 9

1. If $p=5$, $q=-1$, $r=3$, $t=-4$, evaluate $q-2t+r$; $\dfrac{r-q}{t}$; $\sqrt{(p^2-t^2)}$.

2. Subtract $1-3x(1-3x+x^2)$ from $x(2x^2-x-2)$.

Simplify:

3. $6n^3 \times \frac{2}{3}n^2$. 4. $24 \div \dfrac{4}{t^2}$. 5. $\left(\dfrac{a}{b}\right)(-b)(-ab)$.

6. $\dfrac{r-2s}{4r} - \dfrac{2r-3s}{6s}$. 7. $p\left(\dfrac{1}{n}+\dfrac{1}{q}\right)-q\left(\dfrac{1}{q}-\dfrac{1}{p}\right)$.

Solve:

8. $15+1\frac{1}{2}t=0$. 9. $\frac{4}{5}(x-1)=\frac{1}{2}x$.

10. Make n the subject of the formula, $l=a+(n-1)d$.

Test 10

1. If $m=-3$, $p=4$, $r=-2$, evaluate $4m-p-3r$; $\dfrac{p}{m-r}$; $\sqrt[3]{(pr)}$.

2. Multiply $a-(b-c)$ by -1, and subtract the result from $a-b-c$.

Simplify:

3. $h-\dfrac{h+k}{2}$. 4. $(-3a)^3 \div (-3a)$. 5. $\dfrac{12xy^3-9x^3y}{6xy}$.

6. $3\{2a-4(b-c)\}-2[5b-3(c-a)]$.

7. $2yz-y(z-y)-z(y-z)$.

Solve:

8. $\dfrac{2}{3t}-\dfrac{1}{6t}=1$. 9. $x-\dfrac{x-1}{3}=\dfrac{x+1}{4}$.

10. If $p=n(l+b)$ and $A=lb$, express A in terms of n, p, b only.

Test 11

1. If $p = 3$, $q = -1$, $r = 4$, evaluate $2p + 5q - r$; $\dfrac{p - r}{q}$; $\dfrac{\sqrt{(pr - 4q)}}{p^2 + q^3}$.

2. By how much does $2x - 3(y - z)$ exceed $3z - 2(y - x)$?

Simplify:

3. $(3a^2)^2 \times 2a^2$.

4. $(10b^3 + 6b^2 - 8b) \div (-2b)$.

5. $6c^6 \times 12c^4 \div (9c^2)$.

6. $d - 3e - \{3e - 2(d - e)\}$.

7. $\frac{3}{4}(p + q) - \frac{1}{4}(p - q)$.

8. $\dfrac{8x^4 - 6x^2y^2}{2x^2}$.

Solve:

9. $\dfrac{x}{1\frac{1}{2}} = \dfrac{1}{2\frac{1}{2}}$.

10. $\dfrac{y + 6}{2} - \dfrac{y - 2}{5} = \dfrac{y + 9}{3}$.

Test 12

1. If $a = 2$, $b = 3$, $c = -1$, evaluate $\dfrac{a - b - c}{a + b + c}$; $\dfrac{\sqrt{(a^2b - 4bc + c^2)}}{\sqrt[3]{(a^3 - 2bc - 6c^2)}}$.

2. If $bc = b - c$ and $c = -1$, find the value of b.

Simplify:

3. $2a^2 \times (-3ab) \times 5b^2$.

4. $c - \{2c - (1 - c)\}$.

5. $\dfrac{2d^6}{(2d)^2}$.

6. $\dfrac{-1}{x} \div \dfrac{1}{-x}$.

7. $1 - \dfrac{2p - 6q}{4q}$.

Solve:

8. $x(x + 1) = x(x + 3) - (x + 3)$.

9. $\dfrac{3x - 3}{5} - \dfrac{2x + 1}{3} = x + 2$.

10. If $4y = 3x + 7$, express $x - y$ in terms of y only.

D.C.A.

F

TESTS 13–18 (Ch. I–VIII)

Test 13

1. If $a = -2$, $b = 3$, $c = -4$, evaluate $(b-c)(c-a)(a-b)$.

2. If $\frac{1}{2}x - \frac{1}{3}y = 1$, express y in terms of x.

Simplify:

3. $a - \frac{1}{2}a + \frac{1}{3}a$.   **4.** $1 - \dfrac{5b - 10c}{5b}$.   **5.** $(3a)^3(4b)^2 \div (6ab)^2$.

6. $2(p - q - r) - \{3p - 5\overline{q-r}\}$.   **7.** $(6r^6 - 9r^3s^3) \div (-3r^2)$.

Solve:

8. $\dfrac{3x - 1}{5} = x$.   **9.** $4(t+1) = 3 - 3(2t - 7)$.

10. $3y - z = 15$, $7z + 14y = 35$.

Test 14

1. Add together $2x(x^2 - 3x + 6)$, $3x(5 - 4x + x^2)$, $5x^2(1 - x)$.

2. Subtract $\dfrac{a}{5} - \dfrac{3b}{10} + \dfrac{2c}{15}$ from $\dfrac{b}{5} - \dfrac{c}{3} + \dfrac{a}{10}$.

Simplify:

3. $(-x^2)^3(-x^3)^2$.   **4.** $(-4r^3)(-3rs) \div (6r^2s)$.

5. $\dfrac{5b}{6c} - \dfrac{3b}{4c} + \dfrac{b}{3c}$.   **6.** $(4y^6z^2 - 12y^2z^6) \div (-4y^2z^2)$.

Solve:

7. $11x - 4(4x - 3) = 4$.   **8.** $\frac{1}{4}(p - 7) = 8 - \frac{1}{3}(2p - 1)$.

9. $7(x - 3) = y + 1$, $\frac{1}{3}(4x + 1) = \frac{1}{5}(3y - 4)$.

10. If $\dfrac{1}{b} + \dfrac{1}{c} = 1$ and if $b = 1\frac{1}{2}$, find c.

Test 15

1. Find the values of $(2x-1)(x+2)$ if $x = -2, -1, 0, 1, 1\frac{1}{2}, 2$.

2. Subtract $5y(5y^2 - 2y + 3)$ from $4y(4y^2 - 2y - 1) + 2$.

Simplify:

3. $a^6 \div a^2$.   **4.** $2b^2 \times 3b^3 \times 4b^4$.   **5.** $1 - \dfrac{2c-1}{15} + \dfrac{2-c}{6}$.

6. $2\{r - 3(t-3)\} - 3\{t - 2(r+2)\}$.   **7.** $2x\left(\dfrac{2}{x} + 3\right) - 3y\left(\dfrac{3}{y} + 2\right)$.

Solve:

8. $0 \cdot 3x + 5 = 0 \cdot 7x - 3$.

9. $2t(t+5) - 3t(t-7) = 27 - t(5+t)$.

10. $11y - 3z + 5 = 7y - z + 3 = 4z - 5y + 6$.

Test 16

1. If $x = 2a^2 + b^2$ and $y = 3ab - b^2$, find the value of $x + 2y)(x - y)$ when $a = 2, b = -1$.

2. Add together $\dfrac{r}{2} + \dfrac{4s}{3} - \dfrac{t}{6}, \dfrac{t}{2} + \dfrac{4r}{3} - s, \dfrac{s}{6} - \dfrac{r}{6} - t$.

Simplify:

3. $9n^9 \div 3n^3$.   **4.** $(-2p)^3(-3pq)^2$.

5. $12\left(\dfrac{a}{3} - \dfrac{b}{4} - \dfrac{5c}{6}\right) - \dfrac{1}{3}(9a - 12b + 15c)$.   **6.** $\dfrac{5t - \frac{1}{2}}{6} - \dfrac{t - \frac{1}{3}}{2}$.

Solve:

7. $\dfrac{1}{n} + 1\frac{1}{2} = 1\frac{2}{3}$.   **8.** $\frac{2}{3}(x-1) - \frac{1}{7}(3x-4) = 3$.

9. $5x + 6y = \frac{3}{4}x + \frac{1}{3}y = 4$.

10. If $x = \frac{1}{2}y$, express $(x-y)(x^2 - y^2)(x^3 - y^3)$ in terms of y.

Test 17

1. Find the values of $1 - 2x + 3x^2$ if $x = 2, 1, 0, -1, -1\frac{1}{2}, -2$.

2. Simplify and arrange in *ascending* powers of x,

$$2x\left(x^2 - 7x + 1 - \frac{4}{x}\right) - x^2(5 - x) + 3x\left(x + \frac{1}{x} - 3\right).$$

Simplify:

3. $1 - 2[1 - 3\{a - 4(1 - 2a)\} - 2a]$.   **4.** $(3a^2b)(3ab^2) \div (3a^3b^3)$.

5. $(b^2c^2 - b^6c^8) \div (-b^2c^2)$.   **6.** $\frac{1}{2}\left(\frac{4x}{5} - \frac{1}{3}\right) - \frac{2}{3}\left(\frac{x}{4} + \frac{1}{5}\right)$.

Solve:

7. $1 \cdot 4(3r - 1) + 1 \cdot 7(4r + 1) = 0 \cdot 41$.   **8.** $\frac{1}{3x} + \frac{1}{5x} - \frac{1}{4x} = \frac{1}{10}$.

9. $\frac{2x + y}{4} + \frac{x + 3y}{3} = 7x + 36y + 8\frac{1}{2} = 0$.

10. Express a price of n farthings per lb. in £ per ton.

Test 18

1. Prove that the expressions $\dfrac{20}{x(x + 3)}$ and $3x - 4$ are equal if $x = 2$ and if $x = -2$, and find their values if $x = -\frac{5}{3}$.

2. Multiply $x^3 - 2x^2 - 3x + 4$ by x^2 and by $-4x$ and by -3, and add the results.

Simplify:

3. $(-3a)^3 + 3a^3 + (-a)(-3a)^2$.   **4.** $2ad \times 5bd \times 7abd$.

5. $(-6xy)^3 \div (-6xy)$.   **6.** $\frac{x}{2}\left(\frac{y}{3} - \frac{z}{4}\right) - \frac{2y}{3}\left(\frac{x}{2} - \frac{z}{6}\right) + \frac{3z}{4}(2x - y)$.

Solve:

7. $\frac{5}{p} + \frac{1}{4} = \frac{3}{7}$.   **8.** $\frac{3x - 1}{5} - \frac{1 + x}{2} = 3 - \frac{x - 1}{4}$.

9. $\frac{y - 1}{3} + \frac{z + 1}{2} = 1, \quad \frac{2y + 1}{5} - \frac{3z + 1}{4} = 5$.

10. If $a - 2b = 3$ and $2b - c = 4$ and $c - 2d = 5$ and $d + 1 = 0$, find the value of $a + b + c + d$.

REVISION PAPERS, A. 1–8 (Ch. I–III)

A. 1

1. Write more shortly:

    (i) $2a \times 4$;   (ii) $3b \times 3bc$;   (iii) $1\frac{1}{2}t \times 4$.

2. If $y = 3x - 1$, find (i) the value of y if $x = 4$;

                      (ii) the value of x if $y = 14$.

3. Solve the equations, (i) $t + \frac{3}{4}t = 3\frac{1}{2}$;

                    (ii) $\frac{1}{5}(2W + 3) = 7$.

4. A boy is now 6 years old and his father is 30 years old. In how many years' time will the boy be just half as old as his father will be?

5. Fig. 102 represents a rectangle. Find the value of x.

Find also the perimeter of the rectangle.

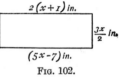

$2(x+1)$ in.

$\frac{3x}{2}$ in.

$(5x-7)$ in.

Fig. 102.

A. 2

1. Simplify: (i) $5y + y - 2y$; (ii) $n - \dfrac{3n}{5}$.

2. (i) If $y = 2x^2 - 3x$, find y if $x = 4$.

    (ii) Subtract $9r$ inches from $2r$ feet. Give the answer (a) in inches, (b) in feet.

3. Solve the quations, (i) $\dfrac{3N}{8} = 9$;

                  (ii) $p + 4 = q - 7 = 20$;

                 (iii) $\dfrac{2r}{5} - \dfrac{r}{3} = 1$.

4. The sum of four consecutive whole numbers is 58. Find the numbers.

5. 12 shillings is shared between 2 boys **A** and **B** so that **A** receives 1s. 6d. more than **B**. How much does **B** receive?

A. 3

1. Write more shortly:

    (i) $3b \times 3ab$;   (ii) $\dfrac{c}{2} \times 6c$;   (iii) $4p \div \frac{1}{2}$.

2. A tram fare is 3d.; what is the cost of n journeys (i) in pence, (ii) in shillings?

3. (i) Simplify $2(3a - 5b) + 5(2a - 3b)$.

    (ii) If $x = 3$, $y = 6$, find the values of $y^2 - 2x^2$ and of $y - 2x$.

4. (i) Find the value of n if $n = \dfrac{n}{3} + 4$.

    (ii) Find the value of z if $1 \cdot 2z = 6$.

    (iii) Find the value of x if $xy + 2y^2 = xy^2 + 2y$ when $y = 3$.

5. Find two consecutive whole numbers such that one-quarter of the smaller exceeds one-fifth of the larger by 4.

A. 4

1. If $p = 1$, $q = 2$, $r = 3$, $s = 4$, find the values of

    (i) $p + q(r + s)$;   (ii) $(p + q)r + s$;

    (iii) $s^3 - 3pqr^2$.

2. Write more shortly:

    (i) $3(x + 5y - 2) - 2x - 5y - 6$;   (ii) $1\frac{1}{3}a \times 6ab$.

3. Find the total cost of 8 lb. of jam at p pence per lb. and 4 lb. of honey at q pence per lb. (i) in pence, (ii) in shillings.

4. Solve the equations:

    (i) $\dfrac{k}{4} = \dfrac{3}{5}$;   (ii) $4 - z = 1 \cdot 8$;   (iii) $17 - r = 2(2 + r)$.

5. A has £100, B has £50; but after B has paid A what he owes him, A has three times as much as B then has. How much did B owe A?

A. 5

1. (i) Simplify $4b + 7c - b - 3c - 3b$.
   (ii) If $p = 2q$ and $q = 5s$ and $s = \frac{1}{2}$, find the values of $p - q$ and pq.

2. (i) Express in shillings the difference between £n and $6n$ half-crowns.
   (ii) A man walks at 4 miles an hour; how long does he take to walk d miles?

3. (i) Find n if $\frac{3}{4}(n + 5) = 9$.
   (ii) Find p if $\dfrac{3}{p} = \dfrac{2}{7}$.
   (iii) If $4(x + a) = 5(x - a) + 4$, find a when $x = 2$.

4. Fig. 103 shows the lengths of the sides of a rectangle in inches. Find the values of x and y. Find also the area of the rectangle.

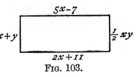
FIG. 103.

5. The total charge for staying n days at a hotel is p shillings where
   (i) $p = 15n$ if n is less than 4.
   (ii) $p = 12(n + 1)$ if n is greater than 4.

What is the *total* charge for 3 days, for 6 days?

A. 6

1. If $p = 1$, $q = \frac{1}{2}$, find the values of
   (i) $2pq$;   (ii) $p^2 + q^2$;   (iii) $\dfrac{p + q}{p - q}$.

2. I buy 6N eggs; how many are left after 6 eggs have been eaten? What is the value of N if 12 eggs are left?

3. Solve the equations, (i) $l = 3(10 - l)$;
   (ii) $2 \cdot 7x - 3 \cdot 4 = 1 \cdot 9x + 1 \cdot 4$.

4. Find in terms of x the third angle of the triangle in Fig. 104.

Show that the triangle is isosceles if $x = 10$ or if $x = 34$ or if $x = 40$.

FIG. 104.

5. I bought 30 pencils for 6s. 6d.; some cost 3d. each and the rest cost 2d. each. How many did I buy at 3d. each?

A. 7

1. If $b=3$, $c=0$, $d=5$, find the values of

    (i) $d-bc$;   (ii) $(b+1)(d-1)$;   (iii) $\dfrac{2b^2-b}{d}$.

2. Simplify (i) $7s+t+3t-3s+t$; (ii) $2\frac{1}{2}k \times 2\frac{1}{2}k$; (iii) $9p \div 15$.

3. Solve the equations:

    (i) $\dfrac{5}{3}=\dfrac{2}{w}$;   (ii) $\dfrac{t-1}{2}=\dfrac{3t+1}{11}$;   (iii) $x^2-ax=10$ if $x=5$.

4. A clerk's salary is £100 a year for the first year and increases by £p a year each year. How much is he paid for the third year, for the sixth year? How much does he receive altogether for the first four years?

5. A greengrocer buys some pears at $1\frac{1}{2}$d. each; 6 of them go bad, but he sells the rest at 2d. each. If his profit is 1s. 6d., find the number he bought.

A. 8

1. (i) Add $3n$ to $5n$ and divide the result by 6.

    (ii) Multiply $2p$ by $6p$ and subtract p from the result.

2. (i) The length of a pole is x yards y feet; express its length in inches.

    (ii) How many $1\frac{1}{2}$d. stamps can be bought for 3s., for c shillings, for d half-crowns?

3. Solve the equations:

    (i) $\dfrac{r}{5}=2\cdot4$;   (ii) $t-0\cdot3t=3\cdot5$;   (iii) $\frac{1}{2}(3z-7)=4$.

4. A rectangular block is $3c$ inches long, $2c$ inches broad, c inches high.

    (i) Find the sum of the lengths of all its edges (a) in inches, (b) in feet.

    (ii) Find the total area of its surface in square inches.

5. The value of 15 coins is £1, 4s.; some of them are half-crowns and the rest are shillings. Find the number of half-crowns.

REVISION PAPERS, A. 9–25 (Ch. I–IV)

A. 9

1. (i) Add $6ab - 3a - 2b$ to $6a - b - 2ab$.

(ii) Simplify $\dfrac{2c}{3d} - \dfrac{c}{6d}$.

2. (i) Simplify $3(2p + 4q - r) - 2(p - q + r)$.

(ii) If $4x + 3y = 10$, find the value of x when $y = 0$, and the value of y when $x = 1$.

3. Solve the equations:

(i) $3t = 2 \cdot 4$;   (ii) $p - \dfrac{2p}{7} = 10$.

4. A car uses 1 gallon of petrol every 18 miles.

(i) How far can the car run on $\frac{1}{2}k$ gallons of petrol?

(ii) How much petrol does the car use to go 45 miles, $6n$ miles?

5. I buy a second-hand car for a certain sum of money, and then spend $\frac{2}{5}$ of that amount on renewals and repairs. The total cost is £196. How much did I pay for the car?

A. 10

1. (i) If $r = \frac{3}{4}t$ and $t = 20$, find the value of $t^2 - r^2$.

(ii) Square $4xy^3$ and divide the result by $4y^2$.

2. (i) Find the L.C.M. of $4abc^2$, $6a^2b^2c$, $8a^3c^3$.

(ii) Simplify $\dfrac{10xyz^2}{6x^2yz}$.

3. Solve the equations:

(i) $0 \cdot 6m = 9$;   (ii) $\frac{1}{3}n - \frac{1}{5}n = 1$;

(iii) $3(4 + r) - 2(2 - r) = 20$.

4. The perimeter of a rectangle $(3r - 4)$ inches long, $(2r + 1)$ inches high is 2 *feet*. Find the value of r and the area of the rectangle.

5. A spoon costs r pence; also a spoon and 3 forks cost t pence. Find the cost of (i) 1 fork, (ii) a spoon and 5 forks.

A. 11

1. (i) Simplify $3[a - 2(b + 2c)] - 3[a + 3(b - 3c)]$.

   (ii) If $x = 2y$ and $3y = z$, find the value of $xy - 2z$ when $z = 9$.

2. Simplify:

$$\text{(i) } 3a^3 \times 3a^3; \quad \text{(ii) } \frac{5}{6b} - \frac{2}{15b}.$$

3. Solve the equations:

$$\text{(i) } \frac{h}{3} + 12 = h; \quad \text{(ii) } 8(3y - 1) - 5(3y + 2) = 3(2y - 1).$$

4. (i) 2 eggs cost 3 pence; how many can be bought for $2p$ shillings?

   (ii) From a stick whose length is $\frac{1}{2}n$ feet a part of length $(8n - 3r)$ inches is cut off. Find in inches the length of what remains.

5. A is 6 years old and B is 29. How old will each be in t years' time? In how many years' time will A be just half as old as B?

A. 12

1. If $p = 7$, $q = 5$, $r = 3$, find the values of

   (i) $p - r(p - q)$;   (ii) $(p - r)p - q$;   (iii) $(q^2 - r^2) \div (q - r)$.

2. (i) Simplify $16ab \times 6bc \div (12abc)$.

   (ii) Add $3a - b - 5c$ to $3c - b - 2a$ and express the sum in terms of b if $a = b + 1$ and $c = b - 1$.

3. Solve the equations:

$$\text{(i) } \tfrac{1}{5}(z - 3) = \tfrac{1}{2}; \quad \text{(ii) } \frac{3x - 1}{4} - \frac{2x + 1}{5} = 2.$$

4. (i) When the day is t hours long, the night is $\dfrac{3t}{5}$ hours long. Find the value of t and check the answer.

   (ii) 9 shillings is shared between A and B so that A gets 1s. 6d. more than B. How much does B receive?

5. The total length of a stretched spiral spring is $(21 + 2\frac{1}{2}W)$ inches when it is supporting a load of W lb. What is the total length (i) if the load is 4 lb., (ii) if there is no load? What is the load if the total length is 3 *feet*?

A. 13

1. Simplify and write in *ascending* powers of x,
$$4x^4 + 5x^3 - 3x + 7 + 4x - 7x^3 - x - 1 + x^4.$$

What is (i) the coefficient of x^4, (ii) the coefficient of x, (iii) the constant term, in the answer?

2. Simplify (i) $2t^2 \times 3t^3 \div (5t^5)$;   (ii) $\frac{2}{3}(2p+1) - \frac{3}{4}(p+1)$.

3. Solve the equations:

(i) $\dfrac{1}{u} + \dfrac{1}{5} = \dfrac{1}{3}$;   (ii) $n - 1\frac{1}{4}(n-3) = 1$.

Prove that the equation $x^2(11-x) = 36(x-1)$ is satisfied by $x = 2$ and by $x = 3$ and by $x = 6$.

4. The length of wire required to make the network in Fig. 105 is 20 inches.   Find the value of t and the total area of the network.

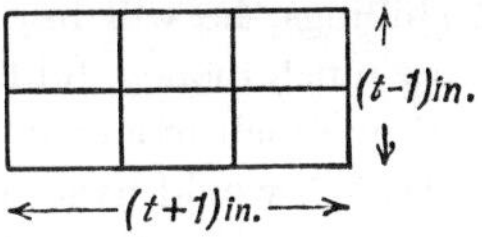

5. A fork costs *half as much again* as a knife costs.

$(t-1)$in.
$(t+1)$in.
FIG. 105.

(i) If the knife costs 1s. 6d., find the cost of a fork.

(ii) If the knife costs p pence, find the *total* cost of 6 knives and 6 forks.

A. 14

1. (i) If $4x - 7y = 3z$, find y when $x = 12$ and $z = 9$.

(ii) If $r = 3s$, simplify $\dfrac{r^2 - s^2}{r^2 + s^2}$.

2. (i) Add $\dfrac{c}{4d}$ to $\dfrac{c^2}{12cd}$;   (ii) Subtract $\frac{1}{2}$ from $\dfrac{p+q}{2q}$.

3. Solve the equations:

(i) $n - 0\cdot3n = 14$;   (ii) $\frac{2}{3}(W-1) = \frac{1}{4}(W+5)$.

4. A hawser, C inches in circumference, breaks under a load of W tons if $W = \frac{2}{5}C^2$.   What load will break the hawser if its circumference is (i) 3 inches, (ii) $5p$ inches?

5. 30 shillings are shared between A, B, C so that A gets 6 shillings more than B, and C gets $\frac{3}{7}$ of the amount A and B together get.   How much does B receive?   How much does C receive?

A. 15

1. If $r = 5$, $s = 0$, $t = 3$, find the values of
     (i) $(r + s)t$;   (ii) $2s(r + t)$;   (iii) $(r + t)^2 - (r - t)^2$.

2. Simplify (i) $2\{r - 3(t - r)\} - 3\{t - 2(r - t)\}$;
        (ii) $(3xy^3)^2 \div 6xy^2$.

3. (i) Solve the equation, $\dfrac{1}{t} + \dfrac{1}{2t} = \dfrac{1}{6}$.

   (ii) If $\frac{3}{4}(n + 1)$ and $\frac{2}{3}n + 1$ are equal, find the value of n, and
        prove that $n^3 - 2 = (n + 2)^2$.

4. A man's holiday lasts 30 days; he spends 16s. a day for
$5n$ days and 24s. a day for the rest of the time. Find in terms of
n how much he spends altogether (i) in shillings, (ii) in £.

5. A has three times as much money as B. If A gives B
4 shillings, he will have left just twice as much as B then has.
How much money did B have at the beginning?

How much money should B have given to A at the beginning
so that A would have five times as much as B would then have?

A. 16

1. Simplify (i) $a - b + c - (b - c + a) - (c - a + b) - (a - b - c)$;
        (ii) $(4x^3y)^2 \div (2x^2y)^3$.

2. (i) Simplify $r - \frac{1}{2}(r + s)$.
   (ii) Express $\frac{1}{4}(n + 3)(2n + 1)(3n - 1)$ in terms of c if $n = 2c + 1$.
        Leave the answer in factors.

3. Solve the equations, (i) $\frac{7}{8}(x - 11) = 3\frac{1}{2}$;
        (ii) $5(y - 2) + 2(y - 6) - 3(y + 5) = 5$.

4. (i) Find the perimeter and area of a rectangle $(n - 2)$ inches
        high, $3n$ inches long. Remove the brackets from the
        answers.
   (ii) Find the cost of $3k$ apples at y pence per dozen.

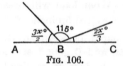

FIG. 106.

5. In Fig. 106, ABC is a straight line; find the value of x.

A. 17

1. If $s = 7$, $t = 4$, find the values of

(i) $2t^2 - st$; (ii) $\frac{3}{4}t^3 - (s-1)^2$; (iii) $\sqrt{(3s+t)}$.

2. Simplify (i) $3x^2(x^2 - 3x - 2) - 2x(x^3 + x - 1)$;

(ii) $1\frac{3}{4}(y+z) - 1\frac{1}{4}(y-z)$.

3. Solve the equations, (i) $0 \cdot 1(n-3) = 0 \cdot 15(n-4)$;

(ii) $\frac{3(2x-1)}{5} - \frac{2(3x+4)}{7} = 1$.

4. (i) A man buys $18n$ eggs for £1 and sells them at 2 pence each. Find in terms of n his profit in shillings.

(ii) $9x$ gallons of beer cost $2y$ shillings, find in pence the cost of 1 pint at the same rate. [1 gallon = 8 pints.]

5. A jug and basin together cost 11 shillings. The jug costs half a crown more than the basin. Find the cost of each.

A. 18

1. Simplify (i) $c - \frac{c-1}{3} - \frac{c+2}{6}$;

(ii) $\frac{y}{z}(y+z) - y\left(1 - \frac{1}{y}\right) + z\left(1 - \frac{1}{z}\right)$.

2. Copy and fill in the blanks in the following:

(i) $6p^2 - 9pq = 3p(\ldots)$; (ii) $a - 5b - 10c = a - 5\ (\ldots)$.

3. (i) Solve the equation $\frac{1}{2z} = \frac{2}{z+2}$.

(ii) Find the value of c if $x = 2$ is a root of the equation

$$3(x-c) - \frac{9c}{x} = \frac{1}{2}x.$$

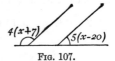

Fig. 107.

4. Fig. 107 shows in degrees the angles at which a line is cut by two parallel lines. Find the value of x.

5. A is paid £250 for his first year's work and receives an increase of £15 a year every following year. B is paid £320 for his first year's work and receives an increase of £10 a year every following year. How much does each receive for (i) his 3rd year, (ii) his 5th year, (iii) his nth year? For which year do they receive equal amounts?

A. 19

1. (i) What must be added to $2(2l - m - 2n)$ to make $5(l + 2m - n)$?

(ii) Simplify $(3c^2)^3 - (2c^3)^2$.

2. Simplify and write in *descending* powers of x,
$$3x^2(x^3 + 6x + 12) - 4x(x^2 + 3x - 3) - 4(2x^2 + 3x - 2).$$
Write down (i) the term of degree 3, (ii) the coefficient of x^2, (iii) the coefficient of x, in the answer.

3. Solve the equations (i) $3(x - 3) - 5(12 - x) = 5$;
$$\text{(ii) } \frac{y - 11}{3} - \frac{y - 3}{4} = \tfrac{1}{2}.$$

4. (i) Invent a problem about numbers which would be solved by the equation
$$n + (n + 1) + (n + 2) + (n + 3) + (n + 4) = c,$$
and find n in terms of c.

(ii) Find four consecutive odd numbers whose sum is 80.

5. A workman is paid 2s. an hour ordinary time, but 4s. for each hour counted as overtime. He receives £6 for working 49 hours one week. How many of these hours are counted as overtime?

A. 20

1. (i) Find the L.C.M. of $6ab^2c^2$, $12b^3$, $9a^3bc$.

(ii) Simplify $18\left(\dfrac{5}{6n} - \dfrac{7}{9n}\right)$.

2. (i) Copy and fill in the blanks in
$$1 - 4x^2 - 8x^4 + 6x^6 = 1 - 2x^2(\ldots).$$

(ii) Express $\tfrac{1}{2}y(2y - 5)(3y + 1)$ in terms of x if $y = 2x + 3$. Leave the answer in factors.

3. (i) Solve the equation $t + 1 - \dfrac{2t + 1}{5} = \dfrac{t + 4}{3}$.

(ii) Find numerical values of x and y such that the expressions $x + 2$ and $2y$ and $5 - x$ are all equal.

4. $\mathsf{P} - (15 \text{ per cent. of } 2\mathsf{P}) = 21$; find P.

5. A bus travels 3 miles an hour faster than a tram. In 80 minutes the tram goes 2 miles farther than the bus goes in 50 minutes. Find the speed of the tram in miles per hour.

A. 21 *

1. (i) Simplify $p^6q^8 \div p^2q^2$; (ii) Subtract $\frac{3}{4}r^2$ from $\frac{5}{6}r^2$.

2. (i) For what value of t does $\dfrac{t}{5}$ exceed $\left(\dfrac{t}{2} - \dfrac{t}{3}\right)$ by 1 ?

(ii) What can you say about h if $10 - h$ is less than $2h + 1$?

3. (i) The least of five consecutive odd numbers is $2l - 1$; what is the greatest number ?

(ii) The greatest of five consecutive even numbers is $4n$; what is the sum of all five numbers ?

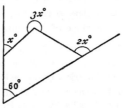

Fig. 108.

4. When Napoleon reached the age of n years, three-quarters of his life was over. Find, in terms of n, his age when he died.

5. In Fig. 108, find x.

A. 22 *

1. Simplify (i) $a \div (a + \tfrac{1}{2}a)$; (ii) $\dfrac{1 + 3b}{6} - \dfrac{b}{2}$.

2. For what value of t is $\tfrac{1}{2}(t - 1)$ equal to $\tfrac{1}{5}t$? Find the value of each expression in this case.

3. How many minutes are there between p minutes past nine and $2p$ minutes to twelve on the same morning. Find the value of p if the number of minutes is $12p$.

4. In an examination a boy who scores n marks fails by k marks. Another boy passes with $\tfrac{1}{2}k$ marks in hand, how many marks did he obtain ?

Fig. 109.

5. Fig. 109 shows the lengths of the sides of a triangle in inches. Find x if the triangle is isosceles. Find also the lengths of the sides. *There is more than one answer.*

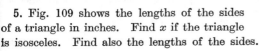

A. 23 *

1. (i) What must be added to $10 - a$ to make 9?

(ii) By what must $a^2 b^2$ be divided to give $\dfrac{1}{b^3}$?

2. From a square plate of side $4t$ inches, four squares each of side t inches are cut away (see Fig. 110). Find (i) the perimeter, (ii) the area of the upper surface of the plate.

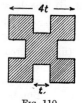

Fig. 110.

3. The marks in an examination run from 30 to 90; they are converted so that an original mark n becomes N where $N = \frac{5}{3}(n - 30)$. What is the new mark if the original mark is (i) 48, (ii) 81? What is the new top mark and the new bottom mark? What mark remains unchanged?

4. A man's ordinary wage is 1s. 6d. per hour; overtime pay is 2s. per hour. He works 54 hours one week and earns £4, 4s.; how many hours are counted as overtime?

5. **A, B, C** are three parcels; **A** and **B** together weigh p lb., **B** and **C** together weigh q lb., **A** and **C** together weigh r lb. (i) What is the total weight of **A, B, C**? (ii) What does **C** weigh by itself?

A. 24 *

1. (i) What is the cube of $3b^3$?

(ii) Divide $5x + y$ by $x - y$ if $x = 7y$.

2. If $a = 3b = 4c = 60$, find the values of (i) $a - c$; (ii) $a + b + c$.

3. (i) By what must $\dfrac{1}{p}$ be multiplied to give p?

(ii) A sheet of paper is $\dfrac{3}{2n}$ inches thick; how many sheets are there in a pile 6 inches high?

4. Three-quarters of an even number equals two-thirds of the next larger even number. Find the numbers.

5. Frying-pans of a certain quality are sold in sizes by the following rule:

Size **N** is of diameter 2(**N** + 3) inches and costs $\frac{1}{2}$(3N + 10) shillings.

(i) Find the diameter and cost of size 2.

(ii) Find the size-number and the cost if the diameter is 16 inches.

(iii) Find the size-number and the diameter if the cost is 14 shillings.

(iv) Find, in terms of d, the size-number and the cost if the diameter is $4d$ inches.

A. 25 *

1. (i) Multiply xy by xz and divide the result by yz.

(ii) Add pq to pr and subtract the result from qr.

2. If a man's holiday lasts n days he spends £p, where

(i) $p = \frac{3}{4}n + 2$ if n is less than 6,

(ii) $p = \frac{2}{3}n + 2\frac{1}{2}$ if n is greater than 6.

What does his holiday cost if it lasts (i) 4 days, (ii) 9 days? How would you try to find the cost if it lasts exactly 6 days, and what do you think it is?

3. In Fig. 111 **BC** = $(r - t)$ inches and **AC** = $(r + t)$ inches; **P** is the mid-point of **AB**. What are the lengths of (i) **AB**, (ii) **PC**? If $r = 4t$, prove that **BC** = 3**AP**.

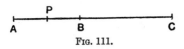

FIG. 111.

4. In Fig. 112 ∠**ACB** = 4∠**ABC**, and **CP** bisects ∠**ACB**, find (i) ∠**ABC**, (ii) ∠**BPC**.

5. A cask of beer weighs **W** lb. when full and w lb. when empty. Find the weight of the cask when half full. Find also the total weight of n full casks and $2n$ half-full casks.

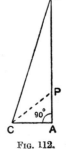

FIG. 112.

REVISION PAPERS A. 26–40 (Ch. I–VI)

A. 26

1. If $p = 6$, $q = -3$, $r = -12$, evaluate

(i) $2p - (r - q)$;   (ii) $\dfrac{pr}{q^2}$.

2. Simplify (i) $(2x)^3 \times (3y)^3 \div (6x^2y)$;

(ii) $a - \dfrac{a+b}{4} - \dfrac{a-b}{3}$.

3. Solve the equations, (i) $6 - \frac{3}{4}(r - 6) = \frac{1}{2}(r + 1)$;

(ii) $4 - \dfrac{3}{t} = \dfrac{18}{t} - 3$.

4. A boy gets 3 marks for each sum right and loses 2 marks for each sum wrong. He does 24 sums and obtains 37 marks. How many were right?

5. The temperature of the water in a boiler is rising at a steady rate.

(i) At 6 a.m. it is $x°$, at 7 a.m. it is $y°$; what is it at 8 a.m.?

(ii) At 1 p.m. it is $p°$, at 3 p.m. it is $q°$; what is it at 2 p.m.?

A. 27

1. Simplify (i) $5a - \dfrac{a}{5}$; (ii) $3 - \dfrac{3b}{b}$; (iii) $\dfrac{3r^2}{s^2} \times \dfrac{s^2}{3r^2}$.

2. (i) Subtract $1 - 5c - 3c^2$ from $2c - 1$.

(ii) If $3x - 2y = 4$, find y in terms of x.

3. Solve the equations, (i) $\dfrac{12}{x} = 96$;

(ii) $\dfrac{5(1 - z)}{3} - \dfrac{3z - 1}{5} = \dfrac{1}{6}$.

4. I think of a number, halve it and subtract 1; the result is double the amount obtained by dividing the number by 3 and subtracting 4. Find the number.

5. I travel 25 miles in $2\frac{1}{2}$ hours, walking part of the way at 3 miles per hour, and motoring the rest at 24 miles per hour. How far do I walk?

A. 28

1. If $a = 3$, $b = -8$, $c = -4$, evaluate

(i) $ab - bc$; (ii) $(a - b)(b - c)$.

2. Simplify (i) $\frac{1}{2}n \div \frac{2}{n}$; (ii) $\frac{2pq}{3pqr} - \frac{q}{6qr}$;

(iii) $\frac{3s^2}{t^2} \times (-3s) \times (-t)^3$.

3. (i) Solve the equation $\frac{y-2}{15} + \frac{1}{20} = \frac{y-1}{20}$.

(ii) Make h the subject of the formula, $V = \pi r^2 h$.

4. An article is reduced from P shillings to $\left(P - \frac{P}{5}\right)$ shillings in a sale. The reduced price is 14 shillings. Find the value of P and the amount by which the price has been reduced.

5. (i) A boy was p years old r years ago. How old is he now? How old will he be in $(p - r)$ years' time?

(ii) What must be added to £x, ys. to make £$(x + 2)$?

A. 29

1. (i) Add together $2a^3 - 4a - 3$, $5 + 3a - 4a^2$, $3(a^3 + a^2 - 1)$.

(ii) Multiply $9c^2d^2$ by $3c^3d^3$ and divide the result by cd^5.

2. If $x = 6$, $y = -3$, $z = -2$, evaluate

(i) $\frac{x}{yz}$; (ii) $x + 4y + 3z$; (iii) $(x - y)(y - z)$.

3. (i) Solve the equation $5(4x + 5) = 5(x + 2\frac{1}{2}) - \frac{1}{2}(7x + 12)$.

(ii) If $x = 2y + 3$ and $y + z = 1$, express x in terms of z only.

4. If a certain number is added both to the numerator and to the denominator of $\frac{9}{17}$, the new fraction reduces to $\frac{5}{7}$. Find the number.

5. C degrees Centigrade is the same temperature as F degrees Fahrenheit if $C = \frac{5}{9}(F - 32)$. Find n if n degrees Centigrade is the same temperature as $(-\frac{1}{3}n)$ degrees Fahrenheit.

A. 30

1. (i) Simplify $3x^2y^4 \times 2x^3y^2$.

   (ii) Add together $\frac{1}{2}(2a+b-c)$, $\frac{1}{2}(2b+c-a)$, $\frac{1}{2}(2c+a-b)$.

2. If $x=2$, $y=-1$, $z=0$, evaluate

   (i) $\dfrac{x}{y}-\dfrac{y}{x}$;   (ii) $2xyz$;   (iii) $(x+y)^2$.

3. (i) Solve the equation, $x(x+5)-2x(3-x)=3(x^2+1)$.

   (ii) For what value of W is $\frac{1}{2}(W+1\frac{1}{2})$ equal to $\frac{1}{3}(W+2\frac{1}{2})$?

4. 4 tickets at $(p+3)$ shillings each cost the same as $(p-3)$ tickets at 8 shillings each. Find the value of p and the cost of $(p+1)$ tickets at $\frac{1}{3}p$ shillings each.

5. A rectangle is $(2n+1)$ inches long, $(3n-4)$ inches high. Find its perimeter in terms of k if $n=2-k$.

A. 31

1. Simplify (i) $\dfrac{a}{2}+\dfrac{a}{3}+\dfrac{a}{6}$; (ii) $r^2s^3 \div \dfrac{r^3}{s^2}$.

2. Simplify (i) $\dfrac{-8x^2}{-2x}$; (ii) $\dfrac{-9y^2}{(-3y)^2}$; (iii) $1-\dfrac{c-d}{c}$.

3. (i) Solve the equation $\frac{1}{5}(7t+5)-12=\frac{1}{7}(2t+1)$.

   (ii) For what value of c is $x=2$ a root of the equation,

   $$c(x^2+6)=x(c+6)?$$

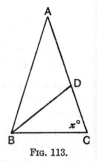

Fig. 113.

4. Find two consecutive even numbers such that one-quarter of the smaller exceeds one-fifth of the larger by 4.

5. In Fig. 113 AB $=$ AC and BD $=$ BC.

   (i) Find $\angle$ BAC in terms of x.

   (ii) Find $\angle$ ADB in terms of x.

   (iii) If $\angle$ ABD $=y°$, find x in terms of y.

A. 32

1. (i) Multiply $2x - 3y + z$ by 5 and subtract the result from $3(z - y - x)$.

(ii) From $a\left(a + \dfrac{1}{a}\right)$ subtract $b\left(b + \dfrac{1}{b}\right)$.

2. Simplify (i) $-\dfrac{(-8c)}{(-c)}$; (ii) $\dfrac{6p^3}{-4p^2q}$.

3. (i) Solve the equation $\frac{1}{2}(x + 18) - \frac{1}{8}(3x - 4) = 5(6 - x)$.

(ii) Make t the subject of the formula, $s = v(t + 2)$.

4. A boy buys 10 dozen papers at 8d. a dozen; he sells some at 1d. each and returns the rest for which he gets 7d. a dozen. He gains 2s. 6d. How many papers does he sell?

5. A rectangle is l inches long, b inches broad.

If $\dfrac{l}{3} = \dfrac{b}{2} = \dfrac{c}{4}$, find (i) the perimeter, (ii) the area of the rectangle in terms of c.

A. 33

1. If $a = 3$, $b = -2$, $c = 0$, $d = 1$, find the values of

(i) $a^2 + b^2 + 2cd$; (ii) $\dfrac{a - b}{c - d}$; (iii) $\dfrac{1}{b} - \dfrac{1}{3b}$.

2. Copy and fill in the blanks in the following:

(i) $4r^2 - 8rt = 4r(\ldots) = -4r(\ldots)$;

(ii) $\dfrac{a}{b} = \dfrac{\ldots}{-b} = \dfrac{-a^2}{\ldots}$.

3. (i) Solve the equation $\dfrac{2 - n}{2} = \dfrac{2 + n}{3} - \dfrac{8 + n}{4}$.

(ii) Find the values of x and y if the expressions $\frac{1}{2}x$, $\frac{1}{6}x + \frac{1}{8}$, $\frac{1}{3}x + \frac{1}{4}y$ are all equal.

4. A car goes from A to B in 3 hours. If its average speed had been 9 miles an hour *slower*, it would have taken 4 hours. Find the distance of B from A.

5. In Fig. 114, AB = AC and BP = BC, find the value of x.

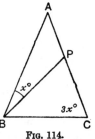

Fig. 114.

A. 34

1. Simplify (i) $\dfrac{2x-1}{4} - \dfrac{1+x}{6}$;

(ii) $\dfrac{4a^2 - 6ab}{2a} - \dfrac{6ab - 4b^2}{2b}$.

2. If $P = c^2 - 3cd$ and $Q = cd - 2d^2$, express $P - 2Q$ in terms of c, d. Also find the value of $\dfrac{P}{Q}$ if $c = -1$, $d = 2$.

3. Solve the equations (i) $d + \frac{1}{2}\pi d = 1$ if $\pi = \frac{22}{7}$;

(ii) $\dfrac{5x-12}{4} - \dfrac{7x+10}{11} = 1$.

4. At an examination, one-quarter of the candidates fail. At the next examination, there are 84 more candidates and 8 more failures; on this occasion, one-fifth of the candidates fail. Find the number of candidates at the first examination.

5. I take $2t$ minutes to go from my house to the station if I walk at 4 miles an hour. Find in terms of t the time I take if I bicycle at 10 miles an hour.

A. 35

1. Simplify (i) $\dfrac{a^3}{b} \div \dfrac{b^2}{a^2}$; (ii) $\dfrac{1}{c} - \dfrac{c-1}{c^2}$.

2. If $\dfrac{1}{x} + \dfrac{1}{3} = \dfrac{1}{2}$ and $\dfrac{1}{y} + \dfrac{1}{4} = \dfrac{1}{5}$, find the values of x and $x + y$.

3. (i) Solve the equation $\dfrac{x+5}{15} - \dfrac{x-5}{10} = 1 + \dfrac{2x}{15}$.

(ii) Make t the subject of the formula, $v = u + at$.

4. I walk at 4 miles an hour and run at 6 miles an hour. I find that I can save 4 minutes by running instead of walking from my house to the station. How far off is the station?

5. If the base of a segment of a circle is $2k$ inches, and if its height is h inches (see Fig. 115), the radius r inches of the circle is given by the formula, $2rh = h^2 + k^2$. Find the radius if the base is 4 inches and the height is 6 inches.

FIG. 115.

A. 36 *

1. (i) Add together $\dfrac{3a+b}{6}$, $\dfrac{a-2b}{9}$, $\dfrac{b-a}{12}$.

   (ii) Simplify $12x^6y^4z^2 \div 6x^3y^2z$.

2. Simplify (i) $(-2r)^3 \times (-\tfrac{1}{4}r)^2$; (ii) $\dfrac{t}{0\cdot6} - \dfrac{2t}{1\cdot5}$.

3. (i) Solve the equation $\tfrac{1}{2}(x+101) - \tfrac{2}{3}(x+99) = 0$.

   (ii) If $\left(\dfrac{4n}{3}+1\right)$ is three times as large as $\left(\dfrac{3n}{5}-2\right)$, find the value of n, and prove that $2n$ is five times as large as $(\tfrac{1}{3}n+1)$.

4. A man walks at a certain rate for the first two hours of a journey of total length 13 miles and then increases his speed by 1 mile per hour. If the total time taken is $3\tfrac{1}{3}$ hours, find the speed at which he starts.

5. A book-shelf will just hold $3x$ books each $1\tfrac{3}{5}$ inches thick or $2(x+1)$ books each $2\tfrac{1}{4}$ inches thick. Find the value of x and the length of the shelf.

A. 37 *

1. (i) Add together $1-3a-a^2$, $2a^2-a-1$ and subtract the sum from 1.

   (ii) Divide $bc^2 - cb^2$ by $-bc$.

2. What is the *change* in the value of $2\tfrac{1}{4} - 7x$ when x increases from -3 to $+2$?

3. (i) Solve the equation, $\dfrac{9-x}{10} + \dfrac{7-x}{15} = \dfrac{1}{30}$.

   (ii) Find the value of z if $\dfrac{x}{3} - \dfrac{y}{4} = \dfrac{7}{z}$ when $x=10$ and $y=11$.

4. The perimeter of the triangle in Fig. 116 is 2 *feet*. If $x+y=2z$ and if $y+z=3x$, find the values of x, y, z.

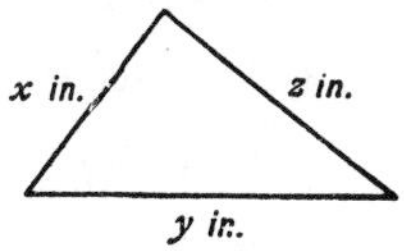

5. An article is bought for $£\left(\dfrac{3c}{4}\right)$ and sold for $£\left(\dfrac{4c}{5}\right)$. Find the profit in shillings in terms of c, and find the gain per cent.

FIG. 116.

A. 38 *

1. (i) If $x = -3$, $y = -2$, $z = -1$, find the value of
$$(y-z)^2 - (x-y)(x-z).$$

(ii) Simplify $\frac{1}{2}(2a - 3b) - \frac{1}{3}(3a - 2b)$.

2. (i) Add $b(4p - 1)$ to $b(1 - p)$ and square the result.

(ii) From N subtract 40 per cent. of N.

3. Solve the equations (i) $3x(x-2) + 2(x^2 + 5) = 5x(1+x)$;

$$\text{(ii) } \frac{2}{1-y} = \frac{3}{1-2y}.$$

4. A leaves X at 9 a.m., walks for half an hour at 5 miles an hour, then halts for 30 minutes and then proceeds on a bicycle at 9 miles an hour. B leaves X at 10 a.m. and pursues A at 12 miles an hour. At what time will B overtake A?

5. At $1\frac{1}{2}$d. per mile, the fare from A to B is n shillings. Find in terms of n the distance of B from A. If the charge is increased to 2d. per mile, find the new fare from A to B.

A. 39 *

1. (i) Simplify $(-x)(y - z - x) + (-y)(z - x - y) + (-z)(x - y - z)$.

(ii) Multiply $8a^3b$ by $\dfrac{18b^3}{a}$, and find the square roots of the result.

2. What is the *change* in the value of $(1 - 2x)(5x - 2)$ when x increases from -1 to $+1$?

3. (i) Solve the equation, $\frac{1}{3}(\frac{2}{3}x - 5) - \frac{1}{4}(\frac{1}{5}x - 1) = 1\frac{1}{2}$.

(ii) If $p(q - r) = q^2(p - r)$, find r when $p = 5$ and $q = 3$.

4. For what income is the tax at 4s. in the £ on the part above £150 equal to the tax at 4s. 6d. in the £ on the part above £200?

5. A bottle weighs ($W - w$) grams when empty and weighs $W + w$) grams when it contains v cu. cm. of oil.   Find the weight f 1 cu. cm. of oil.

A. 40 *

1. (i) Simplify $2x - (-x) + (1 - x)(-3)$.

(ii) What must be added to $2(r - 3s)$ to make $3(s - 2r)$?

2. If $P = x^2 - 3xy + y^2$, $Q = 2x(x - y)$, $R = 3y(3y - x)$ and   if $x = 2y$, express in terms of x (i) P, (ii) $P \frown Q - R$.

3. (i) Solve the equation, $\dfrac{1}{2}\left(\dfrac{x}{7} + 4\right) - \dfrac{2}{3}\left(\dfrac{x}{7} - 3\right) = 3\tfrac{1}{2}$.

(ii) What can you say about the value of p if twice $(3p - 2)$ is less than five times $(12 - 2p)$?

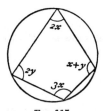

Fig. 117.

4. Fig. 117 shows the angles of a cyclic quadrilateral in degrees. Find the values of x and y.   [The sum of the opposite angles of a cyclic quadrilateral is two right angles.]

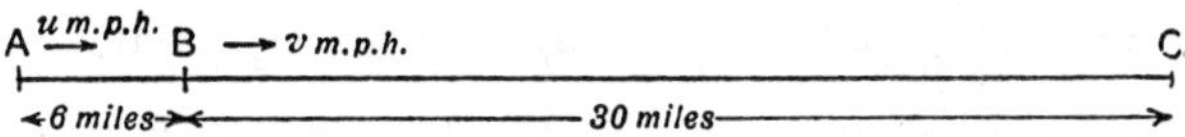

$$\text{A} \xrightarrow{u\,m.p.h.} \text{B} \longrightarrow v\,m.p.h. \qquad\qquad\qquad\qquad \text{C}$$
$$\longleftarrow 6\ miles \longrightarrow\!\longleftarrow\ \text{—}\ 30\ miles \text{—} \longrightarrow$$

Fig. 118.

5. Fig. 118 gives the data of the journey of a man who cycles from A to B and then motors from B to C.   The total time taken is 2 hours.   Find the value of u if $v = 3u$.

REVISION PAPERS A. 41–50 (Ch. I–VIII)

A. 41

1. (i) If $x = -2$, $y = -7$, evaluate $1 - x + y$ and x^3y.

    (ii) Subtract from $2a(1 - a^2) + 5a(1 + 3a^2)$ the   sum   of $3(2 + a) - 4(a^2 - 1)$ and $3(a^3 - 2) + 4(a^2 - a)$.

2. Simplify (i) $16x^4y^3 \div \left(\dfrac{2x}{y}\right)^3$;   (ii) $\left(\dfrac{4a}{5} - \dfrac{3a}{10} + a\right) \div \dfrac{3a}{4}$.

3. Solve (i) $7(x - 3) = 34 - 3(2x + 1)$;

        (ii) $2y - \frac{1}{3}z = 14$, $\frac{1}{4}y + 3z = 20$.

4. Fig. 119 gives the lengths of the sides of a parallelogram in inches. Find the values of x, y and the perimeter.

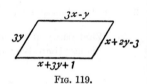

Fig. 119.

5. The value of $2x$ shillings exceeds that of $(x + 3)$ sixpences by the value of $(x - 9)$ half-crowns. Find x.

A. 42

1. Simplify (i) $13(y - x) - 5\{2y - 3(x - y)\}$;

        (ii) $(-3c)(c^2 - 4c) - (-3c)^2 - (-3c)^3$.

2. (i) Divide $6x^6 - 4x^4 - 2x^2$ by $-2x^2$;

    (ii) Add together $x - y + \frac{1}{6}z$, $y + 2z - \frac{1}{3}x$, $\frac{1}{6}z - \frac{1}{2}x + \frac{1}{3}y$.

3. Solve (i) $\dfrac{x - 5}{3} = 5 - \dfrac{2x + 1}{4}$;   (ii) $10r + 3s = 11 = s - 4r$.

4. (i) A man is $4t$ years old when his son is half that age. Find in terms of t the sum of their ages when the son is $3t$ years old.

    (ii) After $\frac{3}{5}$ of a tank has been filled, there is still room for **N** more gallons. Find in terms of **N** the number of gallons the tank will hold.

5. The value of 30 coins, some of which are florins, others shillings, and the rest sixpences, is £1, 12s. If there are two more shillings than florins, find the number of florins and the number of sixpences.

A. 43

1. (i) Evaluate $7 - 2y - 3y^2 + y^3$ when $y = -2$.

  (ii) What must be added to $x^3 - 4x(x - 2) + 3$ to make $x^2(x - 1) - 2(3x - 2)$?

2. (i) Divide $12y^3z^2 - 18y^2z^3 - 9yz^4$ by $-3yz^2$.

  (ii) Simplify $\dfrac{1}{2}\left(\dfrac{c}{3} - 5\right) - \dfrac{2}{3}\left(\dfrac{c}{5} - 2\frac{1}{2}\right) + \dfrac{1}{6}(c - 1)$.

3. Solve (i) $\dfrac{3t - 1}{4} + \dfrac{2t - 10}{3} = t - 2$;

  (ii) $10x + 3y = 35$, $21x + 2y = 52$.

4. Experiments with a screw-jack showed that the load to be raised and the necessary effort were related as follows:

Load in lb. wt. -	100	120	160	180	200
Effort in lb. wt. -	12·0	13·8	17·6	19·6	21·5

Find from a graph (i) the necessary effort if the load is 140 lb. wt., 170 lb. wt., 186 lb. wt.; (ii) the load that can be raised by an effort of 13 lb. wt., 16 lb. wt., 20 lb. wt.

5. The difference between a number of two digits and the number formed by reversing the digits is 36. Also the sum of twice the tens' digit and 9 times the units' digit is 41. Find the number.

A. 44

1. If $x = -1$, $y = -3$, $z = 2$, find the values of

(i) $3x^3z$; (ii) $(y-x)^2$; (iii) $(x-z)(y-z)(x-y)$.

2. Simplify (i) $\dfrac{a+2b}{1\frac{1}{2}} - \dfrac{2a+b}{1\frac{1}{5}}$;

(ii) $(12a^2bc)(-6b^2de) \div \{(-2ae)(-9abd)\}$.

3. (i) If $A = \frac{1}{2}n - 1$ and $B = \frac{1}{3}n + 1$, find the value of n for which $A = \frac{1}{4}B$.

(ii) Solve $\frac{1}{4}x - \frac{1}{5}y = \frac{2}{3}y - \frac{2}{5}x = 2$.

4. A grocer buys a certain number of eggs at 1s. 3d. per dozen; he sells half of them at 2d. each and the rest at 8 for a shilling and thereby gains 10s. on the whole transaction. How many eggs did he buy?

5. (i) If A is 60 per cent. of B, express $B - A$ as a percentage of $B + A$.

(ii) The nth number in the set of numbers, 4, 11, 18, 25, ... is $7n - 3$. Verify this if $n = 5$. Is 200 a number in the set? If so, where does it come?

A. 45

1. Simplify (i) $\dfrac{b}{0\cdot 1} - \dfrac{b}{0\cdot 2}$;

(ii) $15 - [3\{2 - (2c-d)\} - 2\{d - 3(c-3)\}]$.

2. (i) What must be added to $r - 2s + 3t$ to make $t - r + s$?

(ii) Simplify $\dfrac{3x-y}{3x^2y} - \dfrac{x+y}{2xy^2} + \dfrac{x^2+y^2}{2x^2y^2}$.

3. (i) Solve $\frac{1}{3}(2p+9) - \frac{1}{2}(p-4) = 6$.

(ii) If $5x + n = 3$ and $4y + n = 1$, find the value of n for which $2y = 3x$.

4. A man motors for t hours at 24 miles an hour and then walks for $(2-t)$ hours at 3 miles an hour. If he has travelled 34 miles altogether, find the value of t.

5. If a number of two digits is added to the sum of its digits, the result is 69; also the number is increased by 18 if its digits are reversed. Find the number.

A. 46

1. Simplify (i) $(-3b^3)^3$;   (ii) $\dfrac{3}{5}c \div \dfrac{15}{c}$;

     (iii) $\dfrac{6a^3}{-b^2} \times (-4b^2)^2 \div (-2a)^4$.

2. (i) Simplify $2x(3y - z) - 3y(4z + x) + 5z(x - 2y)$.

    (ii) Subtract $\dfrac{a}{10} + \dfrac{b}{4} - \dfrac{2c}{3}$ from $\dfrac{3a}{5} - \dfrac{3b}{4} + \dfrac{5c}{6}$.

3. (i) Solve $\dfrac{2}{15}\left(\dfrac{x}{3} - 1\right) - \dfrac{5}{4}\left(2 - \dfrac{x}{10}\right) = \dfrac{3}{5}\left(\dfrac{x}{12} - 2\right)$.

    (ii) Find the values of b, c if $y = bx^2 + cx$ is satisfied by $x = y = 2$ and by $x = 3$, $y = 9$.

4. With the data of Fig. 120, where the angles are given in degrees, find the values of x and y.

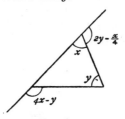

Fig. 120.

5. Draw the travel graph of a man **A** who walks for 48 minutes at 5 miles an hour, then halts for half an hour and then bicycles on at 12 miles an hour for 15 miles.

Draw in the same figure the travel graph of a man **B** who starts from the same place as **A** but $1\frac{1}{2}$ hours later and drives along the same road at 30 miles an hour. Find the distance **B** has gone when he passes **A**.

A. 47

1. If $a = -3$, $b = 5$, $c = 2$, find the values of

(i) $2abc^2$;   (ii) $(2a + b)^3$;

(iii) $(a - b)(b - c) - (a - c)^2$.

2. (i) Express in £ the total value of $6n$ half-crowns and $\dfrac{7n}{2}$ florins.

(ii) Simplify $\dfrac{2r + s}{r^3 s} - \dfrac{r - 3s}{r^2 s^2} - \dfrac{r^2 - s^2}{r^3 s^2}$.

3. Solve (i) $\frac{1}{6}(\frac{1}{2} + \frac{1}{4}x) - \frac{3}{4}(\frac{1}{6} - \frac{2}{5}x) = \frac{3}{8}x$;

(ii) $\frac{1}{3}y = 1 - z$, $\frac{1}{3}(2y - z) = \frac{1}{2}(y - 3z)$.

4. Divide £8, 5s. between **A**, **B**, **C** so that for every shilling **A** gets, **B** gets a florin and **C** gets half a crown.

5. Solve graphically *and* algebraically the following: A man leaves **P** at 1 p.m. and walks along the road to **Q** at 4 miles an hour. Another man leaves **P** at 2 p.m. and cycles at 10 miles an hour to **Q**, 23 miles away, and then turns round and rides back at once to **P** at the same rate. Find the distances from **P** of the places where the men meet.

A. 48

1. (i) Simplify and arrange in *ascending* powers of x,

$$3x\left(5x^2 - 7x + 4 - \frac{1}{x}\right) - 2x\left(4x^2 + 5x - 3 + \frac{1}{x}\right) - (x^3 - 7x^2 + 2x - 7).$$

(ii) For what value of c is $2x^3 - 3x^2 - cx + 6$ zero when $x = -2$?

2. (i) Simplify $18x^3 y^3 z^4 \div \left(\dfrac{3yz^2}{x^3}\right)^2$.

(ii) If $P = 2x^2 - xy - y^2$, $Q = 3y(x - y)$, $R = 2x(3x - 7y)$, and if $x = 4y$, express $P - Q - R$ in terms of y.

3. Solve (i) $\dfrac{5x-11}{4} - \dfrac{4x-7}{3} = x - \tfrac{1}{2}(3x-7) - 1$;

(ii) $4x + \dfrac{x-y}{8} = 17$; $2y + \dfrac{3x-5y-2}{3} = 2$.

4. A man is now 3 times as old as his son. In 10 years' time the sum of their ages will be 76. What was the man's age when his son was born?

5. The ratio of the number of the sides of two convex polygons is 2 : 3, and the ratio of the sums of their angles is 3 : 5. Find the number of sides of each. [The sum of the angles of a polygon with n sides is $(2n-4)$ right angles.]

A. 49

1. (i) Decrease $2\tfrac{1}{2}n$ by 40 per cent.

(ii) Find the change of value in $5 - x + 2x^2 - x^3$ if x increases from -2 to $+2$.

2. (i) From the sum of $\tfrac{2}{3}a - \tfrac{3}{4}b + 2c$ and $\tfrac{1}{6}a + b - \tfrac{1}{2}c$, subtract $\tfrac{1}{2}a - \tfrac{5}{4}b - c$.

(ii) Simplify $(6a^2 - 10ab) \div (-2a) - (12ab - 9b^2) \div (-3b)$.

3. Solve (i) $\tfrac{1}{2}z - z + \tfrac{1}{4}z = \tfrac{1}{5}z - 18$;

(ii) $\dfrac{25}{r} - \dfrac{8}{s} = 4$, $\dfrac{5}{r} + \dfrac{12}{s} = 11$.

4. (i) A train travels v miles an hour, find how many feet it travels in 1 second.

(ii) If a speed of v miles an hour is twice as fast as a speed of $(v-2)$ feet a second, find the value of v and check your answer.

5. Two angles of a triangle are $A°$, $B°$; two angles of another triangle are $(A - 2B)$ degrees and $(B + 70)$ degrees. If the angles of the first triangle are equal to the angles of the second triangle, find the values of A and B. [There are 3 sets of answers.]

A. 50

1. (i) Evaluate $a^2(b-c) + b^2(c-a) + c^2(a-b) + (b-c)(c-a)(a-b)$
if $a = 2$, $b = -1$, $c = -2$.

(ii) Add together $\frac{1}{3}x - \frac{1}{6}y + \frac{1}{4}z$, $\frac{2}{3}y - \frac{1}{2}z + \frac{1}{6}x$, $\frac{3}{4}z - \frac{1}{2}x - \frac{1}{6}y$.

2. A man walks s miles in t hours. (i) How long does he take to walk n miles? (ii) How far does he walk in p hours?

3. Solve (i) $\dfrac{x+1}{5} = \dfrac{x-3}{2} - \dfrac{x-2}{7}$;

(ii) $y(5z-6) = 2$, $y(3z+4) = 5$.

4. In Fig. 121, **AB** = **AC** and **BD** bisects $\angle$ **ABC**, and the angles are all measured in degrees; find the values of x and y.

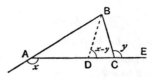

Fig. 121.

5. A walks 16 miles in the same time that B walks 14 miles and B takes half an hour longer to walk 21 miles than A takes to walk 22 miles. Find the speeds at which A and B walk.

CHAPTER IX

PRODUCTS, QUOTIENTS, AND FACTORS

Single Term Factors

IF there is a factor common to each term of an expression, use short division to factorise the expression.

Example 1. Factorise $6a^2 - 12ax + 3a$.

$$3a)\overline{6a^2 - 12ax + 3a}$$
$$\overline{2a - 4x + 1}$$

$$\therefore\ 6a^2 - 12ax + 3a = 3a(2a - 4x + 1).$$

If an expression has been factorised, the quotient, obtained when the expression is divided by one of the factors, can be written down.

Example 2. Divide $6a^2 - 12ax + 3a$ by $2a - 4x + 1$.

$$6a^2 - 12ax + 3a = 3a(2a - 4x + 1);$$
$$\therefore\ (6a^2 - 12ax + 3a) \div (2a - 4x + 1) = 3a.$$

EXERCISE IX. a

Simplify the following:

1. $(6c + 3d) \div 3$. 2. $(8a^2 - 10a) \div 2a$. 3. $(y^2 + y) \div y$.

[4] $(6t^2 + 4t) \div 2t$. [5] $(p^3 - p^2) \div p^2$. [6] $(b^2c - bc) \div bc$.

7. $(10x^2y^2 - 15xy^3) \div 5xy^2$. 8. $(r + nr) \div r$.

9. $(9a^9 - 6a^6) \div 3a^3$. 10. $(6b^2 - 6bc + 3b) \div 3b$.

[11] $(4x^3y - 8x^2y^2 + 12xy^3 - 4xy) \div 4xy$.

Express, *where possible,* the following in factors; *if there are no factors, say so.*

12. $6c - 9$. 13. $4n + 4$. 14. $xy + xz$. 15. $p^2 - 2q$.

16. $6a^2 - 6ab$. 17. $20r^2 + 10r$. 18. $4 + 2s^2$. 19. $b^2c - 2bc^2$.

[20] $5r + 10s$. [21] $bc - cd$. [22] $6y^2 - 2y$. [23] $x^3z + z^3x$.

Express, *where possible*, the following in factors; *if there are no factors, say so.*

24. $ab + a$.　　25. $3d^3 - d$.　　26. $x^2 + y^2$.　　27. $p^2 - rp^2$.

[28] $9pq - 21rs$.　[29] $r^2s^2 + s^2$.　[30] $4ab^2 - 4b$.　[31] $y - cyz$.

32. $ap + aq + ar$.　33. $x^3 - 3x^2 - 3x$.　34. $ab + bc + ca$.

35. $y^2 + yz + y$.　36. $cd + c^2d + cd^2$.　[37] $3r^2 - rs - rt$.

[38] $ax - bx - cx$.　[39] $y^4 - 4y^3 - 2y^2$.　[40] $p^2 - pq + pr$.

41. $2x^2 - x(y + z)$.　42. $6ab - 2b(b - c)$.　[43] $8d^6 - d^2(2e^4 - 4f^4)$.

Divide:

44. $3x - 3y$ by $x - y$.　　　　[45] $8 - 8z$ by $2(1 - z)$.

46. $a^2 + ab$ by $a + b$.　　　　[47] $cd - d^2$ by $c - d$.

48. $n^2 + n$ by $n + 1$.　　　　[49] $xy - x^2y$ by $1 - x$.

50. $a^2b^2 - abc^2$ by $ab - c^2$.　　[51] $8r^2s + 8rs^2$ by $2rs + 2s^2$.

*52. $(a + b)^2 + 3(a + b)$ by $a + b$.　*53. $c(c + d) - d(d + c)$ by $c + d$.

*54. $(x - y)^2 + x - y$ by $x - y$.　*55. $m(p + q) + p + q$ by $p + q$.

Express, *where possible*, the following in factors; *if there are no factors, say so.*

*56. $a(r + s) + b(r + s)$.　　　　*57. $c(x + y) + d(x - y)$.

*58. $x(x + y) - y(y + x)$.　　　　*59. $(a + b)^2 + c(a + b)$.

*60. $a(x + y) + b(y + z)$.　　　　*61. $(r - t)^2 + (r - t)$.

*62. $b(c - d) + x(c - d)$.　　　　*63. $a(p + q) + (p + q)b$.

*64. $r(y + z) + (y + z)$.　　　　*65. $(a + b)^2 - (a + b)$.

Relation between $x - y$ and $y - x$

Statements such as $4 + 6 = 6 + 4$, $2 + 7 = 7 + 2$, $8 + 5 = 5 + 8$, etc., are all included in the single formula, $x + y = y + x$.

Since $6 - 4 = 2$ and $4 - 6 = -2$, $\therefore (6 - 4) = -(4 - 6)$.

Similarly $2 - 7 = -(7 - 2)$, $8 - 5 = -(5 - 8)$, etc.; and all these statements are included in the single formula,

$$x - y = -(y - x).$$

This equality follows from the ordinary rules for removing brackets, $-(y - x) = -y + x = x - y$;

or from short division,　　　$\dfrac{-1)\ \ x - y}{-x + y}$.

Example 3. Divide $2a^2 - 2ab$ by $-2a$.

$$-2a\overline{)2a^2 - 2ab}.$$
$$\underline{-a + b}$$

Quotient, **b − a.**

Example 4. Simplify $\dfrac{5r - 5s}{6s - 6r}$.

$$\frac{5r - 5s}{6s - 6r} = \frac{5(r - s)}{6(s - r)} = \frac{-5(s - r)}{6(s - r)} = -\frac{5}{6}.$$

EXERCISE IX. b

If $a = 7$, $b = 4$, write down the values of:

1. $a - b$; $b - a$.   2. $(a - b)^2$; $(b - a)^2$.

3. $\dfrac{1}{b^2 - a^2}$.   [4] $(a - b)(b - a)$.   [5] $(b - a)^3$.

If $a + b = 9$, $a - b = 5$, write down the values of:

6. $b + a$; $b - a$.   [7] $\dfrac{1}{b - a}$; $(b - a)^2$.

If $x - y = 4$, write down, *where possible*, the *numerical* values of:

8. $y - x$; $1 - y - x$.   9. $(y - x)(x - y)$; $\dfrac{1}{y} - \dfrac{1}{x}$.

10. $\dfrac{2}{x - y} + \dfrac{1}{y - x}$.   [11] $\dfrac{4}{x - y} - \dfrac{1}{y - x}$.

12. $\dfrac{1}{x - y} - \dfrac{1}{y + x}$.   [13] $\dfrac{x - y}{y - x}$.   14. $\dfrac{1 - x + y}{1 - y + x}$.

Simplify the following:

15. $\dfrac{b - a}{a - b}$.   16. $\dfrac{c - d}{3d - 3c}$.   [17] $\dfrac{2x - 2y}{y - x}$.   [18] $\dfrac{-1}{z - y}$.

[19] $\dfrac{4(f + g)}{6(g - f)}$.   [20] $\dfrac{ax - bx}{by - ay}$.   [21] $\dfrac{(r + s)(p - q)}{(s + r)(p + q)}$.

22. $\dfrac{(c + d)(c - d)}{(d + c)(d - c)}$.   23. $\dfrac{(m - n)(m - n)}{(n - m)(n - m)}$.   24. $\dfrac{cxy - xyz}{abz - abc}$.

If $r - s = a$ and $y - z = b$, write down, *where possible*, in terms of a, b only, the following:

25. $1 + s - r$.   26. $1 - y - z$.   27. $(s - r)(z - y)$.

[28] $(r + y) - (s + z)$.   [29] $(s - r)^2$.   [30] $(s + r)(z + y)$.

Write more shortly:

*31. $(p+q)(q+p)$.   *32. $(c-d)(d-c)$.   *33. $(x-y)^2 \div (y-x)$.

*34. $\dfrac{3}{a-b} + \dfrac{1}{b-a}$.   *35. $\dfrac{x}{x-y} + \dfrac{y}{y-x}$.

*36. $\dfrac{x^2}{x-y} \times \dfrac{y-x}{xz}$.   *37. $\dfrac{a-b}{c-d} \div \dfrac{b-a}{d-c}$.

Binomial Products.   Fig. 122 represents a rectangle $(a+b)$ inches high, $(c+d)$ inches long, divided into two compartments, whose areas are $a(c+d)$ sq. in., $b(c+d)$ sq. in.; but the area of the rectangle is $(a+b)(c+d)$ sq. in.; thus

$$(a+b)(c+d) = a(c+d) + b(c+d).$$

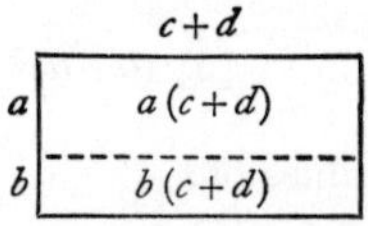

$c+d$	
a	$a(c+d)$
b	$b(c+d)$

Fig. 122.

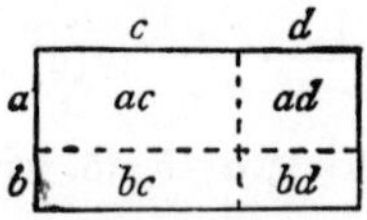

	c	d
a	ac	ad
b	bc	bd

Fig. 123.

Fig. 123 represents the same rectangle divided into four compartments whose areas are ac sq. in., ad sq. in., bc sq. in., bd sq. in.; thus

$$(a+b)(c+d) = ac + ad + bc + bd.$$

The reader should now draw a figure to illustrate that

$$(a-b)y = ay - by.$$

Now write $(c-d)$ instead of y, then

$$
\begin{aligned}
(a-b)(c-d) &= a(c-d) - b(c-d) \\
&= (ac - ad) - (bc - bd) \\
&= ac - ad - bc + bd.
\end{aligned}
$$

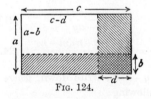

Fig. 124.

This result may be illustrated by Fig. 124.   Other products may be illustrated in the same way.

EXERCISE IX. c (Oral)

1. What product is illustrated by Fig. 125?

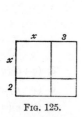

Fig. 125.

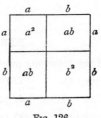

Fig. 126.

2. What product is illustrated by Fig. 126?

3. Draw a figure to illustrate that $(2a)^2 = 4a^2$.

4. Draw a figure to illustrate the value of $(y+7)(y+4)$.

5. What product is illustrated by Fig. 127?

6. Draw a figure to illustrate the value of $(a+b+c)^2$.

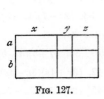

Fig. 127.

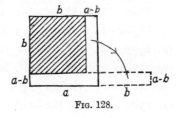

Fig. 128.

7. Fig. 128 shows a square of side a inches, from which a square of side b inches has been removed. Use this figure to express $a^2 - b^2$ as a product.

Example 5. Expand $(2x-3)(x-5)$.

$$(2x-3)(x-5) = 2x(x-5) - 3(x-5)$$
$$= (2x^2 - 10x) - (3x - 15)$$
$$= 2x^2 - 10x - 3x + 15$$
$$= 2x^2 - 13x + 15.$$

Example 6. Expand $(3a + 5b)(3a - 5b)$.

$$(3a + 5b)(3a - 5b) = 3a(3a - 5b) + 5b(3a - 5b)$$
$$= 9a^2 - 15ab + 15ab - 25b^2$$
$$= 9a^2 - 25b^2.$$

EXERCISE IX. d

Expand the following expressions:

1. $(b + c)(y + z)$.   2. $(a - b)(x + y)$.   3. $(c + d)(y - z)$.

4. $(a - d)(x - z)$.   5. $(a + b)(a - c)$.   6. $(x - a)(x - b)$.

[7] $(p - q)(r + s)$.   [8] $(s - t)(y - z)$.   [9] $(b + c)(x - z)$.

[10] $(y - r)(y - t)$.   [11] $(x + a)(x - c)$.   [12] $(p - z)(q + z)$.

13. $(a + 2)(a + 3)$.   14. $(b + 4)(b - 1)$.   15. $(c - 3)(c - 5)$.

[16] $(d - 3)(d + 4)$.   [17] $(e - 1)(e - 5)$.   [18] $(f + 5)(f - 7)$.

19. $(g + 2)(g - 2)$.   20. $(h - 3)(h - 3)$.   21. $(k + 5)(k + 5)$.

22. $(3 - m)(3 - m)$.   23. $(4 + n)(4 - n)$.   24. $(5 + p)(1 - p)$.

[25] $(7 + r)(7 - r)$.   [26] $(6 - s)(6 - s)$.   [27] $(3 - t)(7 + t)$.

28. $(a - 2b)(a - 3b)$.   29. $(c + d)(c - 4d)$.   30. $(x - y)(x + 3y)$.

31. $(2x + 1)(3x - 1)$.   32. $(3y + 2)(2y + 3)$.   33. $(2z - 1)(4z - 3)$.

[34] $(p + 2q)(p - 5q)$.   [35] $(2r + 3s)(4r - 3s)$.

[36] $(2x - 5y)(3x + 2y)$. 37. $(a + b)^2$. 38. $(a - b)^2$. 39. $(a + b)(a - b)$.

40. $(3c - 2d)^2$.   41. $(2p + 5q)^2$.   42. $(3r + 4s)(3r - 4s)$.

[43] $(4x + y)^2$.   [44] $(3y - 4z)^2$.   [45] $(2x + 5z)(2x - 5z)$.

Products by Inspection. The examples in Exercise IX. d show that *the product $(a + b)(c + d)$ is obtained by multiplying each of the terms in the first bracket by each of the terms in the second bracket and then adding the separate products.*

Example 7. Expand $(p - q)(r - s)$.

$$(p - q)(r - s) = pr + p(-s) - qr - q(-s)$$
$$= pr - ps - qr + qs.$$

The middle step should be performed mentally.

Example 8. Expand $(3x - 2)(4x + 5)$.

$$(3x - 2)(4x + 5) = 12x^2 + 15x - 8x - 10$$
$$= 12x^2 + 7x - 10.$$

After a little practice, *the middle step can be performed mentally.*
Inserting links, as shown below, is a help:

$$(3x - 2)(4x + 5).$$

For longer expressions the working may be arranged as in
Arithmetic.

Example 9. Multiply $2x^2 - 5x - 3$ by $3x + 7$.

$$2x^2 - 5x - 3$$
$$3x + 7$$
$$6x^3 - 15x^2 - 9x$$
$$14x^2 - 35x - 21$$
$$6x^3 - x^2 - 44x - 21$$

But even in such cases as this, *it is useful to practise collecting
coefficients of like terms mentally.*

EXERCISE IX. e

Write down the expansions of the following:

1. $(a + b)(x + y)$.   2. $(c - d)(y + z)$.   3. $(q - r)(a - b)$.

[4] $(c + d)(x - y)$.   [5] $(b - x)(b + y)$.   [6] $(p - r)(q + r)$.

7. $(a + b)(a - c)$.   8. $(c - z)(d - z)$.   9. $(m - 1)(n + 2)$.

[10] $(r + s)(s + t)$.   [11] $(a + t)(b + 3)$.   [12] $(p - 2)(q - 2)$.

13. $(y + 4)(y + 7)$.   14. $(z + 1)(z + 10)$.   15. $(a + 5)(a - 2)$.

16. $(b - 7)(b + 3)$.   17. $(c - 3)(c - 5)$.   18. $(1 - n)(5 + n)$.

19. $(3 - p)(3 - p)$.   20. $(4 + q)(4 - q)$.   21. $(4 + t)(3 - t)$.

[22] $(x + 2)(x + 5)$.   [23] $(y - 4)(y + 9)$.   [24] $(z - 7)(z + 7)$.

[25] $(2 - s)(5 - s)$.   [26] $(3 + t)(7 - t)$.   [27] $(4 - r)(10 + r)$.

28. $(3b + 2)(4b + 5)$.   29. $(4y - 1)(3y + 1)$.   30. $(5z - 1)(5z + 1)$.

31. $(3c - 2)(4c - 7)$.   32. $(4p - 3)(3p + 2)$.   33. $(2c - d)(3c - d)$.

34. $(x + y)^2$.   35. $(x - y)^2$.   36. $(x + y)(x - y)$.

Write down the expansions of the following:

[37] $(2a+1)(a+4)$.

[38] $(2b-1)(3b-1)$.

[39] $(3d+2)(4d-5)$.

[40] $(2n-7)(3n-1)$.

[41] $(a+3b)(a+5b)$.

[42] $(x-2y)(x+4y)$.

[43] $(x-3y)^2$.

[44] $(x+5y)^2$.

[45] $(x+4y)(x-4y)$.

46. $(2c+5d)^2$.

47. $(3r-4s)^2$.

48. $(5y+7z)(5y-7z)$.

Expand the following expressions:

49. $(x+3)(x^2+x+2)$.

50. $(a+b)(a^2-ab+b^2)$.

51. $(2c^2-3c-1)(3c-2)$.

52. $(1-7x-3x^2)(2+x)$.

53. $(x^2+2xy+4y^2)(x-2y)$.

54. $(4z-3)(5-3z-2z^2)$.

[55] $(n+1)(n^2-2n+3)$.

[56] $(1-z)(1+z+z^2)$.

[57] $(3r^2-rs-2s^2)(2r+3s)$.

[58] $(2y-3)(2+y-5y^2)$.

Simplify:

59. $(p-1)^2+(\rho+1)^2-2p^2$.

[60] $(r+s)^2-(r-s)^2$.

*61. $(2n+1)(2n+3)+(2n+3)(2n+5)-8(n+1)(n+2)$.

*62. $3(t-3)^2-2(t-1)^2+2(t+1)^2-3(t+3)^2$.

Find the coefficient of x^2 and the coefficient of x in the expansions of the following products:

63. $(x-1)(5x^2-4x-3)$.

64. $(3x+5)(2x^2-x-2)$.

65. $(4x^2+3x-7)(4x-3)$.

66. $(2x-3-5x^2)(3-2x)$.

[67] $(1-2x)(3+7x-2x^2)$.

[68] $(4-5x-8x^2)(4+5x)$.

Solve the following equations:

69. $3(n-1)(n-2)=(1-n)(1-3n)$.

70. $(y+1)^2+y^2+1=(y-1)^2+y^2-1$.

[71] $(x+1)(x-2)+5=(1-x)(2-x)$.

[72] $(t+1)(2-t)+(3+t)(2t+1)+(2+t)(3-t)=6$.

*73. $2(z+4)(z-4)-3(z-3)(z+1)=1-(z-2)^2$.

*74. $5(p+1)^2-3(p-1)(p+2)=2(p+3)^2+8$.

*75. $2(r+3)(r-7)-3(2r+3)^2=14-5(2r-3)(r+1)$.

Answer Nos. 76–85 in a form not containing brackets:

76. Find the area of a rectangle $(l+3)$ inches long, $(l+1)$ inches wide.

77. The average speed of a car is $(n+10)$ miles per hour. How far does it go in $(t-1)$ hours?

[78] Tea costs $(x-6)$ pence per lb.; find the cost of $(w+2)$ lb.

[79] A carpet $(l-3)$ feet long, $(b-2)$ feet wide is laid on the floor of a room l feet long, b feet wide. Find the area of the part of the floor which remains uncovered.

80. By how much does the area of a square of side $(r+3)$ inches exceed the area of a rectangle $(r+5)$ inches long, $(r+1)$ inches high? Find also the perimeter of each figure.

81. The perimeter of a square is $(8m+4)$ inches. Find its area.

[82] Find the product of three consecutive whole numbers, the largest of which is $n+1$.

83. Find the sum of the squares of three consecutive odd numbers, the smallest of which is $2m-1$.

[84] The length of each edge of a cubical block is $(l+1)$ inches. Find the total area of its surface.

*85. A rectangle l inches long, b inches broad has the same perimeter as a square. By how much does the area of the square exceed that of the rectangle? Show that the answer is equal to $\frac{1}{4}(l-b)^2$ sq. inches.

Important Expansions

Three of the expansions in the last exercise should be committed to memory:

$$(A+B)^2 \equiv A^2 + B^2 + 2AB$$
$$(A-B)^2 = A^2 + B^2 - 2AB$$
$$(A+B)(A-B) \equiv A^2 - B^2$$

In words,

The square of the sum of two numbers is equal to the sum of their squares PLUS *twice their product.*

The square of the difference of two numbers is equal to the sum of their squares MINUS *twice their product.*

The product of the sum and the difference of two numbers is equal to the difference of their squares.

Perfect Squares

Example 10. Write down the squares of $2x+3y$ and $5x-7y$.

$$(2x+3y)^2 = (2x)^2 + (3y)^2 + 2(2x)(3y) = 4x^2 + 9y^2 + 12xy.$$
$$(5x-7y)^2 = (5x)^2 + (7y)^2 - 2(5x)(7y) = 25x^2 + 49y^2 - 70xy.$$

After a little practice, the *middle step should be performed mentally*, not written down.

Example 11. Is $16y^2 + 25z^2 - 20yz$ a perfect square?

If it is a perfect square, it must be the square of $4y - 5z$.

Now $\qquad (4y - 5z)^2 = 16y^2 + 25z^2 - 40yz$.

$\therefore \quad 16y^2 + 25z^2 - 20yz$ is not a perfect square.

Square Roots. Any positive number has two square roots; thus the square roots of 25 are $+5$ and -5.

Since $(B - A)^2 = B^2 + A^2 - 2BA = (A - B)^2$, it follows that $A^2 + B^2 - 2AB$ has two square roots, namely $A - B$ and $B - A$; these may be written $A - B$ and $-(A - B)$ or, more shortly, $\pm (A - B)$.

Similarly, $(-A - B)^2 = A^2 + B^2 + 2AB = (A + B)^2$; therefore the two square roots of $A^2 + B^2 + 2AB$ are $A + B$ and $-A - B$; these may be written $A + B$ and $-(A + B)$ or, more shortly, $\pm (A + B)$.

Completing the Square

Geometrical Illustration. What must be added to $x^2 + 6x$ to make the result a perfect square?

Fig. 129 represents a rectangle $(x + 6)$ in. long, x in. high;

$\therefore$ its area $= x(x + 6)$ sq. in. $= (x^2 + 6x)$ sq. in.

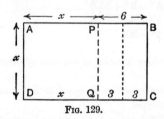

FIG. 129.

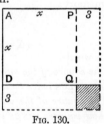

FIG. 130.

Transpose half the rectangle **PBCQ** and fit it on to **DQ**, as in Fig. 130. This gives a square of side x in., bordered with two rectangles, each of width $\frac{6}{2}$ in. $= 3$ in. To complete the square, add the shaded area in Fig. 130; this is a square of side 3 in., area 3^2 sq. in. $= 9$ sq. in. The result is a square of side $(x + 3)$ in., area $(x + 3)^2$ sq. in. $= (x^2 + 6x + 9)$ sq. in.

Hence, to $x^2 + 6x$, add $(\frac{6}{2})^2 = 9$; then the sum is $(x + 3)^2$.

To complete the square, start by looking for an expression whose square is of the required form.

Example 12.   What must be added to $a^2 - 5a$ to make the sum a perfect square ?   Of what expressions is the sum the square ?

Since
$$a^2 - 2ab + b^2 = (a - b)^2,$$
$$a^2 - 5a + ? = a^2 - 2(\tfrac{5}{2})a + ? = (a - \tfrac{5}{2})^2$$
$$= a^2 - 5a + (\tfrac{5}{2})^2.$$

$\therefore$ if $(\tfrac{5}{2})^2$ is added to $a^2 - 5a$, the sum equals $(a - \tfrac{5}{2})^2$, and this is the square of $a - \tfrac{5}{2}$, also of $-(a - \tfrac{5}{2})$, that is, $\tfrac{5}{2} - a$.

Example 13.   What must be added to $25x^2 + 7x$ to make the sum a perfect square ?

$$25x^2 + 7x + ? = (5x)^2 + 2(5x)(\tfrac{7}{10}) + ? = (5x + \tfrac{7}{10})^2$$
$$= 25x^2 + 7x + (\tfrac{7}{10})^2.$$

$\therefore$ if $(\tfrac{7}{10})^2$ is added to $25x^2 + 7x$, the sum equals $(5x + \tfrac{7}{10})^2$.

EXERCISE IX. f

Write down the squares of the following:

1. $a + 5.$ 2. $b - 3.$ 3. $3 - b.$ 4. $-a - 5.$

5. $4c + d.$ 6. $4e - f.$ 7. $2p + 3q.$ 8. $5s - 7r.$

[9] $x - y.$ [10] $y - x.$ [11] $-5r - 3s.$ [12] $4y - 5z.$

13. $x + \dfrac{1}{2}.$ 14. $y - \dfrac{1}{y}.$ 15. $3ab - 4c.$ 16. $y + \dfrac{3z}{2}.$

[17] $a + \dfrac{1}{a}.$ [18] $b - \dfrac{5}{2}.$ [19] $c - \dfrac{3}{d}.$ [20] $5x - 3yz.$

In Nos. 21–35, state whether the expression is a perfect square; if it is, give the *two* square roots.

21. $x^2 - 2x + 1.$ 22. $a^2 + 6a + 9.$ 23. $b^2 + 2b + 4.$

24. $c^2 - 4c + 4.$ 25. $d^2 - 10d - 25.$ 26. $16 - 8k + k^2.$

[27] $x^2 + 2xy + y^2.$ [28] $r^2 - 12r + 36.$ [29] $s^2 - 14s - 49.$

[30] $n^2 - 25.$ [31] $1 - 2p + p^2.$ [32] $4 - 12x + 9x^2.$

33. $9s^2 + 60s + 100.$ 34. $4a^2 - 40ab + 25b^2.$ 35. $t^2 + t + \tfrac{1}{4}.$

What term, added to the following, makes the sum a perfect square ?   Of what expressions is the sum the square ?

36. $x^2 + 10x.$ 37. $y^2 - 8y.$ 38. $a^2 + 6ab.$ 39. $c^2 + 3c.$

[40] $z^2 + 12z.$ [41] $p^2 - 10p.$ [42] $y^2 - 14yz.$ [43] $d^2 - 7d.$

44. $a^2 + a.$ 45. $c^2 - cd.$ *46. $4x^2 + 12x.$ *47. $4y^2 - 5y.$

The Difference of Two Squares

Since
$$A^2 - B^2 = (A + B)(A - B),$$
$$x^2 - 9 = x^2 - 3^2 = (x + 3)(x - 3),$$

and
$$49a^2 - 25b^2 = (7a)^2 - (5b)^2 = (7a + 5b)(7a - 5b),$$

and
$$(x + p)^2 - q^2 = [(x + p) + q][(x + p) - q]$$
$$= (x + p + q)(x + p - q).$$

Example 14. Factorise $16a^2 - 9(b - c)^2$.

$$16a^2 - 9(b - c)^2 = [4a]^2 - [3(b - c)]^2$$
$$= [4a + 3(b - c)][4a - 3(b - c)]$$
$$= (4a + 3b - 3c)(4a - 3b + 3c).$$

Example 15. Factorise $12(2a - b)^2 - 3(a + b)^2$.

$$12(2a - b)^2 - 3(a + b)^2 = 3[4(2a - b)^2 - (a + b)^2]$$
$$= 3[2(2a - b) + (a + b)][2(2a - b) - (a + b)]$$
$$= 3[4a - 2b + a + b][4a - 2b - a - b]$$
$$= 3(5a - b)(3a - 3b)$$
$$= 9(5a - b)(a - b).$$

EXERCISE IX. g

Expand the following:

1. $(a + 3b)(a - 3b)$.
2. $(4x + 5y)(4x - 5y)$.
3. $(4c^4 - 5de^3)(4c^4 + 5de^3)$.
4. $(2p^3 + \frac{1}{2}q)(2p^3 - \frac{1}{2}q)$.
[5] $(1 - 7t)(1 + 7t)$.
[6] $(3x^3 - 2y^2z)(3x^3 + 2y^2z)$.

[7] $(4x^4 + 3)(4x^4 - 3)$.
[8] $\left(y - \dfrac{1}{y}\right)\left(y + \dfrac{1}{y}\right)$.

Factorise the following:

9. $y^2 - z^2$.
10. $9 - x^2$.
11. $c^2 - 16d^2$.
12. $4n^2 - 25$.
13. $1 - 4t^4$.
14. $16p^6 - 49q^8$.
[15] $a^2 - 36b^2c^4$.
[16] $c^8 - 64$.
[17] $a^2b^8 - c^{10}$.
18. $(x + 2y)^2 - z^2$.
19. $(b - c)^2 - 9$.
20. $p^2 - (q - r)^2$.
21. $(a + 3)^2 - 4$.
22. $(b - 4)^2 - 25$.
23. $4c^2 - (c - 4d)^2$.
[24] $(2f - 3g)^2 - h^2$.
[25] $l^2 - (m + n)^2$.
[26] $(2x - 3y)^2 - y^2$.
27. $ab^2 - ac^2$.
28. $3d^2 - 12$.
29. $5 - 45e^2$.

Factorise the following:

[30] $x^4 - 4x^2y^2.$ [31] $9 - 9z^2.$ [32] $p^3 - p(q-r)^2.$

33. $4a^2 - 9(b+c)^2.$ 34. $c^2 - 16(c-d)^2.$ 35. $4e^2 - (e+2)^2.$

[36] $9f^2 - 4(f+3)^2.$ [37] $9(p+2)^2 - 16.$ [38] $18 - 8(r+s)^2.$

39. $(3x+2)^2 - (2x+1)^2.$ 40. $9(y+z)^2 - 4(y-z)^2.$

[41] $(5b-3c)^2 - (2b+9c)^2.$ [42] $16(d-e)^2 - 9(d+e)^2.$

43. $a^4 - b^4.$ 44. $x^4 - 1.$ 45. $y^4 - 2y^2z^2 + z^4.$

Use factors to evaluate the following:

46. $25^2 - 24^2.$ 47. $97^2 - 87^2.$ 48. $5 \cdot 4^2 - 4 \cdot 6^2.$

[49] Evaluate $r^2 - t^2$ when $r = 3\frac{1}{4}$ and $t = 2\frac{1}{4}.$

Simplify:

50. $(b^2 - c^2) \div (b-c).$ 51. $(1 - 9b^2) \div (1 + 3b).$

[52] $(4p^2 - q^2) \div (2p+q).$ [53] $(x^4 - 1) \div (x^2 + 1).$

54. $(x^2 - 2xy + y^2) \div (x-y).$ 55. $(b^2 + 8bc + 16c^2) \div (b+4c).$

[56] $(ab^2 - ac^2) \div (ab-ac).$ [57] $(1 - 4x^2 + 4x^4) \div (1 - 2x^2).$

Factors by Grouping Terms

When factorising an expression, **first see if there is a common factor of each term.** If so, write it down, and find the other factor by short division.

Example 16. Factorise $p(a+b) + q(a+b).$

$(a+b)$ is a factor of each term.

$$[a+b]\underline{p(a+b) + q(a+b)}$$
$$\underline{p+q}$$

$\therefore\ p(a+b) + q(a+b) = (\mathbf{a+b})(\mathbf{p+q}).$

The short division should be done mentally.

Sometimes a common factor can be found by grouping terms together.

Example 17. Factorise $ax - ay + bx - by.$

$$ax - ay + bx - by = a(x-y) + b(x-y).$$

Here $(x-y)$ is a factor of each term;

$\therefore$ by short division, $ax - ay + bx - by = (\mathbf{x-y})(\mathbf{a+b}).$

When dividing by a common factor, write it down first, and treat it as the divisor in a division sum.

When you have obtained the factors, multiply them together mentally, to make sure that their product equals the given expression.

The fact that an expression can be arranged in two groups does not mean, necessarily, that it can be factorised.

Thus, $ac + ax + bc + by = a(c + x) + b(c + y)$.

But there is no factor common to these two terms, so we cannot use the "short division" method.

Actually, this expression has no factors.

An expression, such as $a(c + x) + b(c + y)$, which is written as the *Sum* of two terms **is not in factors**.

Thus, $29 = 15 + 14 = 3 \times 5 + 2 \times 7$, but these numbers are not factors of 29.

Example 18. Factorise $a^2 + bc + ab + ac$.

$$a^2 + bc + ab + ac = (a^2 + bc) + a(b + c).$$

This is not in factors because it is the *sum* of two terms; also there is no factor common to the two terms, so we cannot use the "short division" method.

But $a^2 + bc + ab + ac = a^2 + ab + bc + ac$
$$= a(a + b) + c(b + a).$$

Here, $(a + b)$ is a factor of each term, since $a + b = b + a$;

$\therefore$ by short division, $a^2 + bc + ab + ac = (\mathbf{a} + \mathbf{b})(\mathbf{a} + \mathbf{c})$.

Note. *Group together terms which have a common factor.*

Example 19. Factorise $ad + bc - ac - bd$.

$ad + bc - ac - bd = ad - ac + bc - bd = a(d - c) + b(c - d)$
$$= a(d - c) - b(d - c), \text{ since } c - d = -(d - c),$$
$$= (\mathbf{d} - \mathbf{c})(\mathbf{a} - \mathbf{b}).$$

The *form* of the answer may be altered by grouping differently:
$ad + bc - ac - bd = bc - bd + ad - ac = b(c - d) + a(d - c)$
$$= b(c - d) - a(c - d) = (c - d)(b - a).$$

Since $(c - d) = -(d - c)$ and $(b - a) = -(a - b)$,
$$(c - d)(b - a) = (-1)(-1)(d - c)(a - b)$$
$$= (d - c)(a - b).$$

EXERCISE IX. h (Oral)

In Nos. 1–16, if the answer is yes, state also the other factor.

1. Is $a + 1$ a factor of (i) $2a + 2$; (ii) $3 + 3a$; (iii) $a + 2$?

[2] Is $b + 1$ a factor of (i) $2 + 2b$; (ii) $-b - 1$; (iii) $(1 + b)^2$?

3. Is $c - 1$ a factor of (i) $2c - 1$; (ii) $1 - c$; (iii) $c + 1$?

[4] Is $x - 3$ a factor of (i) $x + 3$; (ii) $3 - x$; (iii) $x^2 - 3$?

5. Is $x + y$ a factor of (i) $2y + 2x$; (ii) $x - y$; (iii) $xz + yz$?

[6] Is $x - y$ a factor of (i) $ax - by$; (ii) $y - x$; (iii) $x^2 - y^2$?

7. Is $a - b$ a factor of (i) $ac - bc$; (ii) $b - a$; (iii) $b^2 - c^2$?

8. Is $c + d$ a factor of (i) $c^2 + d^2$; (ii) $c^2 - d^2$; (iii) $-d - c$?

9. Is $a + b$ a factor of $x(a + b) + y(b + a)$?

10. Is $c + d$ a factor of $x(c + d) - y(c - d)$?

11. Is $x + y$ a factor of $x(a + b) + y(a + c)$?

[12] Is $x - y$ a factor of $a(x - y) + b(y - x)$?

[13] Is $c - d$ a factor of $c(x + y) - d(x - y)$?

14. Is $a + b$ a factor of $x(a + b) + a + b$?

[15] Is $c + d$ a factor of $(c + d)y - c - d$?

16. Is $x + y$ a factor of $a(x + y) - x + y$?

Have the following expressions factors? If so, find them and check by multiplication. *If there are no factors, say so.*

17. $a(c + d) - b(c + d)$.　　18. $p(x + y) - q(x - y)$.

[19] $a(x + y) + b(x + z)$.　　[20] $a(c + d) - b(d + c)$.

21. $c(a - b) + d(b - a)$.　　22. $x(2y + 2) + z(y + 1)$.

[23] $a(b + 1) + b(a + 1)$.　　[24] $x - a + b(a - x)$.

25. $a(x + y) + x + y$.　　26. $x(p + q) - p - q$.

[27] $a(1 + x) - b(1 - x)$.　　[28] $c(y - z) - y + z$.

EXERCISE IX. j

Factorise, *when possible,* the following expressions. *If there are no factors, say so.*

1. $ax - ay + bx - by$.　　2. $a^2 + ab + ac + bc$.

3. $ac + ad - bc - bd$.　　4. $cy - cz - dy - dz$.

5. $x^2 + xy + 3x + 3y$.　　6. $a^2 + ac - 5a - 5c$.

7. $ax + ay + bx + bz$.　　8. $a^2c^2 + a^2d^2 + b^2d^2 + b^2c^2$.

[9] $pr + ps - qr - qs$.　　[10] $cm - cn - km + kn$.

[11] $dp - dq - 4p + 4q$.　　[12] $x^2 - cx - dx + cd$.

Factorise, *when possible*, the following expressions. *If there are no factors, say so.*

13. $5cx + 5dy - 5cy - 5dx$.

14. $6ab - 3bx + 2ay - xy$.

15. $4x^2 - 2xy - 6xz + 3yz$.

16. $ab - 12xy + 3bx - 4ay$.

17. $a^2 - ab - 2a - 2b$.

18. $2ab + 2ac + b + c$.

[19] $6cd + 2cn - 9md - 3mn$.

[20] $10cp - 15pq - 4ac + 6aq$.

[21] $x(a + b + c) + y(a + b + c)$.

[22] $p(x + y) + q(x - y)$.

23. $a(r - s) + b(s - r)$.

24. $a^2(b + c) - bc(c + b)$.

25. $ax - 3 + a - 3x$.

26. $xy + y^2 - x - y$.

27. $x^3 + x^2 + x + 1$.

28. $ac - bc - a + b$.

[29] $ap + pq - a - q$.

[30] $xy^2 - 1 + x - y^2$.

[31] $a(b - c) - d(c - b)$.

[32] $x^2 - (a + b)x + ab$.

33. $ca - cd - bd + ba$.

34. $2px - py + qy - 2qx$.

[35] $ac - a^2 + ad - cd$.

[36] $x^2 - 2x - xy - 2y$.

37. $x^2 - x + y - xy$.

38. $4 - 4x + cx - c$.

[39] $l(a - b) - m(a + b)$.

[40] $r(a - x) + z(x - a)$.

41. $1 + c^2 + cd + c^3d$.

42. $2a^4 - 2a^3x + x - a$.

*43. $x^2 - y^2 + ax + ay$.

*44. $z^2 - 1 + cz - c$.

*45. $a^2 - b^2 - ac + bc$.

*46. $1 - m^2 - t - tm$.

*47. $rt - 2st - r^2 + 4s^2$.

*48. $3cy + dy - 9c^2 + d^2$.

Quadratic Functions. The product of two first-degree functions of x is a quadratic function of x.

Thus, $(2x - 5)(3x + 4) = 2x(3x + 4) - 5(3x + 4)$
$$= 6x^2 + 8x - 15x - 20 = 6x^2 - 7x - 20.$$

To factorise a quadratic function, we express it so that this process can be *worked backwards*.

Example 20. Factorise $8x^2 + 10x + 3$.

Replace $+ 10x$ by two equivalent terms whose product is $8x^2 \times 3 = 24x^2$. Since the product is *positive*, the terms have the *same* sign; since the sum is *positive*, each term is *positive*.

$$24x^2 = 4x \times 6x.$$
$$8x^2 + 10x + 3 = 8x^2 + 4x + 6x + 3$$
$$= 4x(2x + 1) + 3(2x + 1)$$
$$= (2x + 1)(4x + 3).$$

Always check the factors by multiplying mentally.

Example 21. Factorise $y^2 - 22y + 96$.

Replace $-22y$ by two equivalent terms whose product is $y^2 \times 96$, $= 96y^2$.

The terms have the same sign, so each term is negative.

$$96y^2 = 2y \times 48y = 3y \times 32y = 4y \times 24y = 6y \times 16y.$$
$$\begin{aligned} y^2 - 22y + 96 &= y^2 - 6y - 16y + 96 \\ &= y(y - 6) - 16(y - 6). \\ &= (y - 6)(y - 16). \end{aligned}$$

Example 22. Factorise $6x^2 - 11xy - 10y^2$.

Replace $-11xy$ by two equivalent terms whose product is $6x^2 \times (-10y^2)$, $= -60x^2y^2$.

Since the product is *negative*, the terms have *opposite* signs; since the sum is *negative*, the *numerically larger* term is *negative*.

$$-60x^2y^2 = 2xy \times (-30xy) = 3xy \times (-20xy) = 4xy \times (-15xy).$$
$$\begin{aligned} 6x^2 - 11xy - 10y^2 &= 6x^2 + 4xy - 15xy - 10y^2 \\ &= 2x(3x + 2y) - 5y(3x + 2y) \\ &= (3x + 2y)(2x - 5y). \end{aligned}$$

Example 23. Factorise $2 + t - 10t^2$.

Replace $+t$ by two equivalent terms whose product is $2 \times (-10t^2)$, $= -20t^2$. The terms have *opposite* signs and the *numerically larger* term is positive:

$$-20t^2 = (-4t) \times (+5t).$$
$$\begin{aligned} 2 + t - 10t^2 &= 2 - 4t + 5t - 10t^2 \\ &= 2(1 - 2t) + 5t(1 - 2t) \\ &= (1 - 2t)(2 + 5t). \end{aligned}$$

If the coefficient of the term of degree 2 is negative and if the constant term is positive, work in *ascending* powers as in Example 23. *Do not turn the expression round.*

The above examples show that we need only consider the *coefficient* of the product and that if this coefficient is **positive**, the numerical factors required have a known **sum**; and if this coefficient is **negative**, the numerical factors required have a known **difference**.

If this coefficient has a large number of factors, as in the next Example, it saves time to express it in *prime factors* before looking for the pair which have a known sum or difference.

Example 24.   Factorise $12a^2 - 16a - 35$.

Replace $-16a$ by two equivalent terms whose product is $12a^2 \times (-35)$.

Look for two numbers whose product is 12×35 and which *differ* by 16.

$$12 \times 35 = 2^2 \times 3 \times 5 \times 7 = 14 \times 30.$$
$$12a^2 - 16a - 35 = 12a^2 + 14a - 30a - 35$$
$$= 2a(6a + 7) - 5(6a + 7)$$
$$= (6a + 7)(2a - 5).$$

EXERCISE IX. k

Write down the coefficient of x in Nos. 1–9:

1. $(2x + 3)(x + 4)$.   2. $(2x - 3)(x - 4)$.   3. $(2x + 3)(x - 4)$.

4. $(2x - 3)(x + 4)$.   5. $(1 - 2x)(2 + 5x)$.   6. $(7 - 3x)(2 - 3x)$.

[7] $(3x - 7)(2x + 3)$.   [8] $(x + 1)(7x - 5)$.   [9] $(1 - 4x)(2 - 7x)$.

Find *by inspection* two numbers satisfying the conditions in Nos. 10–25:

10. Product $= 15$, sum $= 8$.   11. Product $= 15$, sum $= 16$.

12. Product $= 45$, difference $= 4$.

13. Product $= 48$, difference $= 13$.

[14] Product $= 12$, sum $= 8$.   [15] Product $= 108$, sum $= 24$.

[16] Product $= 60$, difference $= 11$.

[17] Product $= 54$, difference $= 3$.

18. Product $= 24$, sum $= -11$.   19. Product $= -18$, sum $= 7$.

20. Product $= -45$, sum $= 12$.   21. Product $= -96$, sum $= -10$.

[22] Product $= 36$, sum $= -15$.   [23] Product $= -18$, sum $= -7$.

[24] Product $= -28$, sum $= -3$.   [25] Product $= -40$, sum $= 3$.

Factorise the following: *check your answers mentally.*

26. $3x^2 + 5x + 2$.   27. $2y^2 + 7y + 3$.   28. $3z^2 + 8z + 4$.

29. $a^2 + 6a + 8$.   30. $b^2 + 10b + 9$.   31. $c^2 - 7c + 12$.

32. $d^2 - 5d - 14$.   33. $x^2 + 7xy - 30y^2$.   34. $r^2 - 8rs - 84s^2$.

35. $2z^2 + 5z - 3$.   36. $2p^2 - 11p + 12$.   37. $3t^2 + 13t + 4$.

[38] $2a^2 + 11a + 5$.   [39] $3b^2 - 10b + 8$.   [40] $4c^2 + 11c - 3$.

[41] $d^2 + 7d + 10$.   [42] $t^2 + 6t - 16$.   [43] $n^2 + 7n - 18$.

[44] $x^2 - 3x - 28$.   [45] $y^2 + 15y + 14$.   [46] $z^2 + 3z - 70$.

Factorise the following: *check your answers mentally.*

47. $15 + 2a - a^2$.   **48.** $4 - 3b - b^2$.   **49.** $12 + 11c - c^2$.

50. $6d^2 + 5d - 6$.   **51.** $4x^2 + 13xy + 3y^2$.

52. $12a^2 - 11ab + 2b^2$.   **53.** $2y^2 - 22y + 48$.

54. $2c^2 - 22cd + 60d^2$.   **55.** $9r^2 - 39rs - 30s^2$.

[**56**] $c^2 - 13cd + 40d^2$.   [**57**] $12a^2 - 7ab + b^2$.

[**58**] $8m^2 - 10mn - 3n^2$.   [**59**] $2 - k - 6k^2$.   [**60**] $18 - 3x - x^2$.

[**61**] $6 + 5y - 6y^2$.   [**62**] $3a^2 + 60a - 63$.   [**63**] $2b^2 - 16b - 96$.

[**64**] $40c^2 - 50cd - 15d^2$.   **65.** $60k^2 - 25k - 10$.

66. $12n^2 + 33n - 9$.   **67.** $27t^2 + 18t - 24$.   **68.** $60 + 3y - 3y^2$.

[**69**] $4z^2 + 16z + 15$.   [**70**] $24 - 14x - 20x^2$.   [**71**] $6a^2 - 13ab + 6b^2$.

72. $12c^2 + 7cd - 12d^2$.   **73.** $24 + 50y - 25y^2$.

Factors by Inspection

After a little practice, *simple* quadratic functions can often be factorised at sight, without using the grouping method. But always check the answer by (mental) multiplication.

Example 25. Factorise (i) $x^2 + 11x + 24$; (ii) $x^2 - 2x - 35$.

(i) Find two numbers whose product is $+24$ and sum $+11$. These are $+8$, $+3$.

$$x^2 + 11x + 24 = (\mathbf{x} + 8)(\mathbf{x} + 3).$$

(ii) Find two numbers whose product is -35 and sum -2. These are -7, $+5$.

$$x^2 - 2x - 35 = (\mathbf{x} - 7)(\mathbf{x} + 5).$$

Check by mental multiplication in each case.

Example 26. Factorise $2y^2 + 5y - 3$.

Write down pairs of factors whose products introduce $2y^2$ and -3, and select that pair which also introduces $+5y$. Possible pairs are

$(2y + 3)(y - 1)$; $(2y - 3)(y + 1)$; $(2y - 1)(y + 3)$; $(2y + 1)(y - 3)$.

$$2y^2 + 5y - 3 = (\mathbf{2y} - 1)(\mathbf{y} + 3).$$

Use the grouping method, whenever you are not able to obtain the factors by inspection, *quickly.*

If there is a common factor, write it down first and find the other factor by short division.

EXERCISE IX. 1

Factorise the following: *check your answers mentally.*

1. $a^2 + 5a + 6$.   2. $b^2 + 6b + 9$.   3. $c^2 - 7c + 12$.

4. $d^2 - 3d - 10$.   5. $k^2 + 2k - 8$.   6. $n^2 - n - 6$.

7. $p^2 + p - 30$.   8. $r^2 + 12r + 36$.   9. $t^2 - 5t - 50$.

10. $x^2 + 14x + 45$.   11. $y^2 + 7y - 60$.   12. $z^2 - 9z - 70$.

13. $m^2 + 16m + 64$.   14. $n^2 - 64$.   15. $r^2 - 16r + 64$.

[16] $a^2 + 8a + 12$.   [17] $b^2 - 8b + 16$.   [18] $c^2 + 4c - 5$.

[19] $d^2 + 9d + 18$.   [20] $k^2 - 3k - 28$.   [21] $n^2 - 11n + 30$.

[22] $p^2 - 14p + 49$.   [23] $q^2 + 6q - 27$.   [24] $r^2 - 18r + 72$.

[25] $t^2 - 36$.   [26] $x^2 + x - 90$.   [27] $y^2 - 2y - 63$.

[28] $z^2 - 7z - 120$.   [29] $m^2 - 20m + 100$.   [30] $s^2 - 100$.

31. $x^2 - 12xy + 32y^2$.   32. $a^2 + 3ab - 10b^2$.

33. $c^2 - 4cd - 32d^2$.   34. $1 + 3a - 10a^2$.

35. $1 - 2b - 24b^2$.   36. $1 - 12c + 35c^2$.

37. $1 - 14d + 49d^2$.   38. $1 - 49e^2$.

39. $1 + 14g + 49g^2$.   40. $1 - k - 20k^2$.

41. $24 - 5n - n^2$.   42. $28 - 11p + p^2$.

[43] $a^2 + ab - 6b^2$.   [44] $c^2 - 4cd - 5d^2$.

[45] $r^2 + 8rs + 16s^2$.   [46] $x^2 + 6xy + 5y^2$.

[47] $p^2 - 9q^2$.   [48] $y^2 - 6yz + 9z^2$.

[49] $12 - a - a^2$.   [50] $10 + 7b + b^2$.

[51] $35 - 2c - c^2$.   52. $3k^2 - 12k - 15$.

53. $2x^2 + 6xy - 20y^2$.   54. $3 - 27z^2$.

55. $a^2b^2 - 7abc + 10c^2$.   56. $1 - 3xy - 18x^2y^2$.

57. $24r^2 + 2rs - s^2$.   58. $2p^2 - 7p - 15$.

59. $5q^2 - 16q + 3$.   60. $4r^2 + 5r - 6$.

61. $10x^2 - 13x + 4$.   62. $12y^2 - 11y - 5$.

63. $10z^2 - 21z + 9$.   [64] $2a^2 + 2a - 12$.

[65] $5b^2 - 5b - 150$.   [66] $4c^2 - 100$.

[67] $2d^2 - 5d + 2$.   [68] $3e^2 + 5e - 2$.

[69] $6k^2 - 11k + 3$.   [70] $5m^2 + 14m - 3$.

[71] $4n^2 - 11n + 6$.   [72] $5p^2 + 3p - 2$.

[73] $12x^2 + 19x + 5$.   [74] $10y^2 + 3y - 4$.

Factorise the following: *check your answers mentally.*

[75] $10z^2 + 9z - 1$.   76. $6a^2 + 7a - 10$.

77. $4b^2 - 12b + 9$.   78. $9c^2 + c - 10$.

79. $9m^2 - 64n^2$.   80. $25x^2 + 40xy + 16y^2$.

81. $42c^2 - cd - 30d^2$.   [82] $10y^2 - 43y + 12$.

[83] $8z^2 + 7z - 15$.   [84] $6t^2 - 17t + 10$.

85. If $x + 2$ is a factor of $x^2 + ax + 10$, what is the other factor?
Hence find a.

86. Find b if $x + 3$ is a factor of $x^2 + bx - 12$.

87. Find c if $x - 6$ is a factor of $x^2 + cx + 30$.

[88] Find a if $x - 4$ is a factor of $x^2 + ax - 4$.

[89] Find b if $x - 3$ is a factor of $x^2 + bx - 9$.

90. Find c if $x + 4$ is a factor of $x^2 + 7x + c$.

91. Find a if $x + 2$ is a factor of $x^2 - 5x + a$.

92. Find b if $2x - 3$ is a factor of $6x^2 + bx - 12$.

Factorise:

*93. $-6 + 5x - x^2$.   *94. $-y^2 + 6y - 5$.

*95. $-16 + 8z - z^2$.   *96. $7ab - a^2 - 10b^2$.

*97. $17cd - 3d^2 - 10c^2$.   *98. $24pq - 9p^2 - 16q^2$.

Long Multiplication and Division

Example 27.   Multiply $2x^3 - 4x^2 + 2x + 3$ by $3x^2 - x - 5$.

$$
\begin{array}{l}
2x^3 - 4x^2 + 2x + 3 \\
3x^2 - x - 5 \\
\hline
6x^5 - 12x^4 + 6x^3 + 9x^2 \\
 - 2x^4 + 4x^3 - 2x^2 - 3x \\
 - 10x^3 + 20x^2 - 10x - 15 \\
\hline
\mathbf{6x^5 - 14x^4 + 27x^2 - 13x - 15}
\end{array}
$$

Example 28.   Multiply $a^2 - ab + b^2$ by $a^2 + ab + b^2$.

$$
\begin{array}{l}
a^2 - ab + b^2 \\
a^2 + ab + b^2 \\
\hline
a^4 - a^3b + a^2b^2 \\
 + a^3b - a^2b^2 + ab^3 \\
 + a^2b^2 - ab^3 + b^4 \\
\hline
\mathbf{a^4 + a^2b^2 + b^4}
\end{array}
$$

Example 29.   Divide $3x^3 + 5x^2 - 14x + 4$ by $x + 3$.

First Method : *Inverse Multiplication.*

Fill in the blank spaces in the following:

$$3x^3 + 5x^2 - 14x + 4 = (x + 3)(\ldots\ldots) + \ldots\ldots$$

$(x + 3) \cdot 3x^2 = 3x^3 + 9x^2$; but we want $5x^2$ instead of $9x^2$, so we must arrange for a term, $-4x^2$.

$(x + 3)(3x^2 - 4x) = 3x^3 + 5x^2 - 12x$; but we want $-14x$ instead of $-12x$, so we must arrange for a term, $-2x$.

$(x + 3)(3x^2 - 4x - 2) = 3x^3 + 5x^2 - 14x - 6$; but we want $+4$ instead of -6, so we add 10 to each side.

$\therefore$ $(x + 3)(3x^2 - 4x - 2) + 10 = 3x^3 + 5x^2 - 14x + 4$.

$\therefore$ the quotient is $\mathbf{3x^2 - 4x - 2}$, and the remainder is **10.**

Second Method : *The Arithmetical Process.*

$$
\begin{array}{r}
\mathbf{3x^2 -\ 4x - 2} \\
x + 3{\overline{)3x^3 + 5x^2 - 14x + 4}} \\
\underline{3x^3 + 9x^2} \\
-4x^2 - 14x \\
\underline{-4x^2 - 12x} \\
-\ 2x + 4 \\
\underline{-\ 2x - 6} \\
\underline{10}
\end{array}
$$

Note.   The second method is a short-hand form of writing down the argument used in the first method.

Example 30.   Divide $a^3 + b^3$ by $a + b$.

$$
\begin{array}{r}
a^2\ -ab\ +b^2 \\
a + b{\overline{)a^3\ +b^3}} \\
\underline{a^3 + a^2b} \\
-a^2b \\
\underline{-a^2b - ab^2} \\
ab^2 + b^3 \\
\underline{ab^2 + b^3}
\end{array}
$$

$\therefore$ the quotient is $\mathbf{a^2 - ab + b^2}$, and there is no remainder.

From Example 30, we see that

$$a^3 + b^3 = (a + b)(a^2 - ab + b^2).$$

Similarly it can be proved that

$$a^3 - b^3 = (a - b)(a^2 + ab + b^2).$$

These results are given in Ch. XIII; examples on factorising the sum and difference of two cubes are given on pp. 286, 287.

EXERCISE IX. m

Find the products of the following:

1. $x^2 + 3x - 1$, $x - 4$.　　　　　2. $a^2 + ab + b^2$, $a - b$.

3. $x^2 + x + 1$, $x^2 - x + 1$.　　　4. $2y^2 - y + 3$, $2y^2 + y - 1$.

[5] $3z^2 - z + 4$, $2z - 1$.　　　　[6] $a^2 + 2ab + b^2$, $a - b$.

[7] $3x^2 - x - 2$, $x^2 + 2x + 3$.　　[8] $2y^2 + 3y - 1$, $2y^2 - 3y - 1$.

9. $x^2 + 2xy + y^2$, $x^2 - 2xy + y^2$.　10. $a - 2b + 3c$, $a + 2b - 3c$.

[11] $a^4 - a^2b^2 + b^4$, $a^2 + b^2$.　　[12] $x + y + z$, $x - y + z$.

Divide:

13. $x^3 + x^2 - 5x - 6$ by $x + 2$.　　14. $6x^3 + 5x^2 - 3x - 2$ by $3x - 2$.

[15] $2x^3 - 5x^2 + x + 2$ by $x - 1$.　[16] $6x^3 + x^2 - 9x - 4$ by $2x + 1$.

17. $3y^3 + 4y^2 - 17y - 9$ by $y + 3$.

[18] $8z^3 + 14z^2 - 23z - 6$ by $4z - 3$.

19. $a^3 - b^3$ by $a - b$.　　　　20. $x^3 - 3x^2y + 3xy^2 - y^3$ by $x - y$.

[21] $x^3 + 8y^3$ by $x + 2y$.　　[22] $a^4 - 3a^3b + 2b^4$ by $a - b$.

23. $x^4 + x^3 - 8x^2 - 11x - 3$ by $x^2 - 2x - 3$.

24. $10y^4 + 11y^3 - 2y^2 - 13y - 6$ by $2y^2 + 3y + 2$.

25. $2z^4 - 9z^3 - 9z^2 - 13z + 6$ by $z^2 - 5z - 3$.

[26] $6a^4 + a^3 - 16a^2 + 8$ by $3a^2 + 2a - 4$.

[27] $6b^4 + 15b^3 - 17b^2 - 20b + 12$ by $2b^2 + 5b - 3$.

[28] $10c^4 - c^3 + 13c^2 - 14c + 2$ by $5c^2 - 3c - 2$.

29. $a^4 + a^2b^2 + b^4$ by $a^2 - ab + b^2$.　　[30] $x^6 + y^6$ by $x^2 + y^2$.

31. $8x^4 + x$ by $4x^2 - 2x + 1$.　　　　[32] $z^4 - z$ by $z^2 + z + 1$.

REVISION EXERCISE R. 5 (Ch. IX)

Expand the following:

1. $(r+4)(s-3)$.   2. $(3-2c)(2+3d)$.   3. $(3x-7y)^2$.
4. $(4p-5q)(4p+5q)$.   5. $(t-1)(1-t)$.   6. $(3z+\frac{1}{2})^2$.
[7] $(1-a)(1+b)$.   [8] $(2c+5d)^2$.   [9] $(2-3n)(2n-1)$.

Write down the coefficient of x^2 and the constant term in the expansions of the following products:

10. $(3x-1)(2x^2-x-4)$.   11. $(6x-x^2-1)(6+x)$.
[12] $(3+2x-5x^2)(4+3x)$.   [13] $(2x+7)(4x-3x^2-2)$.

Find the products of the following expressions:

14. $y^2+2y+1,\ y+1$.   [15] $z^2+z+1,\ z-1$.
16. $2a^2-3a-5,\ 3a+2$.   [17] $3b^2-2bc-c^2,\ 2b-3c$.
18. $2x^2-7xy-5y^2,\ 4x+3y$.   [19] $3ab-2a^2-4b^2,\ 3b+2a$.

20. If $x+4y=1$, express $x^2+6xy+10y^2+y-3x+2$ in terms of y only.

Divide:

21. x^3-5x^2+7x-2 by $x-2$.   [22] $y^3+4y^2-4y-21$ by $y+3$.
23. $4y^3+2y^2z-14yz^2+15z^3$ by $2y+5z$.
[24] $a^3-6a^2b+18ab^2-27b^3$ by $a-3b$.
25. $x^4+20x-21$ by x^2+2x-3.
26. $6y^4-11y^3-49y^2+18y+8$ by $2y^2-7y-2$.
[27] $27a^3-b^3$ by $3a-b$.   [28] $8x^3+125y^3$ by $2x+5y$.

29. Find the quotient and remainder when x^3-1 is divided by x^2+2x+1, and *deduce* the quotient and remainder when 999 is divided by 121.

Copy and complete the following:

30. $b^2-5bc\ldots=(\ldots.)^2$.   31. $d^2+d\ldots=(\ldots.)^2$.
[32] $n^2+16n\ldots=(\ldots.)^2$.   [33] $9p^2-5p\ldots=(\ldots.)^2$.

34. If a, b, c, d, e are consecutive integers, prove that $ae+c^2=ad+be$.

Factorise:

35. $36 - a^2$.   **36.** $b^2 - 12b + 36$.   **37.** $c^4 - 25c^2$.

[38] $1 - 4d^2$.   **[39]** $4e^2 + 20e + 25$.   **[40]** $3f^2 - 12$.

41. $ap + cp - cd - ad$.   **42.** $6ac - 2ad + 3bd - 9bc$.

43. $xy + xz - y - z$.   **44.** $t^3 + t^2 - t - 1$.

[45] $b^2 + bd + bc + cd$.   **[46]** $a^2 - ab - a + b$.

[47] $x^2 - xz + yz - xy$.   **[48]** $py - 6 + 3p - 2y$.

49. $a^2 - 3a - 4$.   **50.** $b^2 + 4b - 21$.   **51.** $1 - 11c + 24c^2$.

52. $3d^2 + 5d - 2$.   **53.** $3f^2 + 9f - 30$.   **54.** $4k^2 + 12k - 72$.

55. $3r^2 + rs - 2s^2$.   **56.** $3 - 3m - 36m^2$.   **57.** $3 - 5n^2 - 12n^4$.

[58] $p^2 - 7p + 12$.   **[59]** $2t^2 + t - 6$.   **[60]** $12x^2 - x - 6$.

[61] $1 - 2y - 15y^2$.   **[62]** $10a^2 - 19ab + 6b^2$.   **[63]** $15 + 14c - 8c^2$.

[64] $12d^2 + 32de + 5e^2$.   **[65]** $x^2 - (p - q)x - pq$.

[66] $16 - n^4$.   **67.** $(2a + b)(c + d) + c + d$.

68. $m - n + (n - m)^2$.   **69.** $a(x + y) - xy - a^2$.

70. $l^2 - 4(m - n)^2$.   **[71]** $1 + x^2 + xy + x^3y$.

[72] $(y + 1)^2 - (y + 1)(2y - 3)$.   **[73]** $(a - b)^2 + a^2 - ab$.

[74] $4(2c - 3)^2 - 9(c - 1)^2$.   **75.** $r^4 - 5r^2s^2 + 4s^4$.

[76] $y(6x - 3y) + yz - 2xz$.   **77.** $(3x - 5)(5x + 3) - (x + 4)(6x - 10)$.

[78] $a^2b^2 - abc - 156c^2$.   **79.** $(ac + bdx)^2 - x(ad + bc)^2$.

[80] $(a + b)^3 - (a - b)^3$.   **81.** $ab(c^2 + 1) - c(a^2 + b^2)$.

[82] $y(x^2 - y + 2) - (x^2 + y^2)$.   **83.** $(x + 2y)^2 - 5(x + 2y) + 6$.

[84] $c^2 - 5c(d - e) - 6(d - e)^2$.   **85.** $a^2x^2 + 2abx + b^2 - c^2$.

[86] $y^2 + 2ay - c^2 - 2ac$.   **87.** $x(x - 2) - y(y - 2)$.

[88] $c^2 + 12ab - 4a^2 - 9b^2$.

89. Factorise $20y^2 + 17y + 3$ and *deduce* the factors of 2173 and of 201703.

[90] If $x = p - 2q$ and $y = 2p - q$, prove that
$$x^2 - 2xy + y^2 = p^2 + 2pq + q^2.$$

91. Express $(5x^2 + 14x + 13)^2 - 16(x^2 + x - 2)^2$ as the product of four factors.

92. Simplify $(x^2 - 3x + 2)(x^2 - 2x - 3) \div (x^2 - 1)$.

[**93**] Simplify:

$$(2a^2 - 19ab + 35b^2)(2a^2 - 13ab + 15b^2) \div (4a^2 - 16ab + 15b^2).$$

94. Find the square root of

$$(a^2 + 2a - 15)(a^2 + 3a - 10)(a^2 - 5a + 6).$$

[**95**] Divide $(3x^2 - 2x + 4)^2 - (2x^2 + x - 1)^2$ by $x^2 - 3x + 5$.

96. What is the expression of lowest degree by which $(x^2 + 3x - 10)(x^2 + x - 20)$ must be multiplied to give a perfect square?

[**97**] Is $a^2 + 2$ a factor of $a^4 + 4$?

[**98**] Find the value of c if $x - 2$ is a factor of $x^2 + cx - 10$.

99. Complete the relation, $a^4 + a^2b^2 + b^4 = (a^2 + b^2)^2 - (\ldots)^2$, and hence factorise $a^4 + a^2b^2 + b^4$.

100. Find the numerical value of c if $xy - 3x + 5y + c$ has factors.

CHAPTER X

QUADRATIC EQUATIONS

Statements as Equations

IF all we know about two expressions, A and B, is that $A \cdot B = 5$, it is impossible to find the value of either, unless we know the value of the other.

But if $$A \cdot B = 0,$$

we know that **either** $A = 0$ or $B = 0$, because the product of two numbers is zero if, and only if, one of them is zero.

Example 1. What can be said about the value of x, if
$$x(2x - 3) = 0?$$

Since the product of x and $2x - 3$ is zero, one of the numbers x and $2x - 3$ must be zero.

$$\therefore \ x = 0 \ or \ 2x - 3 = 0; \qquad \therefore \ x = 0 \ or \ 2x = 3;$$
$$\therefore \ x = 0 \ or \ \frac{3}{2}.$$

Check: If $x = 0$, $x(2x - 3) = 0(-3) = 0$.

If $x = \frac{3}{2}$, $x(2x - 3) = \frac{3}{2}(3 - 3) = \frac{3}{2} \times 0 = 0$.

Do not say $x = 0$ *and* $x = \frac{3}{2}$, because x cannot equal both 0 and $\frac{3}{2}$ at the same time.

Example 2. Combine into a single statement:
$$\text{Either } y = 3 \text{ or } y = -\tfrac{1}{2}.$$

Either $y = 3$ or $2y = -1$; either $y - 3 = 0$ or $2y + 1 = 0$.

$$\therefore \text{ in either case, } (y - 3)(2y + 1) = 0;$$
$$\therefore \ 2y^2 - 5y - 3 = 0.$$

EXERCISE X. a (Oral)

1. If $x = 2$, what is the value of $(x - 2)(x + 10)$?

[2] If $y = 5$, what is the value of $(y + 3)(y - 5)$?

3. If $z = 0$, what is the value of $z(2z + 3)$?

4. If $xy = 0$ and $x = 3$, what is y?

[5] If $xy = 0$ and $y = 0$, what can you say about the value of x?

219

6. If $xy = 1$, can you say anything about the numerical value of x?

7. What conclusion can be drawn from $(a - b)x = 0$?

8. If $(y - 3)(z - 2) = 0$, what do you know about z (i) if $y = 2$, (ii) if $y = 100$, (iii) if $y = 3$?

[9] What conclusion can be drawn from the equation $(x - 5)(y + 3) = 0$?

[10] If $\dfrac{x + 1}{y + 2} = 0$, can you say anything about the value (i) of x, (ii) of y?

11. What conclusion can you draw if $(x - 5)(x + 3) = 0$? What do you get if you multiply out?

12. Combine into a single statement: Either $x = 2$ or $x = 4$. Multiply out the result.

13. Combine into single statements the following, and multiply out each result:

(i) Either $x = -2$ or $x = -5$;   (ii) Either $x = -3$ or $x = 4$;
(iii) $y = \pm 7$;   (iv) Either $y = 6$ or $y = 0$;
(v) Either $t = 0$ or $t = -8$;   (vi) Either $x = 2$ or $x = 3$ or $x = -1$.

14. What conclusion can you draw if $(3x - 2)(2x + 5) = 0$? What do you get if you multiply out?

15. Combine into single statements, free from fractions, the following, and multiply out each result:

(i) Either $x = \frac{1}{2}$ or $x = \frac{2}{3}$;   (ii) Either $y = -\frac{1}{4}$ or $y = \frac{3}{5}$;
(iii) Either $z = -\frac{3}{4}$ or $z = -\frac{2}{7}$;   (iv) Either $x = 0$ or $x = -\frac{2}{5}$.

Solve the following equations:

16. $(x - 3)(x - 7) = 0$.   **17.** $(y + 4)(y - 5) = 0$.
18. $(t + 7)(t + 2) = 0$.   **19.** $z(z - 10) = 0$.
20. $(x - 3)^2 = 0$.   **21.** $(t + 5)^2 = 0$.
[22] $(y + 1)(y + 2) = 0$.   **[23]** $n(n + 4) = 0$.
[24] $5x^2 = 0$.   **[25]** $5(y - 2)(y + 8) = 0$.
26. $(2z - 1)(3z - 5) = 0$.   **[27]** $(3p + 1)(p + 3) = 0$.
28. $7(x - 7)(4x - 3) = 0$.   **[29]** $5(5t + 2)(5t - 3) = 0$.
30. $6x(3x + 7) = 0$.   **[31]** $(n - 2)(n - 5)(n + 8) = 0$.
32. $r(r + 3)(r - 6) = 0$.   **[33]** $y^2(y + 4) = 0$.
34. $4x(x - 4)^2 = 0$.   **[35]** $2z(2z + 1)(3z - 10) = 0$.

Solution by Factors

Example 3.   Solve $x^2 = 25$.

First Method. $x^2 - 25 = 0$; $\therefore$ $(x+5)(x-5) = 0$;

$\therefore$ either $x + 5 = 0$ or $x - 5 = 0$;

$\therefore$ $x = -5$ *or* 5.

Second Method. $x^2 = 25$.

Take the square root of each side; the square root of 25 is either $+5$ or -5 because $(+5)(+5) = 25$ and $(-5)(-5) = 25$;

$\therefore$ $x = 5$ or -5, as before.

The answer is usually written, $x = \pm 5$.

Example 4.   Solve $(x+3)(x-5) = 20$.

Multiply out, $\therefore$ $x^2 - 2x - 15 = 20$.

$\therefore$ $x^2 - 2x - 35 = 0$; $\therefore$ $(x-7)(x+5) = 0$;

$\therefore$ either $x - 7 = 0$ or $x + 5 = 0$;

$\therefore$ $x = 7$ *or* -5.

Check: If $x = 7$, $(x+3)(x-5) = 10 \times 2 = 20$.

If $x = -5$, $(x+3)(x-5) = (-2)(-10) = 20$.

Do not shorten this argument. If you leave out the step, "either $x - 7 = 0$ or $x + 5 = 0$," you may make mistakes in sign.

Example 5.   Solve $8x^2 + 6x = 9$.

$8x^2 + 6x - 9 = 0$; $\therefore$ $(2x+3)(4x-3) = 0$;

$\therefore$ either $2x + 3 = 0$ or $4x - 3 = 0$.

$\therefore$ $2x = -3$ or $4x = 3$;

$\therefore$ $x = -\frac{3}{2}$ *or* $\frac{3}{4}$.

Example 6.   Solve $4x^2 = 12x - 9$.

$4x^2 - 12x + 9 = 0$; $\therefore$ $(2x-3)^2 = 0$;

$\therefore$ $2x - 3 = 0$;

$\therefore$ $2x = 3$;

$\therefore$ $x = 1\frac{1}{2}$.

Each of the quadratic equations in Examples 3–5 has *two* distinct roots, but the quadratic equation in Example 6 is satisfied by only *one* value of x; it is convenient to say that this quadratic equation has *two equal roots* or that the root is $x = 1\frac{1}{2}$ (repeated), just as we say in geometry that a straight line which *touches* a circle meets it at "two coincident points."

EXERCISE X. b

Solve the following equations: check one answer of each.

1. $x^2 - 5x + 6 = 0$.   **2.** $x^2 + 5x + 6 = 0$.   **3.** $x^2 - 5x - 6 = 0$.

4. $x^2 + 5x - 6 = 0$.   **5.** $x^2 - x - 6 = 0$.   **6.** $x^2 + 4x - 5 = 0$.

7. $x^2 + 6x = 0$.   **8.** $x^2 - 9 = 0$.   **9.** $x^2 = 7x$.

10. $x^2 - 6x + 9 = 0$.   **11.** $x^2 + 10x + 25 = 0$. **12.** $x^2 = 1$.

[13] $x^2 - 3x + 2 = 0$.   [14] $x^2 + 3x + 2 = 0$.   [15] $x^2 + x - 12 = 0$.

[16] $x^2 + 9x + 14 = 0$. [17] $x^2 + 5x = 0$.   [18] $x^2 - 49 = 0$.

[19] $x^2 - 3x - 70 = 0$.   [20] $x^2 + 9x - 36 = 0$.

[21] $x^2 - 11x - 60 = 0$.   [22] $x^2 - 12x + 36 = 0$.

[23] $x^2 + 20x + 100 = 0$.   [24] $x^2 + x = 0$.

25. $x^2 - 3x = 10$.   **26.** $x^2 + 21 = 10x$.   **27.** $x^2 + 2x = 99$.

28. $2x^2 - 5x + 2 = 0$. **29.** $3x^2 + x - 2 = 0$. **30.** $4x^2 + 13x + 3 = 0$.

31. $2x^2 + 5 = 11x$.   **32.** $6x^2 = x + 2$.   **33.** $15x^2 + 2x = 8$.

34. $4x^2 + 1 = 4x$.   **35.** $9x^2 = 100$.   **36.** $9x^2 + 12x + 4 = 0$.

[37] $x^2 + 2x = 24$.   [38] $x(x - 1) = 72$.   [39] $x^2 + 49 = 14x$.

[40] $2x^2 - 7x + 6 = 0$. [41] $6x^2 - 7x - 3 = 0$. [42] $3x^2 + 8x - 3 = 0$.

[43] $6x^2 = 11x + 7$.   [44] $4x^2 = 6x$.   [45] $2x^2 + x = 15$.

[46] $9x^2 + 25 = 30x$.   [47] $6x^2 + 6 = 13x$.   [48] $20x^2 = 7x + 6$.

49. $(x + 1)(x + 2) = 30$.   **50.** $(2x - 1)(x - 2) = 5$.

51. $(2x - 1)(1 + 3x) = 4$.   **52.** $(2x + 1)^2 = 7(2x + 1)$.

53. $(x - 3)^2 = 25$. **54.** $(3x + 7)^2 = 1$. **55.** $x^2 + \frac{1}{4} = x$.

[56] $(x - 3)(x + 2) = 14$.   [57] $(3x + 1)(2x + 3) = 3$.

[58] $(3x + 4)^2 = 7(3x + 4)$.   [59] $(4x - 5)^2 = 49$.

[60] $(x + 8)(x - 3) = 3x$.   [61] $(x - 1)^2 + (x + 3)^2 = 26$.

62. $(2x + 1)^2 = (2x + 7)^2$.   **63.** $(2x + 1)^2 = (3x + 2)^2$.

*64. $x + 1 = \dfrac{6}{x}$.   *65. $x + 2 = \dfrac{28}{x - 1}$.   *66. $x^3 = 9x$.

*67. $(x + 1)(x + 2)(x + 3) = 15(x + 2)$.   *68. $x^3 - x = 6(x - 1)$.

*69. $x^2 - cx = 0$; find x.   *70. $y^2 - b^2 = 0$; find y.

*71. $x^2 = px + qx$; find x.   *72. $y^2 + ay = 6a^2$; find y.

*73. Find x in terms of y if $x^2 - 6xy + 8y^2 = 0$.

*74. Find x and y if $y = x(x - 2)$ and $y = 3(x + 2)$.

*75. Find x and y if $xy = 21$ and $y = x + 4$.

The Sum and Product of the Roots

Form the equation whose roots are 3 and 5.
Either $x = 3$ or $x = 5$; either $x - 3 = 0$ or $x - 5 = 0$;

$$\therefore \text{ in either case, } (x - 3)(x - 5) = 0;$$
$$\therefore x^2 - 8x + 15 = 0.$$

Here, the sum of the roots, 5 and 3, equals *the coefficient of x with the sign changed*; and the product of the roots equals *the constant term*.

This holds for any quadratic equation, if all the terms are brought to one side and if the coefficient of x^2 is $+1$.

Form the equation whose roots are e, f.
Either $x = e$ or $x = f$; either $x - e = 0$ or $x - f = 0$;

$$\therefore \text{ in either case, } (x - e)(x - f) = 0;$$
$$\therefore x^2 - ex - fx + ef = 0;$$
$$\therefore x^2 - (e + f)x + ef = 0.$$

$\therefore$ *if the coefficient of x^2 is $+1$, and if all terms are brought to one side of the equation,*

(i) the sum of the roots, $e + f$, = the coefficient of x with the sign changed.

(ii) the product of the roots, ef, = the constant term.

This gives a useful method for checking answers.

Example 7. Solve $2x^2 = x + 10$.

$$2x^2 - x - 10 = 0; \quad \therefore (2x - 5)(x + 2) = 0;$$
$$\therefore \text{ either } 2x - 5 = 0 \text{ or } x + 2 = 0;$$
$$\therefore x = 2\tfrac{1}{2} \text{ or } - 2.$$

Check: First make the coefficient of x^2 unity, and bring all the terms to one side.

$$x^2 = \tfrac{1}{2}x + 5; \quad \therefore x^2 - \tfrac{1}{2}x - 5 = 0.$$

Sum of roots = coefficient of x with sign changed = $+\tfrac{1}{2}$, and product of roots = constant term = -5.

But sum of roots = $2\tfrac{1}{2} - 2 = \tfrac{1}{2}$,
and product of roots = $2\tfrac{1}{2} \times (-2) = -5$.

General Statement. If the quadratic equation is

$$ax^2 + bx + c = 0,$$

divide throughout by a, then $x^2 + \dfrac{b}{a}x + \dfrac{c}{a} = 0.$

Hence

$$\text{The sum of the roots} \quad = -\frac{b}{a}.$$

$$\text{The product of the roots} = \frac{c}{a}.$$

EXERCISE X. c

What are the roots of the following equations? Multiply out and verify the relations between the sum and product of the roots and the coefficients.

1. $(x-2)(x-3)=0.$ 2. $(x+1)(x-5)=0.$ 3. $(x-5)(x+5)=0.$

4. $(x+3)(x+3)=0.$ 5. $(2x-1)(x+3)=0.$

6. $(3x+2)(x+2)=0.$ [7] $(x+2)(x+4)=0.$

[8] $(x+7)(x-2)=0.$ [9] $(2x-5)(3x-4)=0.$

Solve the following equations, and check your answers by finding the sum and product of the roots:

10. $x^2-8x+12=0.$ 11. $x^2+12x+35=0.$ 12. $x^2+5x=24.$

13. $x^2-8x=9.$ 14. $2x^2-3x+1=0.$ 15. $2x^2+5x=12.$

16. $x^2=16.$ 17. $9x^2+6x+1=0.$ 18. $6x^2=5x+6.$

[19] $x^2-3x-28=0.$ [20] $x^2+x=20.$ [21] $3x^2+5=8x.$

[22] $4x^2+5x=6.$ [23] $x^2=8x.$ [24] $3x^2+2x=5.$

Write down the sum and the product of the roots of the following equations; check by solving.

25. $x^2+10x+21=0.$ 26. $x^2+18=9x.$

27. $x^2+6x=27.$ 28. $2x^2-x=3.$

29. $4x^2+3x=10.$ 30. $5-x-6x^2=0.$

[31] $x^2+6x-16=0.$ [32] $x^2-6x=40.$

[33] $x^2-55=6x.$ [34] $3x^2=2x+8.$

[35] $16x=4x^2+15.$ [36] $x+2=6x^2.$

*37. Show that $x=1$ satisfies $x^2+99x-100=0.$ What is the sum of the roots? What is the other root?

*38. One root of $x^2 - 5x - 12 = 0$ is $x = 6 \cdot 77$ correct to 2 places of decimals. Assuming this fact, *write down* the other root correct to 2 places of decimals.

*39. What is the product of the roots of $x^2 + bx - 28 = 0$? If $x = 4$ is one root, what is the other? Hence state the value of b.

*40. What is the sum of the roots of $3x^2 - 5x + c = 0$? If $x = 2$ is one root, what is the other? Hence state the value of c.

*41. Form the equations whose roots are

(i) $+5, +7$; (ii) $-3, +8$; (iii) $4c, -3c$.

*42. Invent an equation such that the sum of its roots is 19 and the product of its roots is 60.

*43. Invent an equation such that the sum of its roots is $2\frac{1}{2}$ and the product of its roots is $-1\frac{1}{3}$.

*44. Prove that one root of the equation $6x^2 - 25x - 1 = 0$ is greater than 4, *without* solving the equation.

*45. If $a^2 - b^2 = 2(a - b)^2$ and if a, b are unequal, find a in terms of b.

*46. If $(p - 1)(p - 2) = (q - 1)(q - 2)$ and if p, q are unequal, find p in terms of q.

Graphical Solution

The use of graphs in solving equations has been illustrated in Ch. VIII; the next two exercises provide further practice.

Example 8. Draw the graph of $2x^2 - 7x - 2$ for values of x from -1 to 4.

When making a table of values, work by rows.

First take the values $x = -1$, 0, 1, 2, 3, 4; write above the table the values of x^2 to help you to find $2x^2$.

When these values have been plotted, it becomes clear that the graph can be drawn more accurately if the value, $x = 1.5$, is added to the table; add this at the end.

x^2	1	0	1	4	9	16	2·25
x	-1	0	1	2	3	4	1·5
$2x^2$	2	0	2	8	18	32	4·5
$-7x$	7	0	-7	-14	-21	-28	$-10·5$
$2x^2 - 7x - 2$	7	-2	-7	-8	-5	2	-8

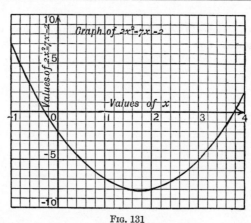

Fig. 131

The required graph is shown in Fig. 131.

The various uses that can be made of this graph are indicated in Ex. X. *d.*

EXERCISE X. d (Oral)

Use Fig. 131 *to answer the following questions, Nos.* 1–11.

1. What is approximately the value of $2x^2 - 7x - 2$ when $x = 0\cdot4$, $1\cdot2$, $2\cdot5$, $2\cdot8$, $3\cdot5$, $3\cdot9$, $-0\cdot5$, $-0\cdot9$?

2. What is the least value of $2x^2 - 7x - 2$? For what value of x is $2x^2 - 7x - 2$ least?

3. State approximately the values of x for which $2x^2 - 7x - 2$ is equal to (i) 2, (ii) 1, (iii) -2, (iv) 0, (v) -5, (vi) -6.

4. For what value of x is $2x^2 - 7x - 2$ equal to 5? Is there more than one answer? If so, why cannot you find it?

5. Is there a value of x for which $2x^2 - 7x - 2$ equals -10?

6. Can you draw a line up the paper about which the curve is symmetrical? Where will the line cut the x-axis?

7. For what values of x is $2x^2 - 7x - 2$ negative?

8. Solve graphically the equation, $2x^2 - 7x - 2 = 0$. Use the results on p. 224 to say what the sum and the product of the roots should be; then test the answers obtained from the graph.

9. Solve graphically the following equations, and find in each case the sum of the roots:

 (i) $2x^2 - 7x - 2 = 1$;   (ii) $2x^2 - 7x - 2 = -2$;

 (iii) $2x^2 - 7x - 2 = -6$; (iv) $2x^2 - 7x - 2 = 2$.

10. If $2x^2 - 7x + 5 = 0$, that is, if $2x^2 - 7x = -5$, find the value of $2x^2 - 7x - 2$. Hence solve graphically $2x^2 - 7x + 5 = 0$.

11. Solve, *where possible,* the following equations graphically:

 (i) $2x^2 - 7x = -1$;   (ii) $2x^2 - 7x = -4$;

 (iii) $2x^2 - 7x = 5$;   (iv) $2x^2 - 7x = 7$;

 (v) $2x^2 - 7x = -6$;   (vi) $2x^2 - 7x = -9$;

 (vii) $7x - 2x^2 = 3$;   (viii) $7x - 2x^2 + 6 = 0$.

EXERCISE X. e

[Throughout this exercise, use the statement on p. 224 about the sum of the roots of a quadratic equation, as a check.]

1. Draw the graph of $4x - x^2$ from $x = -1$ to $x = 5$, and solve graphically the following equations:

   (i) $4x - x^2 = 2$;   (ii) $4x - x^2 = -3$;   (iii) $4x - x^2 = 2\cdot5$;

(iv) $4x - x^2 = -1$; (v) $x^2 - 4x - 4 = 0$; (vi) $x^2 - 4x + 3 = 0$.

For what values of d has $4x - x^2 = d$ two roots?

2. Draw the graph of $y = x^2 - 5x + 6$ from $x = 0$ to $x = 5$.

What are the roots of the following equations?

        (i) $x^2 - 5x + 6 = 0$;   (ii) $x^2 - 5x + 1 = 0$;

       (iii) $x^2 - 5x + 3 = 0$;   (iv) $x^2 - 5x + 4 = 0$.

Has $x^2 - 5x + 6$ a greatest value or a least value, and how much is it?

3. Draw, on the same scale and axes used for No. 2, the graph of $y = x^2 - 5x + 8$ from $x = 0$ to $x = 5$. Use this graph to solve

   (i) $x^2 - 5x + 8 = 5$; (ii) $x^2 - 5x + 3 = 0$; (iii) $x^2 - 5x + 2 = 0$.

Is there a value of x for which $x^2 - 5x + 8 = 0$? What is the least value of $x^2 - 5x + 8$?

[4] By drawing the graph of $y = x^2 + 4x$ from $x = -5$ to $x = 1$, solve, *where possible,* the equations:

        (i) $x^2 + 4x = 1$;   (ii) $x^2 + 4x + 2 = 0$;

       (iii) $x^2 + 4x + 4 = 0$;   (iv) $x^2 + 4x + 5 = 0$.

[5] By drawing the graph of $y = 2x^2 - 3x$ from $x = -1$ to $x = 3$, solve, *where possible,* the equations:

        (i) $2x^2 - 3x = 3$;   (ii) $2x^2 - 3x + 1 = 0$;

      (iii) $2x^2 - 3x + 2 = 0$;   (iv) $10x^2 - 15x + 3 = 0$.

[6] Draw the graph of $7x - 4x^2$ from $x = -1$ to $x = 3$. Solve the following:

       (i) $7x - 4x^2 = 2$;   (ii) $7x - 4x^2 = -3$;

     (iii) $7x - 4x^2 + 10 = 0$;   (iv) $8x^2 - 14x = 11$.

What is the greatest value of $7x - 4x^2$?

What can you say about the value of c if there is no value of x which satisfies the equation $7x - 4x^2 = c$?

7. By drawing the graph of $y = 3x^2 - 5x$ from $x = -1$ to $x = 3$, solve, *where possible*, the equations:

(i) $3x^2 - 5x = 2$; (ii) $3x^2 - 5x + 1 = 0$;
(iii) $3x^2 - 5x + 2 = 0$; (iv) $3x^2 - 5x + 3 = 0$;
(v) $6x^2 - 10x + 1 = 0$; (vi) $9x^2 - 15x = 4$.

8. Draw the graph of $y = x^2$ from $x = -2$ to $x = +2$.

(i) Draw with the same scale and axes the graph of $y = x + 1$ and solve the equation $x^2 = x + 1$.

(ii) Draw with the same scale and axes the graph of $y = \frac{1}{2}x + 2$. State what quadratic equation can be solved from this figure and solve it.

(iii) Repeat (ii) with the graph of $y = \frac{1}{3}(5x - 2)$.

(iv) Draw also the graph of $y = x - 1$. What can you say about the equation $x^2 = x - 1$?

9. Draw the graph of $y = x^2$ from $x = -2$ to $x = +2$. By drawing on the same diagram suitable straight-line graphs, solve

(i) $x^2 = \frac{1}{2}(x + 1)$; (ii) $2x^2 = 3x + 1$;
(iii) $2x^2 + x - 4 = 0$; (iv) $4x^2 + 3x = 2$.

*10. Draw the graph of $y = x + \dfrac{12}{x} - 6$ from $x = 1 \cdot 5$ to $x = 8$.

(i) Solve (a) $x + \dfrac{12}{x} - 6 = 1 \cdot 5$; (b) $x + \dfrac{12}{x} = 9$.

(ii) Find the least value of $x + \dfrac{12}{x}$ when x is positive.

(iii) Use the same graph to solve $x^2 + 12 = 8 \cdot 5x$.

*11. Draw the graphs of $y = \dfrac{x^2 + 4}{x + 1}$ for values of x from 0 to 4.

(i) What is the least positive value of $\dfrac{x^2 + 4}{x + 1}$? (ii) Use the graph to solve the equation $x^2 + 4 = 3(x + 1)$. (iii) What is the value of y if $2x^2 = 5x - 3$? Hence solve this equation by means of the graph; solve also by calculation.

*12. Draw the graphs of $y = \dfrac{x^2}{x + 3}$ and $y = 1 - \frac{1}{2}x$ for values of x from -2 to $+6$. What is the quadratic equation whose roots are given by the intersections of the two graphs? Obtain its roots graphically.

Solution by " Completing the Square "

The process of "completing the square" of a quadratic function has been explained on pp. 202, 203.

Thus $x^2 + 6x$ becomes a perfect square if we add 3^2 to it,

$$x^2 + 6x + 3^2 = (x+3)^2;$$

$x^2 - 7x$ becomes a perfect square if we add $(\frac{1}{2}$ of $7)^2$ to it,

$$x^2 - 7x + (\tfrac{7}{2})^2 = (x - \tfrac{7}{2})^2.$$

In general, $x^2 + bx$ becomes a perfect square if we add $(\frac{1}{2}b)^2$ to it,

$$x^2 + bx + (\tfrac{1}{2}b)^2 = (x + \tfrac{1}{2}b)^2.$$

Example 9.   Solve $x^2 + 6x = 27$.

Add 3^2 to each side, $x^2 + 6x + 3^2 = 27 + 9;$

$$\therefore \ (x+3)^2 = 36.$$

Take the square root of each side: the square root of 36 is *either* $+6$ *or* -6.

$$\therefore \ x + 3 = +6 \quad \text{or} \quad x + 3 = -6;$$
$$\therefore \ x = 3 \quad \text{or} \quad -9.$$

For this equation it is quicker, and therefore better, to use the method of solution by factors:

$$x^2 + 6x - 27 = 0; \quad \therefore \ (x-3)(x+9) = 0;$$
$$\therefore \ x - 3 = 0 \quad \text{or} \quad x + 9 = 0;$$
$$\therefore \ x = 3 \quad \text{or} \quad -9.$$

EXERCISE X. f

Solve the following equations, using where necessary the following approximate square roots:

$$\sqrt{2} \simeq 1\cdot41, \quad \sqrt{3} \simeq 1\cdot73, \quad \sqrt{5} \simeq 2\cdot24, \quad \sqrt{10} \simeq 3\cdot16.$$

1. $(x-5)^2 = 9$.   2. $(x+3)^2 = 25$.   3. $(x-3)^2 = \frac{4}{9}$.

4. $(x-2)^2 = 3$.   5. $(x+3)^2 = 10$.   6. $(x-\frac{3}{2})^2 = 9$.

[7] $(x-4)^2 = 1$.   [8] $(x+1)^2 = \frac{1}{4}$.   [9] $(x-2)^2 = 2\frac{1}{4}$.

[10] $(x+1)^2 = 2$.   [11] $(x+\frac{1}{2})^2 = 4$.   [12] $(x-\frac{5}{2})^2 = 6\frac{1}{4}$.

13. $(x+\frac{4}{3})^2 = \frac{49}{9}$.   14. $(x-\frac{1}{2})^2 = \frac{5}{4}$.   15. $(x+\frac{1}{3})^2 = \frac{10}{9}$.

[16] $(x-\frac{3}{4})^2 = \frac{25}{16}$.   [17] $(x+\frac{2}{5})^2 = \frac{16}{25}$.   [18] $(x+\frac{3}{4})^2 = \frac{5}{8}$.

The method of " completing the square " should only be used when no simple factors can be found, as in the next two examples.

Example 10. Solve $x^2 - 7x - 5 = 0$.

$$x^2 - 7x = 5;$$

Add to each side $\left(\frac{7}{2}\right)^2$, $\therefore x^2 - 7x + \left(\frac{7}{2}\right)^2 = 5 + \frac{49}{4};$

$$\therefore \left(x - \frac{7}{2}\right)^2 = \frac{20 + 49}{4} = \frac{69}{4};$$

Take the square root of each side,

$$\therefore x - \frac{7}{2} = \pm \frac{\sqrt{69}}{2};$$

$$\therefore x = \frac{7}{2} + \frac{\sqrt{69}}{2} \quad \text{or} \quad x = \frac{7}{2} - \frac{\sqrt{69}}{2}.$$

To find the values of the roots to (say) 2 places of decimals, we find the square root of 69 to 3 places of decimals; $\sqrt{69} = 8 \cdot 307$.

$$\therefore x = \frac{7}{2} + \frac{8 \cdot 307}{2} = \frac{7 + 8 \cdot 307}{2} = \frac{15 \cdot 307}{2} = 7 \cdot 65$$

or $$x = \frac{7}{2} - \frac{8 \cdot 307}{2} = \frac{7 - 8 \cdot 307}{2} = -\frac{1 \cdot 307}{2} = -0 \cdot 65.$$

$$\therefore x = 7 \cdot 65 \text{ or } -0 \cdot 65.$$

Check: The sum of the roots $\simeq 7 \cdot 65 + (-0 \cdot 65) = 7$, which is the coefficient of x with the sign changed.

The product of the roots $\simeq 7 \cdot 65 \times (-0 \cdot 65) \simeq -4 \cdot 97$, and this is, approximately, equal to the constant term.

The roots, $x = \frac{7}{2} + \frac{\sqrt{69}}{2}$ or $\frac{7}{2} - \frac{\sqrt{69}}{2}$, are usually written more shortly as $\frac{7 \pm \sqrt{69}}{2}$.

It is impossible to find any whole number or fraction whose square is exactly 69. The square root of 69 is therefore called an **irrational number**; and we call the roots of the equation, $x^2 - 7x - 5 = 0$, *irrational*. The roots of the equation, $8x^2 + 6x = 9$ (see Example 5, p. 221) are $\frac{3}{4}$, $-\frac{3}{2}$; we call the roots of this equation *rational*, because their *exact* values can be expressed as whole numbers or fractions, *i.e.* as the *ratios* of two integers.

Example 11. Solve $3x^2 + 11x + 4 = 0$, giving the roots correct to 2 places of decimals.

$$3x^2 + 11x = -4; \qquad \therefore x^2 + \frac{11}{3}x = -\frac{4}{3};$$

Add to each side $\left(\frac{11}{6}\right)^2$, $\qquad \therefore x^2 + \frac{11}{3}x + \left(\frac{11}{6}\right)^2 = -\frac{4}{3} + \frac{121}{36};$

$$\therefore \left(x + \frac{11}{6}\right)^2 = \frac{-48 + 121}{36} = \frac{73}{36};$$

Take the square root of each side,

$$\therefore x + \frac{11}{6} = \pm \frac{\sqrt{73}}{6};$$

$$\therefore x = -\frac{11}{6} + \frac{\sqrt{73}}{6} \quad \text{or} \quad -\frac{11}{6} - \frac{\sqrt{73}}{6}.$$

From the tables, $\sqrt{73} = 8 \cdot 544$,

$$\therefore x = \frac{-11 + 8 \cdot 544}{6} = -\frac{2 \cdot 456}{6} = -0 \cdot 41$$

or $\qquad x = \frac{-11 - 8 \cdot 544}{6} = -\frac{19 \cdot 544}{6} = -3 \cdot 26;$

$$\therefore x = -0 \cdot 41 \quad \text{or} \quad -3 \cdot 26, \text{ to 2 places of decimals.}$$

Example 12. Solve $7x^2 = 14x + 10$, giving the roots correct to 2 places of decimals.

$$7x^2 - 14x = 10; \qquad \therefore x^2 - 2x = \frac{10}{7};$$

$$\therefore x^2 - 2x + 1 = \frac{10}{7} + 1;$$

$$\therefore (x - 1)^2 = \frac{17}{7};$$

$$\therefore \ x - 1 = \pm \sqrt{\left(\frac{17}{7}\right)} \eqsim \pm \sqrt{2 \cdot 429};$$

$$\therefore \ x - 1 = \pm 1 \cdot 559;$$

$$\therefore \ x = 1 + 1 \cdot 559 = 2 \cdot 559,$$

or

$$x = 1 - 1 \cdot 559 = -0 \cdot 559.$$

$$\therefore \ x = 2 \cdot 56 \quad \text{or} \quad -0 \cdot 56, \text{ to 2 places of decimals.}$$

Note. An approximate value of $\sqrt{\left(\frac{17}{7}\right)}$ may also be found by saying $\sqrt{\left(\frac{17}{7}\right)} = \sqrt{\left(\frac{119}{49}\right)} = \frac{\sqrt{119}}{7} \eqsim \frac{10 \cdot 91}{7} \eqsim 1 \cdot 559.$ Either of these methods is *much shorter* than saying $\sqrt{\left(\frac{17}{7}\right)} = \frac{\sqrt{17}}{\sqrt{7}} \eqsim \frac{4 \cdot 123}{2 \cdot 646}$, and evaluating this fraction.

Example 13. If α and β are the roots of the equation $3x^2 + 11x + 4 = 0$, find the values of (i) $\dfrac{1}{\alpha} + \dfrac{1}{\beta}$; (ii) $\alpha^2 + \beta^2$.

Write the equation in the form, $x^2 + \frac{11}{3}x + \frac{4}{3} = 0$; then the sum of the roots is $-\frac{11}{3}$ and the product is $\frac{4}{3}$;

$$\therefore \ \alpha + \beta = -\tfrac{11}{3} \ . \qquad . \qquad . \qquad . \qquad (1)$$

and

$$\alpha\beta = \tfrac{4}{3} \qquad . \qquad . \qquad . \qquad . \qquad (2)$$

(i) $\dfrac{1}{\alpha} + \dfrac{1}{\beta} = \dfrac{\beta + \alpha}{\alpha\beta} = -\dfrac{11}{3} \div \dfrac{4}{3}$, from equations (1), (2),

$$= -\tfrac{11}{4} = -2\tfrac{3}{4}.$$

(ii) From equation (1), by squaring each side,

$$\alpha^2 + 2\alpha\beta + \beta^2 = \tfrac{121}{9},$$

also

$$2\alpha\beta = \tfrac{8}{3}, \text{ from equation (2);}$$

$$\therefore \text{ by subtraction,} \qquad \alpha^2 + \beta^2 = \tfrac{121}{9} - \tfrac{8}{3} = \tfrac{97}{9}$$

$$= 10\tfrac{7}{9}.$$

Note. This method is simpler than substituting the values of α and β which were found in Example 11.

EXERCISE X. g

What numbers must be added to the expressions in Nos. 1–8 to make the results perfect squares? Of what are they then the squares?

1. $x^2 - 10x$.　　2. $x^2 + 3x$.　　3. $x^2 - x$.　　4. $x^2 + \frac{6}{7}x$.

5. $x^2 - \frac{7}{9}x$.　　[6] $x^2 - 5x$.　　[7] $x^2 + \frac{10}{3}x$.　　[8] $x^2 - \frac{11}{5}x$.

The equations in Nos. 9–17 have rational roots. First solve them by completing the square, and then solve by the direct factor method. Which method is the easier? Check your answers also by calculating the sum and the product of the roots.

9. $x^2 - 6x = 40$.　　10. $x^2 + 5x = 14$.　　11. $x^2 + x = 12$.

[12] $x^2 - 10x + 21 = 0$.　　[13] $x^2 + 3x = 10$.　　[14] $x^2 - 7x = 18$.

15. $3x^2 + 2x = 8$.　　16. $2x^2 - x = 6$.　　[17] $3x^2 - 4x = 15$.

In solving the following equations, **use the direct factor method whenever it is easier to do so.** If the roots are not rational, give each root correct to two places of decimals.

18. $x^2 = 3$.　　19. $2x^2 = 3$.　　20. $x^2 + 2x = 5$.

21. $x^2 - 2x = 5$.　　22. $x^2 + 6x = 0$.　　23. $x^2 - 10x + 15 = 0$.

24. $x^2 - 2x = 8$.　　25. $x^2 + 20x = 33$.　　26. $x^2 + 14x + 33 = 0$.

27. $x^2 - 8x = 0$.　　28. $x^2 + 16x = 17$.　　29. $x^2 - 16x = 10$.

[30] $7x^2 = 5$.　　[31] $x^2 + 6x = 8$.　　[32] $x^2 - 6x = 16$.

[33] $x^2 - 6x = 12$.　　[34] $x^2 - 12x = 0$.　　[35] $x^2 - 12x + 36 = 0$.

36. $x^2 + 3x = 2$.　　37. $x^2 - 7x + 9 = 0$.　　38. $x^2 - 7x = 30$.

39. $x^2 + x = 8$.　　40. $x^2 + x = 0$.　　41. $x^2 - x = 12$.

[42] $x^2 - 5x = 3$.　　[43] $x^2 + 5x = 24$.　　[44] $x^2 - x = 1$.

[45] $x^2 + 9x + 8 = 0$.　　[46] $x^2 + 15 = 9x$.　　[47] $x^2 + 9x = 0$.

48. $3x^2 + 4x = 2$.　　49. $5x^2 - 8x + 2 = 0$.　　50. $3x^2 + 5x = 2$.

51. $2x^2 + 7x = 3$.　　52. $2x^2 - 5x = 1$.　　53. $3x^2 + x = 2$.

54. $2x^2 - 4x = 5$.　　55. $3x^2 + 12x = 10$.　　56. $5x^2 = 30x + 18$.

[57] $3x^2 - 2x = 2$.　　[58] $3x^2 - 2x = 1$.　　[59] $2x^2 + 3x = 4$.

[60] $7x^2 - 4x = 4$.　　[61] $2x^2 - 12x = 15$.　　[62] $7x^2 + 15 = 28x$.

[63] $4x^2 - 6x = 3$.　　[64] $2x^2 = 3x + 6$.　　[65] $2x^2 + 5x = 3$.

Find the value of $\alpha^2 + \beta^2$ in Nos. 66–69:

66. $\alpha + \beta = 7$, $\alpha\beta = 10$.   [67] $\alpha + \beta = 8$, $\alpha\beta = 11$.

68. $\alpha + \beta = -6$, $\alpha\beta = -3$.   [69] $\alpha + \beta = -7$, $\alpha\beta = -12$.

Find the sum of the squares of the roots of the following equations:

70. $x^2 - 5x = 24$.   71. $x^2 - 5x = 3$.   72. $x^2 + 7x + 4 = 0$.

[73] $x^2 + 3x = 40$.   [74] $x^2 - 9x + 15 = 0$.   [75] $x^2 + x - 1 = 0$.

76. $2x^2 + 5x = 3$.   77. $2x^2 - 9x - 4 = 0$.   78. $5x^2 - 7x + 1 = 0$.

79. If α, β are the roots of $x^2 - 7x = 3$, find the values of
(i) $(\alpha + 1)(\beta + 1)$; (ii) $\dfrac{1}{\alpha} + \dfrac{1}{\beta}$; (iii) $\dfrac{\alpha}{\beta} + \dfrac{\beta}{\alpha}$.

[80] If α, β are the roots of $2x^2 + 5x + 1 = 0$, find the values of
(i) $(\alpha - 2)(\beta - 2)$; (ii) $\dfrac{\alpha}{\beta} + \dfrac{\beta}{\alpha}$; (iii) $(\alpha - \beta)^2$.

81. If α, β are the roots of $3x^2 - 10x + 5 = 0$, find the values of
(i) $\dfrac{1}{\alpha^2} + \dfrac{1}{\beta^2}$; (ii) $\dfrac{\alpha}{\alpha - 1} + \dfrac{\beta}{\beta - 1}$.

[82] If α, β are the roots of $2x^2 + 7x = 3$, find the values of
(i) $\dfrac{\alpha}{\beta + 1} + \dfrac{\beta}{\alpha + 1}$; (ii) $(\alpha - 2\beta)(2\alpha - \beta)$.

Example 14. Is it possible to find a value of x such that $x^2 - 6x + 13 = 0$?

$$x^2 - 6x = -13.$$

Add to each side 3^2,

$$\therefore\ x^2 - 6x + 3^2 = -13 + 9;$$
$$\therefore\ (x - 3)^2 = -4.$$

But it is impossible to find a number whose square is negative; $2 \times 2 = 4$ and $(-2) \times (-2) = 4$. $\therefore$ there is no value of x such that $(x - 3)^2 = -4$, that is, such that $x^2 - 6x + 13 = 0$. We therefore say that the equation $x^2 - 6x + 13 = 0$ has **no roots**.

If the graph of $y = x^2 - 6x + 13$ is drawn, it will be found that the *least* value of y is 4. There is no value of x for which $x^2 - 6x + 13$ is less than 4; this also follows from the fact that $x^2 - 6x + 13$ equals $(x - 3)^2 + 4$.

Problems

Example 15. If a stone is projected vertically upwards from the ground with a velocity of 80 feet per second, its height above the ground after t seconds is $(80t - 16t^2)$ feet. After what time is it 75 feet above the ground? Is there a time when the stone is 104 feet above the ground?

[This formula neglects the effect of air-resistance.]

(i) If it is 75 feet above the ground after t seconds,

$$80t - 16t^2 = 75;$$
$$\therefore \ 16t^2 - 80t + 75 = 0;$$
$$\therefore \ (4t - 15)(4t - 5) = 0; \quad \therefore \ 4t - 15 = 0 \text{ or } 4t - 5 = 0;$$
$$\therefore \ t = \tfrac{15}{4} \text{ or } \tfrac{5}{4}.$$

The stone is therefore 75 feet above the ground after $1\frac{1}{4}$ sec. and after $3\frac{3}{4}$ sec. The first answer refers to the upward motion, and the second to the downward motion.

(ii) If it is 104 feet above the ground after t seconds,

$$80t - 16t^2 = 104; \quad \therefore \ 16t^2 - 80t + 104 = 0;$$
$$\therefore \ t^2 - 5t + \tfrac{104}{16} = 0;$$
$$\therefore \ t^2 - 5t + (\tfrac{5}{2})^2 = \tfrac{25}{4} - \tfrac{26}{4} = -\tfrac{1}{4};$$
$$\therefore \ (t - \tfrac{5}{2})^2 = -\tfrac{1}{4}.$$

But it is impossible to find a number whose square is negative; $\frac{1}{2} \times \frac{1}{2} = \frac{1}{4}$ and $(-\frac{1}{2}) \times (-\frac{1}{2}) = \frac{1}{4}$.

$\therefore$ there is no value of t such that $(t - \tfrac{5}{2})^2 = -\tfrac{1}{4}$, that is, such that $80t - 16t^2 = 104$.

This means that the stone never rises as high as 104 feet above the ground; and we say that the equation $80t - 16t^2 = 104$ has no roots.

EXERCISE X. h

1. I think of a number, then square it and add the original number; the result is 56. What is the number? (Two answers.)

2. I think of a number, multiply it by 3, then subtract 1 and square the result. I shall obtain the same answer if I simply square the original number. What is the number?

[3] The length of a room is 3 feet more than the breadth, and the area of the floor is 270 sq. ft. Find the length and breadth.

[4] Find two consecutive odd numbers such that the sum of their squares is 650.

5. The rectangles in Fig. 132 are of equal area, and the dimensions are shown in inches. Find the value of x and the difference between their perimeters.

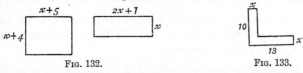

Fig. 132.   Fig. 133.

[6] In Fig. 133, all the corners are right-angled and the dimensions are shown in inches. If the area of the figure is 60 sq. in., find the value of x.

7. A marble is rolling down a sloping groove and travels $(4t + \frac{1}{2}t^2)$ inches in t seconds, for values of t from 0 to 5. How long will it take to roll 10 feet?

[8] A stone is thrown up so that its height above the ground after t seconds is $(88t - 16t^2)$ feet. After what times is it 105 feet above the ground?

9. The product of two consecutive odd numbers exceeds twelve times the intermediate even number by 27. What is the even number?

10. a, b, c, d are four consecutive integers such that the sum of the squares of a and b exceeds the square of d by 4. Find c.

[11] The sum of two numbers is 12, and the sum of their squares is $2\frac{1}{2}$ times their product. Find the numbers.

12. Divide 1 into two parts such that the sum of their cubes is $\frac{1}{3}$.

[13] If $\frac{1}{2}(x-1)(x-2)$ and $\frac{1}{6}(x-1)(x+3)$ are consecutive integers, find the value of x and find the integers.

14. A piece of wire 44 cm. long is cut into two parts, each of which is bent into a square. The total area of the two squares is $68\frac{1}{2}$ sq. cm.; find the lengths of the two parts.

[15] The sum of the first n integers 1, 2, 3, 4, 5, . . . is $\frac{1}{2}n(n+1)$. How many must be taken to add up to 120?

16. The sum of the first n numbers of the set 3, 7, 11, 15, 19, . . . is $n(2n+1)$. How many must be taken, starting from the beginning, to add up to 210? What will then be the last number?

17. An n-sided figure has $\frac{1}{2}n(n-3)$ diagonals. How many sides has a figure if it has 135 diagonals?

[18] A man is x^2 years old and his son is x years old. If the man lives to the age of $13x$, his son will then be x^2 years old. Find the present age of the man.

19. If x^2 degrees east of north is the same direction as $3x$ degrees east of south, find the value of x and the direction.

[20] If $7t$ minutes past two is the same time as t^2 minutes to three, find the value of t and the time.

21. Fig. 134 represents a rectangular lawn with a rectangular flower-bed in the middle. If the area of the grass is 720 sq. yd., find the dimensions of the flower-bed.

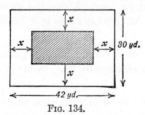
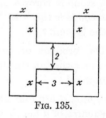

FIG. 134.   FIG. 135.

[22] The corners of Fig. 135 are all right-angled, and the dimensions are shown in inches. Find the value of x if the area of the figure is 126 sq. in.

23. A rectangle is of area 1 sq. in.; its length exceeds its breadth by 1 inch. Find its breadth, correct to $\frac{1}{100}$ inch.

24. The perimeter of a rectangle is 12 inches; if its length is l inches, what is its breadth? Can you make a rectangle (i) perimeter 12 inches, area 7 sq. in.; (ii) perimeter 12 inches, area 10 sq. in.? If so, find the length correct to $\frac{1}{100}$ inch.

[25] A marble is rolling down a sloping groove and travels $(5t + 2t^2)$ inches in t seconds, for values of t from 0 to 5. How long, correct to $\frac{1}{10}$ second, does it take to roll 2 feet?

26. In Fig. 136 the dimensions are shown in inches. Find the value of x and the perimeter of the triangle.

Fig. 136.

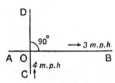

Fig. 137.

27. Fig. 137 shows two cross-roads AOB, COD; P passes O at 2 p.m. walking at 3 miles per hour along AB; Q passes O at 2.30 p.m. walking at 4 miles per hour along CD. When are P and Q 3 miles apart?

[28] The sides of a right-angled triangle are x, $x + 1$, $x + 3$ inches. Find the perimeter, correct to $\frac{1}{10}$ inch.

29. If the area of Fig. 133, p. 237 in which all the corners are right-angled and the dimensions are shown in inches is 40 sq. in., find the value of x correct to one place of decimals.

Which of the following equations (Nos. 30–33) have no roots? *Do not solve any of them.*

30. (i) $x^2 - 9 = 0$; (ii) $x^2 + 4 = 0$; (iii) $x^2 - 3 = 0$.

31. (i) $x^2 - 2x - 3 = 0$; (ii) $x^2 - 2x + 1 = 0$; (iii) $x^2 - 2x + 5 = 0$.

[32] (i) $x^2 + 8x + 17 = 0$; (ii) $x^2 + 8x + 16 = 0$; (iii) $x^2 + 8x + 15 = 0$.

[33] (i) $x^2 - x - 1 = 0$; (ii) $x^2 - x + \frac{1}{4} = 0$; (iii) $x^2 - x + 1 = 0$.

34. What can you say about the value of c if the equation $x^2 + 10x + c = 0$ has no roots? What does this tell you about the graph of $y = x^2 + 10x$?

[35] What can you say about the value of b if the equation $x^2 - 12x + b = 0$ has two unequal roots? What does this tell you about the graph of $y = x^2 - 12x$?

[36] Find the distance from B of a point P on **BC** in Fig. 138 such that **PA = PD**. [The point P is not shown in the figure.]

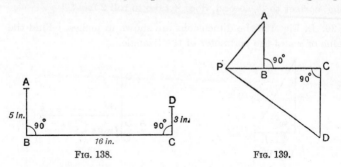

FIG. 138.

FIG. 139.

37. In Fig. 139, **AB** = 4 in., **BC** = 5 in., **CD** = 6 in. If **PD** = 2**PA**, find **PB**.

*38. Fig. 140 represents a circle of radius r inches, inscribed in the quadrant of a circle of radius 10 inches. Calculate the value of r, correct to one place of decimals.

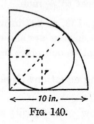

←——— 10 in. ———→

FIG. 140.

*39. The hypotenuse of a right-angled triangle is 4 inches, and the other two sides differ by 1 inch. Find the area of the triangle without finding the length of each side separately.

*40. Find three positive consecutive integers such that their product is 40 times their sum.

*41. Find a whole number such that the sum of its square and cube is sixteen times the next greater whole number.

*42. I buy an old car for £x and sell it after an accident for £12, 15s. at a loss of x per cent. Find x.

*43. A stone is thrown up so that its height above the ground after t seconds is $(88t - 16t^2)$ feet.

> (i) Find the length of time before the stone strikes the ground.
>
> (ii) Does the stone reach a height of 125 feet above the ground?
>
> (iii) Find, correct to $\frac{1}{10}$ second, after what times it is 100 feet above the ground.

*44. If, with the data of Fig. 141, the area of a rectangle with sides equal to **AD** and **BD** is 48 sq. cm., find the length of **AD**. [The area of this rectangle is often denoted by **AD** . **BD**.]

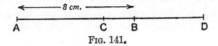

FIG. 141.

*45. If, with the data of Fig. 141, $AC^2 + CB^2$ is 40 sq. cm., find the length of **AC**. [AC^2 denotes the area of a square whose side is equal to **AC**.]

Can you find **AC** so that $AC^2 + CB^2$ is 24 sq. cm.?

*46. If, with the data of Fig. 141, $DA . DB = AB^2$, find the length of **DB**, correct to the nearest mm.

*47. If **OT** is a tangent to the circle in Fig. 142, it can be proved that $OT^2 = OP . OQ$. Find the length of **OQ** if **PQ** $= 9$ in. and **OT** $= 6$ in.

FIG. 142.

FIG. 143.

*48. Fig. 143 shows 3 circular arcs touching each other at **A**, **B**, **C**; the radii of the arcs **AC**, **BC** are 3 in., 5 in., and the arc **AB** is a quarter of a circle. Calculate the radius of the arc **AB**, correct to $\frac{1}{10}$ inch.

In Nos. 49–52, *the unit on each axis is* 1 *inch ; the graphs are not drawn to scale.*

*49. Fig. 144 represents the graph of $y = 3x - x^2$; **NP** is perpendicular to the x-axis. (i) What is the length of **OA**? (ii) Calculate the length of **ON** if **PN** = 2 in., also if **PN** = 1 in.

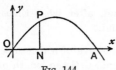

Fig. 144.

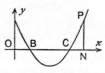

Fig. 145.

*50. Fig. 145 represents the graph of $y = (x - 1)(x - 4)$; **NP** is perpendicular to the x-axis. (i) What are the lengths of **OB** and **OC**? (ii) Calculate the length of **ON** if **PN** = 4 in., also if **PN** = 5 in.

*51. Fig. 146 represents the graphs of $y = x(2 - x)$ and $y = 1 - \frac{1}{3}x$. (i) What are the co-ordinates of **A, B, C**? (ii) Calculate, correct to one place of decimals, the values of such that $x(2 - x) = 1 - \frac{1}{3}x$, and explain the connection of the answers with the figure.

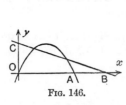

Fig. 146.

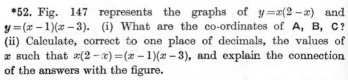

Fig. 147.

*52. Fig. 147 represents the graphs of $y = x(2 - x)$ and $y = (x - 1)(x - 3)$. (i) What are the co-ordinates of **A, B, C**? (ii) Calculate, correct to one place of decimals, the values of x such that $x(2 - x) = (x - 1)(x - 3)$, and explain the connection of the answers with the figure.

CHAPTER XI

FRACTIONS

FRACTIONS in Algebra are simplified by precisely the same methods as are used in Arithmetic.

EXERCISE XI. a (Revision)

Simplify the following expressions:

1. $\dfrac{ax}{ay}$.　　[2] $\dfrac{6ab}{3bc}$.　　3. $\dfrac{p^2}{pq}$.　　[4] $\dfrac{-x}{xy}$.

5. $\dfrac{bc^2}{-bc}$.　　[6] $\dfrac{-10}{5c}$.　　7. $\dfrac{a^8}{a^4}$.　　8. $\dfrac{-6bc}{-9cd}$.

[9] $\dfrac{2xy^2}{6yz^2}$.　　[10] $\dfrac{a^3}{-3a}$.　　11. $\dfrac{a}{ab} - \dfrac{1}{b}$.　　[12] $1 + \dfrac{x-3}{3}$.

13. $\dfrac{a}{b} - \dfrac{a^2}{b^2}$.　　[14] $\dfrac{x}{3} - \dfrac{3}{x}$.　　15. $\dfrac{3}{4ab} + \dfrac{1}{6b^2}$.

[16] $\dfrac{y-4}{8} - \dfrac{y-3}{6}$.　　[17] $1 \div \dfrac{p}{q}$.　　18. $-ab \div \dfrac{-1}{a}$.

[19] $\dfrac{1}{2}xy \times \dfrac{2y}{-x}$.　　　　20. $\dfrac{a^2b}{b^2c} \times \dfrac{bc}{a^2}$.

[21] $\dfrac{6x^2 \times 4xy}{9y^2 \times 2xz}$.　　　　22. $\dfrac{5r^6s^6}{15r^2s^2}$.

[23] $\dfrac{a-1}{2b} - \dfrac{a-2}{3b} - \dfrac{1}{b}$.　　24. $\dfrac{a-b}{ab} + \dfrac{b-c}{bc} + \dfrac{c-a}{ca}$.

[25] $\dfrac{x+y}{6x} - \dfrac{x-y}{4x} - \dfrac{2x+y}{12x}$.　　26. $1 + \dfrac{2b-c}{4c} - \dfrac{b+3c}{10c}$.

[27] $\dfrac{a^2-2a}{a} - \dfrac{a^2-a^3}{a^2} - a$.　　28. $\dfrac{x^2-xy}{xy} - \dfrac{yz-z^2}{yz}$.

[29] $y\left(1 - \dfrac{1}{y}\right) - z\left(1 - \dfrac{1}{z}\right)$.　　30. $\dfrac{1}{r}(2r^2 - rs) - \dfrac{1}{s}(2s^2 + rs)$.

243

Reduction to Lowest Terms

Example 1. Express $\dfrac{x^2 + xy}{x^2 - y^2}$ in its lowest terms.

$$\frac{x^2 + xy}{x^2 - y^2} = \frac{x(x+y)}{(x+y)(x-y)};$$

Divide numerator and denominator by $(x+y)$,

$$\therefore \frac{x^2 + xy}{x^2 - y^2} = \frac{x}{x - y}.$$

This fraction cannot be *reduced* any further, because there is no factor common to x and $x - y$.

If we divide numerator and denominator by x, we shall have

$$\frac{x}{x - y} = \frac{1}{1 - \dfrac{y}{x}}; \quad \text{but } \textit{this is a less simple form.}$$

Example 2. Simplify (i) $\dfrac{x + \frac{1}{2}}{x + \frac{1}{3}}$;   (ii) $\dfrac{1}{\dfrac{1}{u} + \dfrac{1}{v}}$.

(i) Multiply numerator and denominator by 6.

$$\frac{x + \frac{1}{2}}{x + \frac{1}{3}} = \frac{6x + 3}{6x + 2} = \frac{3(2x + 1)}{2(3x + 1)}.$$

(ii) Multiply numerator and denominator by uv.

$$\frac{1}{\dfrac{1}{u} + \dfrac{1}{v}} = \frac{uv}{\dfrac{uv}{u} + \dfrac{uv}{v}} = \frac{uv}{v + u}.$$

Or
$$\frac{1}{\dfrac{1}{u} + \dfrac{1}{v}} = 1 \div \left(\frac{1}{u} + \frac{1}{v} \right) = 1 \div \left(\frac{v + u}{uv} \right)$$

$$= 1 \times \frac{uv}{v + u} = \frac{uv}{v + u}.$$

Example 3. Simplify $\dfrac{b^2 - a^2}{2a^2 + ab - 3b^2}$.

$$\frac{b^2 - a^2}{2a^2 + ab - 3b^2} = \frac{(b+a)(b-a)}{(a-b)(2a+3b)};$$

but $b + a = a + b$ and $b - a = -(a - b)$;

$$\therefore \text{ the fraction} = \frac{-(a+b)(a-b)}{(a-b)(2a+3b)}$$

$$= -\frac{a + b}{2a + 3b}.$$

EXERCISE XI. b

Simplify the following. *If there is no simpler form, say so.*

1. $\dfrac{a^2 + ab}{ab}$.

2. $\dfrac{a^2 + ab}{a^2 - ab}$.

3. $\dfrac{b^2}{b^2 - bc}$.

4. $\dfrac{4p + 4q}{6p - 6q}$.

5. $\dfrac{r + r^2}{s + rs}$.

6. $\dfrac{4b + c}{4b - c}$.

7. $\dfrac{r^2 - s^2}{(r - s)^2}$.

8. $\dfrac{x}{x^2 + xy}$.

9. $\dfrac{b - c}{c - b}$.

10. $\dfrac{n^2 - 9}{n + 3}$.

11. $\dfrac{y^2 - z^2}{z - y}$.

12. $\dfrac{2x + 3y}{2y + 3x}$.

[13] $\dfrac{8u + 8v}{6u + 6v}$.

[14] $\dfrac{4m + 4n}{4m - 4n}$.

[15] $\dfrac{xy - xz}{xy + xz}$.

[16] $\dfrac{p^2 - pq}{pq - q^2}$.

[17] $\dfrac{a^2 + b^2}{a^2 - b^2}$.

[18] $\dfrac{c^2 - 1}{c^2 - c}$.

[19] $\dfrac{(a - b)^2}{b - a}$.

[20] $\dfrac{c + d}{(d + c)^2}$.

[21] $\dfrac{r - t}{4t - 4r}$.

22. $\dfrac{r^2 - r - 6}{r - 3}$.

23. $\dfrac{a^2 - b^2}{(b - a)^2}$.

24. $\dfrac{(2c - 2d)^2}{(3c - 3d)^2}$.

25. $\dfrac{x^2 + 4x - 32}{xy - 4y}$.

26. $\dfrac{y^2 - 6y + 5}{1 - y}$.

27. $\dfrac{2(a + b) + 3(a - b)}{(a + b)(a - b)}$.

28. $\dfrac{3x^2 + 5xy - 2y^2}{4x^2 + 7xy - 2y^2}$.

29. $\dfrac{(1 - a)(1 - b)}{(a - 1)(b - 1)}$.

30. $\dfrac{6p^2 + 5pq - 6q^2}{6p^2 - pq - 2q^2}$.

[31] $\dfrac{a - 2}{a^2 + a - 6}$.

[32] $\dfrac{3x + 2(x + y)}{x(x + y)}$.

[33] $\dfrac{xy + ax}{xy + ay}$.

[34] $\dfrac{3a^3b - 3ab^3}{a^2 + ab}$.

[35] $\dfrac{t^2 + t}{t^2 + 1}$.

[36] $\dfrac{2x^2 - 7x + 3}{(2x - 6)^2}$.

37. $\dfrac{1}{a + \frac{1}{2}}$.

38. $\dfrac{\frac{1}{2}a}{b - \frac{1}{3}}$.

39. $\dfrac{c + \dfrac{1}{d}}{c - \dfrac{1}{2d}}$.

40. $\dfrac{t - \dfrac{1}{t}}{(t - 1)^2}$.

[41] $\dfrac{\frac{1}{4}c}{c + \frac{1}{4}}$.

[42] $\dfrac{\dfrac{1}{a} + \dfrac{1}{b}}{a + b}$.

[43] $\dfrac{\dfrac{x}{2} - y}{x^2 - 4y^2}$.

[44] $\dfrac{1 - \dfrac{1}{z^2}}{1 - \dfrac{1}{z}}$.

45. $\dfrac{p + \dfrac{1}{q}}{q + \dfrac{1}{p}}$.

46. $\dfrac{1 - \dfrac{1}{c^2}}{c + \dfrac{1}{c} + 2}$.

47. $\dfrac{x + 1 - \dfrac{2}{x}}{x^2 - x - 6}$.

Addition and Subtraction

Two fractions are called *equivalent,* if either can be reduced to the other by dividing (or multiplying) numerator and denominator by equal expressions.

Thus, $\dfrac{x}{x - y}$ is equivalent to $\dfrac{x(x + y)}{(x - y)(x + y)}$ or $\dfrac{x^2 + xy}{x^2 - y^2}$.

As in Arithmetic, fractions are added and subtracted by replacing any of them by equivalent fractions, so arranged that all the denominators are equal.

Example 4.   Simplify $\dfrac{2}{x} + \dfrac{1}{x + y}$.

Make the denominator of each fraction $x(x + y)$.

$$\frac{2}{x} + \frac{1}{x + y} = \frac{2(x + y)}{x(x + y)} + \frac{x}{x(x + y)} = \frac{2(x + y) + x}{x(x + y)}$$

$$= \frac{2x + 2y + x}{x(x + y)} = \frac{3x + 2y}{x(x + y)}.$$

Leave the denominator in factors.

Example 5.   Simplify $\dfrac{a + b}{a^2 - ab} - \dfrac{a + 2b}{a^2 - b^2}$.

The expression $= \dfrac{a + b}{a(a - b)} - \dfrac{a + 2b}{(a + b)(a - b)}$.

The L.C.M. of $a(a - b)$ and $(a + b)(a - b)$ is $a(a - b)(a + b)$; make the denominator of each fraction $a(a - b)(a + b)$.

The expression $= \dfrac{(a + b)(a + b)}{a(a - b)(a + b)} - \dfrac{(a + 2b)a}{a(a + b)(a - b)}$

$$= \frac{(a^2 + 2ab + b^2) - (a^2 + 2ab)}{a(a + b)(a - b)}$$

$$= \frac{a^2 + 2ab + b^2 - a^2 - 2ab}{a(a + b)(a - b)} = \frac{b^2}{a(a + b)(a - b)}.$$

Example 6.   Simplify $x - \dfrac{x^2}{x-y}$.

$$x = \frac{x}{1} = \frac{x(x-y)}{x-y};$$

$\therefore$ the expression $= \dfrac{x(x-y)}{x-y} - \dfrac{x^2}{x-y} = \dfrac{x(x-y) - x^2}{x-y}$

$$= \frac{x^2 - xy - x^2}{x-y} = \frac{-xy}{x-y}$$

$$= -\frac{\mathbf{xy}}{\mathbf{x-y}}.$$

We may write this answer, $\dfrac{xy}{y-x}$

because $\dfrac{-xy}{x-y} = \dfrac{+xy}{(-1)(x-y)} = \dfrac{xy}{y-x}.$

EXERCISE XI. c

Copy and complete the following:

1. (i) $\dfrac{3}{5} = \dfrac{\cdots}{25}$; (ii) $\dfrac{3x}{y} = \dfrac{\cdots}{xy} = \dfrac{\cdots}{y^2}$; (iii) $\dfrac{3x}{x+y} = \dfrac{\cdots}{y(x+y)}.$

[2] $\dfrac{1}{a} = \dfrac{\cdots}{a^2} = \dfrac{\cdots}{ab}.$ 3. $\dfrac{1}{a-b} = \dfrac{\cdots}{a(a-b)} = \dfrac{\cdots}{a^2-b^2} = \dfrac{\cdots}{(a-b)^2}.$

4. $\dfrac{b}{c} = \dfrac{\cdots}{2c} = \dfrac{\cdots}{c+c^2}.$ [5] $\dfrac{pq}{p+2q} = \dfrac{\cdots}{q(p+2q)} = \dfrac{\cdots}{(p+2q)(p+3q)}.$

6. $t = \dfrac{\cdots}{t+2} = \dfrac{\cdots}{s-t}.$ [7] $x+y = \dfrac{\cdots}{a} = \dfrac{\cdots}{x-y}.$

Find the L.C.M. of the following:

8. $4a+4b$, $6a-6b$.   9. $3x^2-3$, $5x+5$.

10. $4y-4z$, $10z-10y$.   11. $x^2-7x+10$, $6-x-x^2$.

[12] $2x-2y$, $3y-3x$.   [13] p^2-pq, $pq-q^2$.

[14] $x^3y+x^2y^2$, $x^2y^2-xy^3$.   [15] $a^2-2ab+b^2$, b^2-a^2.

Replace the following pairs of fractions by equivalent fractions with denominators equal to each other:

16. $\dfrac{1}{a}$; $\dfrac{1}{a+b}$.

17. $\dfrac{3}{2x+2}$; $\dfrac{5}{3x+3}$.

18. $\dfrac{y^2}{y^2-z^2}$; $\dfrac{y}{y-z}$.

[19] $\dfrac{1}{n+1}$; $\dfrac{1}{n-1}$.

[20] $\dfrac{b}{b+c}$; $\dfrac{c}{b-c}$.

[21] $\dfrac{5}{6z}$; $\dfrac{z+2}{2z+6}$.

Express the following as single fractions in their lowest terms. *Leave the denominator in factors.*

22. $\dfrac{1}{x+3} - \dfrac{1}{x-3}$.

23. $\dfrac{3}{y+1} - \dfrac{2}{y-1}$.

24. $\dfrac{1}{b} + \dfrac{1}{b-c}$.

25. $\dfrac{p}{p+q} + \dfrac{q}{p-q}$.

26. $1 - \dfrac{x}{x-y}$.

27. $\dfrac{1}{2} + \dfrac{b}{a-2b}$.

28. $\dfrac{1}{m} - \dfrac{n}{m^2+mn}$.

29. $\dfrac{1}{t^2} - \dfrac{1}{t^2+t}$.

30. $\dfrac{1}{x} - \dfrac{2y}{xy-y^2}$.

[31] $\dfrac{1}{a+2} + \dfrac{1}{a-2}$.

[32] $\dfrac{c}{c-d} - \dfrac{c}{c+d}$.

[33] $r - \dfrac{rs}{r+s}$.

[34] $b + \dfrac{bc}{b-c}$.

[35] $\dfrac{1}{x} - \dfrac{x}{x^2-y^2}$.

[36] $\dfrac{a}{2a+b} - \dfrac{1}{2}$.

37. $\dfrac{ab}{a^2-b^2} - \dfrac{b}{a+b}$.

38. $\dfrac{d}{c^2-cd} - \dfrac{c}{cd-d^2}$.

39. $\dfrac{1}{x-2} - \dfrac{7}{2x^2-x-6}$.

40. $\dfrac{2z}{z^2-y^2} - \dfrac{1}{z-y}$.

41. $\dfrac{1}{a^2+a-6} - \dfrac{1}{a^2-a-12}$.

42. $\dfrac{x}{x^2-4xy+3y^2} - \dfrac{2y}{x^2-xy-6y^2}$.

[43] $\dfrac{1}{2a-2b} - \dfrac{1}{3a-3b}$.

[44] $y+z + \dfrac{z^2}{y-z}$.

[45] $\dfrac{1}{x-1} + \dfrac{2}{x^2+2x-3}$.

[46] $\dfrac{c}{c-d} + \dfrac{c}{d-c}$.

47. $\dfrac{1}{y} + \dfrac{1}{z} - \dfrac{1}{y+z}$.

48. $\dfrac{a+b}{a-b} - \dfrac{a-b}{a+b}$.

49. $\dfrac{r^2+s^2}{r^2-s^2} - \dfrac{r+s}{r-s}$.

50. $\dfrac{2b}{b+c} + \dfrac{c}{b-c} - \dfrac{2b^2}{b^2-c^2}$.

[51] $\dfrac{3}{2-n} - \dfrac{6}{4-n^2}.$ [52] $\dfrac{p+2}{p+1} - \dfrac{p+1}{p+2}.$

[53] $\dfrac{3}{a+b} - \dfrac{2(a-2b)}{a^2-b^2}.$ [54] $\dfrac{c}{b^2+bc} + \dfrac{b-c}{b^2+2bc+c^2}.$

[55] $\dfrac{1}{z^2-4} - \dfrac{1}{z^2+2z-8}.$ [56] $\dfrac{x+2y}{x^2+xy} + \dfrac{x-y}{xy+y^2}.$

57. $\dfrac{x-3y}{x^2-3xy-4y^2} - \dfrac{x-y}{x^2-xy-2y^2}.$

58. $\dfrac{p+q}{p^2-4q^2} - \dfrac{p+2q}{3p^2-5pq-2q^2}.$

Multiplication and Division

Example 7.   Simplify $\dfrac{x^2-xy}{x+y} \times \dfrac{x^2-4y^2}{2x^2-5xy+2y^2} \div \dfrac{y^2-xy}{2x-y}.$

The expression $= \dfrac{x(x-y)}{x+y} \times \dfrac{(x+2y)(x-2y)}{(2x-y)(x-2y)} \times \dfrac{2x-y}{y(y-x)}$

$\qquad = \dfrac{x(x-y)}{x+y} \times \dfrac{(x+2y)(x-2y)}{(2x-y)(x-2y)} \times \dfrac{2x-y}{-y(x-y)}.$

Divide numerator and denominator by the common factors, $(x-y)$, $(x-2y)$, $(2x-y)$.

$\therefore$ the expression $= \dfrac{x(x+2y)}{-y(x+y)} = -\dfrac{\mathbf{x(x+2y)}}{\mathbf{y(x+y)}}.$

EXERCISE XI. d

Simplify the following:

1. $\dfrac{x^2-x}{2x+2} \times \dfrac{6x}{x^2-1}.$ 2. $\dfrac{x^2-5x+6}{x} \div \dfrac{x-2}{x^2-3x}.$

3. $\dfrac{b-c}{c+b} \div \dfrac{c-b}{b+c}.$ 4. $\dfrac{a-b}{a-c} \times \dfrac{b-c}{b-a} \times \dfrac{c-a}{c-b}.$

5. $\dfrac{a^2+2ab}{ab} \div (a^2-4b^2).$ 6. $\dfrac{x^2-y^2}{x^2-2xy+y^2} \times \dfrac{1}{xy+y^2}.$

[7] $\dfrac{2y}{2y+z} \times \dfrac{2yz+z^2}{6y^2}.$ [8] $\dfrac{a}{b} \times \dfrac{b}{c} \times \dfrac{c}{d} \times \dfrac{d}{a}.$

[9] $\dfrac{1}{2}x \times \dfrac{x^2-1}{x^2-x}.$ [10] $\dfrac{x^2-3x}{2x^2+7x+3} \div \dfrac{x^2-5x+6}{2x^2-3x-2}.$

11. $\dfrac{y^2 + y - 6}{y + 1} \div \dfrac{y + 3}{2y^2 + y - 1}$.   12. $\dfrac{3x - x^2 - 2}{x^2 - 2x - 3} \times \dfrac{6x - x^2 - 9}{x^2 - 5x + 6}$.

13. $\dfrac{x^2 - 2xy + y^2}{x^2 - y^2} \times \dfrac{x^2 + 2xy + y^2}{x^2 + xy}$.   14. $\dfrac{b^2 - 4c^2}{b^2 - 4bc + 4c^2} \div \dfrac{c}{b^2 - 2bc}$.

[15] $\dfrac{r^2 + 2rs + s^2}{r^2 + 2rs} \times \dfrac{r}{r^2 - s^2}$.   [16] $\dfrac{a^2 - 4ab + 4b^2}{a^2 + ab - 6b^2} \div \dfrac{a^2 + 3ab}{a^2 + 6ab + 9b^2}$.

[17] $\dfrac{a^2 - 4a + 4}{2 - 6a} \times \dfrac{9a^2 - 6a + 1}{3a^2 - 12}$.   [18] $\dfrac{x^2 + (a + 1)x + a}{x^2 + 2ax + a^2} \times \dfrac{a + x}{a + 1}$.

19. $\dfrac{x^2 + 2x - 8}{5 - x} \times \dfrac{x^2 - 8x + 15}{1 - x} \times \dfrac{x^2 + 2x - 3}{2 - x}$.

20. $\left(y + \dfrac{12}{y} - 7 \right) \times \left(y + \dfrac{5}{y} - 6 \right) \div \left(y + \dfrac{3}{y} - 4 \right)$.

21. $\dfrac{b^2 + 3bc + 2c^2}{b^3 - 3b^2c} \times \dfrac{b^3 + b^2c}{b^2 + 5bc + 6c^2} \div \dfrac{b^2 + 3bc}{b - 3c}$.

[22] $\dfrac{a^2 - 4ab - 5b^2}{a^2 - 2ab - 15b^2} \times \dfrac{a^2}{a^2 - 4ab} \div \dfrac{a^2 - ab - 2b^2}{a^2 - ab - 12b^2}$.

Further Simplification

Example 8. Find the L.C.M. of

$$x^2 + x - 6, \ x^2 - x - 12, \ 16 - x^2, \ 2x - x^2.$$

Use the method of factors, as in Arithmetic.

$$x^2 + x - 6 = (x + 3)(x - 2); \ x^2 - x - 12 = (x + 3)(x - 4);$$
$$16 - x^2 = (4 + x)(4 - x) = -(x + 4)(x - 4);$$
$$2x - x^2 = x(2 - x) = -x(x - 2).$$

$$\therefore \text{the L.C.M. is } \mathbf{x(x - 2)(x + 3)(x - 4)(x + 4)}.$$

Example 9. Simplify $\left(\dfrac{a}{b} - \dfrac{b}{a} \right)\left(1 + \dfrac{b}{a - b} \right) \div \left(1 - \dfrac{b}{a + b} \right)$.

First reduce the contents of each bracket to a single fraction.

The expression $= \left(\dfrac{a^2 - b^2}{ab} \right) \times \left(\dfrac{a - b + b}{a - b} \right) \div \left(\dfrac{a + b - b}{a + b} \right)$

$$= \dfrac{(a + b)(a - b)}{ab} \times \dfrac{a}{a - b} \times \dfrac{a + b}{a}$$

$$= \dfrac{(a + b)^2}{ab}.$$

Example 10.   Simplify $\dfrac{3(x+y)}{x^2+xy-2y^2} + \dfrac{3x+y}{y^2-x^2}$.

The expression

$$= \frac{3(x+y)}{(x-y)(x+2y)} + \frac{3x+y}{(y+x)(y-x)}$$

$$= \frac{3(x+y)}{(x-y)(x+2y)} - \frac{3x+y}{(x+y)(x-y)}, \text{ since } (y-x) = -(x-y),$$

$$= \frac{3(x+y)(x+y)}{(x+y)(x-y)(x+2y)} - \frac{(3x+y)(x+2y)}{(x+y)(x-y)(x+2y)}$$

$$= \frac{3(x^2+2xy+y^2) - (3x^2+7xy+2y^2)}{(x+y)(x-y)(x+2y)}$$

$$= \frac{3x^2+6xy+3y^2-3x^2-7xy-2y^2}{(x+y)(x-y)(x+2y)}$$

$$= \frac{y^2-xy}{(x+y)(x-y)(x+2y)} = \frac{-y(x-y)}{(x+y)(x-y)(x+2y)}$$

$$= -\frac{\mathbf{y}}{\mathbf{(x+y)(x+2y)}}.$$

Fractions should always be expressed in their lowest terms. Before showing up an answer, *see whether the numerator and denominator have any common factor*; if so, simplify the fraction.

EXERCISE XI. e

Copy and complete the following:

1. $\dfrac{a}{b-c} = \dfrac{\ldots}{c-b} = \dfrac{\ldots}{c^2-b^2}$.

2. $\dfrac{1}{(b-c)(a-c)} = \dfrac{\ldots}{(b-c)(c-a)(a-b)}$.

Find the L.C.M. of the following:

3. $x^2+x-2,\ x^2-3x-10,\ x^2-4x-5$.

[4] $y^2-yz,\ z^2-yz,\ 2yz-y^2-z^2$.

5. $a^2+a,\ a^2+2a+1,\ a^2+ab+a+b$.

[6] $x^3+x^2,\ x^2+2x-8,\ 2+x-x^2,\ x-x^3$.

Simplify the following:

7. $\dfrac{1}{c^2 - d^2} + \dfrac{1}{d^2 - c^2}$.

[8] $\dfrac{2x}{x^2 - y^2} + \dfrac{1}{y - x}$.

9. $\left(1 + \dfrac{b}{a}\right) \div \left(1 + \dfrac{a}{b}\right)$.

[10] $\left(\dfrac{1}{p} - \dfrac{1}{q}\right) \div \left(\dfrac{p}{q} - \dfrac{q}{p}\right)$.

11. $\dfrac{4}{x+2} - \dfrac{3}{x+3} - \dfrac{1}{x}$.

[12] $\dfrac{4}{x-2} - \dfrac{1}{x+3} - \dfrac{5}{x^2 + x - 6}$.

13. $\dfrac{z+1}{z^2 - 4z + 3} - \dfrac{z-3}{z^2 - 1}$.

[14] $\dfrac{2}{x-a} - \dfrac{3}{x+a} + \dfrac{6x}{x^2 - a^2}$.

15. $\dfrac{2}{a^2 - 1} + \dfrac{1}{1 - a}$.

[16] $\dfrac{p}{p-q} + \dfrac{q}{q-p}$.

17. $\left(1 - \dfrac{c}{d}\right) \div \left(1 - \dfrac{d}{c}\right)$.

[18] $\left(1 - \dfrac{b}{a}\right) \div \left(\dfrac{a}{b} - \dfrac{b}{a}\right)$.

19. $\left(x + \dfrac{x}{y}\right) \div \left(x - \dfrac{x}{y}\right)$.

[20] $\left(1 - \dfrac{a}{a+c}\right)\left(\dfrac{1}{a} + \dfrac{c}{a^2}\right)$.

21. $\dfrac{x+1}{(x+2)(x+3)} + \dfrac{6}{x(x+3)} - \dfrac{2}{x}$.

[22] $\dfrac{a}{2a+b} + \dfrac{2b}{a-2b} - \dfrac{5ab}{2a^2 - 3ab - 2b^2}$.

23. $\dfrac{x^2 + a^2}{a^2 - ax} + \dfrac{x^2 + 2a^2}{ax + a^2} - \dfrac{9a^2}{a^2 - x^2}$.

24. $\dfrac{3}{x^2 + x - 2} - \dfrac{2}{x^2 + 2x - 3} + \dfrac{1}{x^2 + 5x + 6}$.

25. $\left(\dfrac{x}{y} + \dfrac{y}{x} - 2\right)\left(\dfrac{1}{x} + \dfrac{1}{y}\right) \div \left(\dfrac{x^2}{y^2} - \dfrac{y^2}{x^2}\right)$.

[26] $\dfrac{5}{a+b} - \dfrac{4}{a-b} - \dfrac{8a}{b^2 - a^2}$.

27. $\dfrac{1}{(a-b)(a-c)} + \dfrac{1}{(c-a)(c-b)}$.

[28] $\left(\dfrac{a}{b} + \dfrac{a+b}{a-b}\right) \div \left(\dfrac{b}{a} + \dfrac{a-b}{a+b}\right)$.

29. $\dfrac{x+2y}{x^2 - y^2} + \dfrac{2y}{xy - x^2}$.

[30] $\dfrac{b+c}{b-c} + \dfrac{b-c}{b+c} + \dfrac{4bc}{c^2 - b^2}$.

31. $\dfrac{3}{y+3} + \dfrac{4}{y+4} - \dfrac{7}{y+7}$.

[32] $\left(\dfrac{1}{x} + \dfrac{1}{y}\right)(x+y) \div \left(\dfrac{1}{x^2} - \dfrac{1}{y^2}\right)$.

33. $\dfrac{a}{b + \frac{1}{2}} + \dfrac{a}{b - \frac{1}{2}} - \dfrac{2a}{b}$.

[34] $\left(a - \dfrac{10}{a} - 3\right) \div \left(\dfrac{1}{2}a + 1\right)$.

35. $\left(\dfrac{1}{1-a} - \dfrac{2a}{1-a^2}\right) \times \dfrac{a^2 - 2a - 3}{a^2 - 6a + 9}$.

36. $\dfrac{2x+1}{x^2+x-6} - \dfrac{x+3}{2x^2-3x-2} + \dfrac{5x}{2x^2+7x+3}.$

*37. $\dfrac{2}{3x^2-4xy+y^2} + \dfrac{2}{2x+y} - \dfrac{5}{y^2-xy-6x^2}.$

*38. $\dfrac{b+c}{(b-a)(c-a)} + \dfrac{c+a}{(c-b)(a-b)} + \dfrac{a+b}{(a-c)(b-c)}.$

*39. $\left(\dfrac{x}{x-y} + \dfrac{y}{y-x}\right)\left(\dfrac{x-y}{x} - \dfrac{y-x}{y}\right).$

*40. $\left\{\dfrac{p}{(p-1)^2} + \dfrac{1}{1-p}\right\}\left\{\dfrac{1}{p} - 1\right\}.$

*41. $\left(x+y+\dfrac{y^2}{x}+\dfrac{y^3}{x^2}\right) \div \left(\dfrac{x^2}{y^2} - \dfrac{y^2}{x^2}\right).$

*42. $\dfrac{1}{a+\dfrac{1}{b}} + \dfrac{1}{b+\dfrac{1}{a}} - \dfrac{1}{\dfrac{1}{2}a+\dfrac{1}{2}b}.$

*43. $\dfrac{1}{x+\frac{1}{2}} + \dfrac{1}{2x-1} + \dfrac{x}{2x+1} - \dfrac{x}{1-2x} - 1.$

Equations

Example 11. Solve $\dfrac{x}{x-2} - \dfrac{3}{x+1} = 1.$

Multiply each side by $(x-2)(x+1)$.

$$\therefore\ x(x+1) - 3(x-2) = (x-2)(x+1).$$
$$\therefore\ x^2 + x - 3x + 6 = x^2 - x - 2;$$
$$\therefore\ -x = -8; \qquad \therefore\ x = 8.$$

Check. If $x=8$, left side $= \frac{8}{6} - \frac{3}{9} = \frac{4}{3} - \frac{1}{3} = 1.$

Example 12. Solve $\dfrac{5}{x-6} - \dfrac{4}{x-4} = \dfrac{3}{x+2}.$

Multiply each side by $(x-6)(x-4)(x+2)$.

$$\therefore\ 5(x-4)(x+2) - 4(x-6)(x+2) = 3(x-6)(x-4).$$
$$\therefore\ 5(x^2-2x-8) - 4(x^2-4x-12) = 3(x^2-10x+24).$$
$$\therefore\ 5x^2-10x-40-4x^2+16x+48 = 3x^2-30x+72.$$
$$\therefore\ -2x^2+36x-64 = 0; \quad \therefore\ x^2-18x+32 = 0;$$
$$\therefore\ (x-2)(x-16) = 0; \quad \therefore\ x-2=0 \text{ or } x-16=0;$$
$$\therefore\ x = 2 \text{ or } 16.$$

The reader should check these answers, see p. 254.

$$\frac{5}{x-6} - \frac{4}{x-4} = \frac{3}{x+2}.$$

Check. If $x = 2$, left side $= \dfrac{5}{-4} - \dfrac{4}{-2} = -1\frac{1}{4} + 2 = \frac{3}{4}$;

right side $= \frac{3}{4}$.

If $x = 16$, left side $= \frac{5}{10} - \frac{4}{12} = \frac{1}{2} - \frac{1}{3} = \frac{1}{6}$;

right side $= \frac{3}{18} = \frac{1}{6}$.

EXERCISE XI. f

Solve the following equations:

1. $\dfrac{1}{x} = 2\frac{1}{2}$.

2. $\dfrac{1}{y-1} = \dfrac{2}{7}$.

3. $\dfrac{1}{z} + \dfrac{1}{z+2} = 0$.

[4] $\dfrac{1}{t} - \dfrac{5}{3t} = \dfrac{5}{12}$.

[5] $\dfrac{2}{p-1} = \dfrac{5}{p}$.

[6] $\dfrac{x-3}{x+6} = 4$.

7. $r = \dfrac{1}{r}$.

8. $t - 1 = \dfrac{8}{t+1}$.

[9] $z = \dfrac{6}{z+1}$.

10. $\dfrac{1}{t} - \dfrac{2}{t+1} + \dfrac{1}{t+3} = 0$.

11. $\dfrac{3}{p} = \dfrac{2}{p+1} + \dfrac{3}{3p-1}$.

12. $3x + 5 = \dfrac{3x^2 + 5}{5x + 3}$.

13. $\dfrac{3}{x+4} - \dfrac{2}{x+3} = \dfrac{1}{x+1}$.

14. $\dfrac{6}{y+1} + \dfrac{1}{1-y} = \dfrac{2}{y}$.

15. $\dfrac{1}{2z-3} = \dfrac{5}{z} + \dfrac{3}{2z^2 - 3z}$.

[16] $\dfrac{2x-1}{3x+1} = \dfrac{6x-1}{9x-3}$.

[17] $\dfrac{1}{y-2} + \dfrac{3}{y-3} + \dfrac{5}{2-y} = 0$.

[18] $\dfrac{5}{z-8} = \dfrac{2}{z-3} + \dfrac{3}{z+2}$.

[19] $\dfrac{1}{t-2} - \dfrac{1}{t+1} = \dfrac{1}{6}$.

20. $\dfrac{x-1}{x+2} + \dfrac{x+3}{x-2} = 2$.

21. $\dfrac{y-1}{y+2} + \dfrac{y+3}{y^2-4} = \dfrac{3y-1}{5(y-2)}$.

[22] $\dfrac{3p-1}{p-1} - \dfrac{2p+1}{p+1} = 1$.

[23] $\dfrac{3x^2}{x^2-1} = \dfrac{4}{x-1}$.

*24. $\dfrac{4}{y-3} + \dfrac{3y-3}{y^2-y-6} = \dfrac{10y+10}{3y+6}$.

*25. $z - 1 = \dfrac{z^2+2}{z-1} + \dfrac{z+2}{z-6}$.

In Nos. 26–27, give the answers correct to 2 places of decimals:

26. $\dfrac{1}{x-2} + \dfrac{2}{x-1} - \dfrac{2}{x-3} = 0$.

*27. $\dfrac{2x+2}{x-1} - \dfrac{x-1}{x+1} = \dfrac{x}{x-2}$.

Miscellaneous Fractions and Equations

EXERCISE XI. g

Simplify the given expressions, and solve the given equations:

1. $\dfrac{1}{2} - \dfrac{1}{x-2}$.   2. $\dfrac{1}{2} - \dfrac{1}{x-2} = \dfrac{1}{4}$.   3. $1 - \dfrac{1}{x+1}$.

4. $\dfrac{x}{3} - \dfrac{x+1}{5}$.   5. $\dfrac{x}{3} - \dfrac{x+1}{5} = 1$.   6. $x+3 - \dfrac{x^2}{x-3}$.

7. $\dfrac{x}{x-1} - \dfrac{1}{x} - 1$.   8. $\dfrac{x}{2x-4} - \dfrac{x}{3x-6}$.   9. $\dfrac{x}{x-1} + \dfrac{1}{x} = 1$.

[10] $\dfrac{1}{x} + \dfrac{1}{2x} - \dfrac{1}{3x}$.   [11] $\dfrac{1}{x} + \dfrac{1}{2x} - \dfrac{1}{3x} = \dfrac{1}{9}$.   [12] $2 + \dfrac{1}{2x+1} = 1$.

[13] $\dfrac{1}{3x} - \dfrac{1}{3x+3}$.   [14] $\dfrac{1}{3x} - \dfrac{1}{3x+3} = \dfrac{1}{4x}$.   [15] $\dfrac{x}{x+2} - \dfrac{1}{x} = 1$.

16. $\left(\dfrac{1}{x} - \dfrac{1}{y}\right) \div \left(\dfrac{1}{x^2} - \dfrac{1}{y^2}\right)$.   17. $\left(1 - \dfrac{1}{x-1}\right)\left(1 + \dfrac{1}{x-2}\right)$.

18. $x+4 - \dfrac{x^2}{x-4} = 1$.   19. $\dfrac{a^2 - 2ab + b^2}{a^2 - b^2} - \dfrac{a^2 - b^2}{a^2 + 2ab + b^2}$.

20. $\left(b + \dfrac{bc}{b-c}\right) \div \left(b - \dfrac{bc}{b+c}\right)$.   21. $\dfrac{3}{c+2} + \dfrac{4}{c+3} = \dfrac{7}{c+6}$.

[22] $\left(\dfrac{a}{b} - 1\right) \div \left(\dfrac{b}{a} - 1\right)$.   [23] $\left(c - 2 - \dfrac{3}{c}\right) \div \left(1 - \dfrac{1}{c^2}\right)$.

[24] $\dfrac{x}{x+1} + \dfrac{3x}{2+2x} - 2$.   [25] $\left(\dfrac{b}{c} + \dfrac{c}{b} + 2\right) \div \left(1 + \dfrac{b}{c}\right)$.

26. $\dfrac{2}{x-1} + \dfrac{1}{2-x} - \dfrac{1}{x-3}$.   27. $\dfrac{5}{x-2} - \dfrac{3}{x} = \dfrac{12}{x(x-2)}$.

28. $\dfrac{(x+y)^2 - z^2}{(x+y-z)^2}$.   29. $\left(a - 6 + \dfrac{10}{a+5}\right)\left(a - 1 - \dfrac{6}{a+4}\right)$.

[30] $\dfrac{1}{x} - \dfrac{x+1}{x(x-1)} + \dfrac{1}{x-1}$.   [31] $\dfrac{x}{2x-4} - \dfrac{x}{3x-6} = 1$.

[32] $[(r+s)^2 + (r-s)^2] \div \left[\dfrac{r}{s} + \dfrac{s}{r}\right]$.   [33] $\dfrac{1}{r+2} = \dfrac{3}{r-20} - \dfrac{2}{r-5}$.

34. $\dfrac{x+6}{y-2} = \dfrac{2}{3}$, $\dfrac{x+4}{y+1} = \dfrac{4}{7}$.   35. $\dfrac{4(a-b)}{b-1} = 2\tfrac{1}{2}$, $\dfrac{b+1}{5a} = \dfrac{1}{8}$.

Problems

Example 13. From London to Bristol is 120 miles. The average speed of one train is 9 miles an hour more than that of another train and the first train takes 40 minutes less time over the journey. Find the speed of each train.

Let the speed of the faster train be x miles an hour.

∴ the speed of the slower train is $(x - 9)$ miles an hour.

Then the faster train goes 120 miles in $\dfrac{120}{x}$ hours, and the slower train goes 120 miles in $\dfrac{120}{x - 9}$ hours.

But the time taken by the faster train is 40 min. or $\frac{2}{3}$ hour less than the time taken by the slower train.

$$\therefore \ \frac{120}{x} + \frac{2}{3} = \frac{120}{x - 9};$$
$$\therefore \ 360(x - 9) + 2x(x - 9) = 360x;$$
$$\therefore \ 360x - 9 \times 360 + 2x^2 - 18x = 360x;$$
$$\therefore \ 2x^2 - 18x - 9 \times 360 = 0; \quad \therefore \ x^2 - 9x - 9 \times 180 = 0;$$
$$\therefore \ (x - 45)(x + 36) = 0; \quad \therefore \ x - 45 = 0 \text{ or } x + 36 = 0;$$
$$\therefore \ x = 45 \text{ or } -36.$$

But the conditions of the problem require that x should be positive; therefore we take $x = 45$ and disregard $x = -36$.

Also if $x = 45$, $x - 9 = 45 - 9 = 36$.

∴ the faster train averages **45 miles an hour**,

and the slower train averages **36 miles an hour**.

Check:

The faster train takes $\frac{120}{45}$ hours $= \frac{8}{3}$ hours $= 2$ hr. 40 min.;

The slower train takes $\frac{120}{36}$ hours $= \frac{10}{3}$ hours $= 3$ hr. 20 min.;

　　　3 hr. 20 min. $-$ 2 hr. 40 min. $= 40$ min.

Note. Every value of x which satisfies the data of the problem must satisfy the equation, $\dfrac{120}{x} + \dfrac{2}{3} = \dfrac{120}{x - 9}$. The converse is not necessarily true; it does not follow that every value of x which satisfies the equation must satisfy *all* the data of the problem. Here, there is another condition to be satisfied, namely x must be positive.

EXERCISE XI. h

1. The bill at a shop for a luncheon party is 24 shillings. f one of the party has no money, the others will have to pay an xtra 4 pence each. How many were in the party?

2. If the average speed of a train could be increased by 10 miles an hour, a journey of 180 miles would take 54 minutes less ime. What is the average speed?

3. A train running between two towns arrives at its destination 0 minutes late when it averages 48 miles an hour and 16 minutes ate when it averages 45 miles an hour. What is the distance etween the towns?

4. When the price of coal rises 8s. a ton, I obtain $\frac{1}{4}$ ton less or £2. Find the original price.

[5] Find the speed of a train if an increase of 6 miles an hour owers the time for a journey of 72 miles by 10 minutes.

[6] Two cars make the journey between two towns, 112 miles apart, both starting from the same town; one travels 7 miles n hour faster than the other, but starts 48 minutes later. If hey arrive at the same time, find the speed of each car.

[7] When the price of eggs rises by $\frac{1}{2}$d. each, I obtain 20 fewer ggs for 10 shillings. Find the original price.

[8] From London to Crewe is 160 miles. An express train averages 10 miles an hour more than another train and does he journey in 32 minutes less time. Find the average speed of the express.

[9] A man bought some chickens for £3. If he had obtained 5 more for the same money, they would have cost 1 shilling less each. How many did he buy?

10. My coal bill last year was £28. This year I have to pay 5s. a ton more for my coal. If I can manage to use 2 tons less, my coal bill will remain the same. How much coal did I use last year?

[11] A cricketer has scored 368 runs. In his next match he is out for 12 and 16 in the two innings and thereby reduces his average by 1. What is his final average?

12. A man bought some cows for £540. Two of them died and he sold the rest at £6 per head more than he gave for them. On the whole transaction he gained 10 per cent. on his outlay. How many cows did he buy?

[13] For what value of x has the expression $\dfrac{x(x+3)}{(x-1)(x+2)}$ the same value as it has when $x=2$?

14. For what value of x are $\dfrac{5x-1}{x-2}$ and $\dfrac{3x+2}{x-6}$ equal to consecutive integers?

15. Two rectangles are each 1 sq. foot in area. Their lengths differ by 2 inches and their breadths by 1 inch. Find their lengths.

[16] In a one-thousand mile race, A's average speed is 10 miles an hour more than B's; and A beats B by 200 miles. Find A's average speed.

17. An aeroplane takes 25 minutes longer to fly 100 miles against a steady wind than with it. The aeroplane travels at 100 miles an hour in still air. Find the speed of the wind.

[18] A man can swim 50 yards per minute in still water. He takes $3\frac{3}{4}$ minutes longer to swim 100 yards against a current than with it. Find the speed of the current.

[19] A housekeeper sent 7s. 7d. for the purchase of a certain number of tablets of soap; the price of the soap had, however, fallen 1d. per tablet so that she received 2 tablets more than she expected and also 3d. in change. Find the original price of the soap per tablet.

20. In Fig. 148, where TA is a tangent to the circle, it can be proved that

$$\frac{\text{CT}}{\text{AT}}=\frac{\text{AT}}{\text{BT}}=\frac{\text{AC}}{\text{AB}}.$$

Find the lengths of CT and AB.

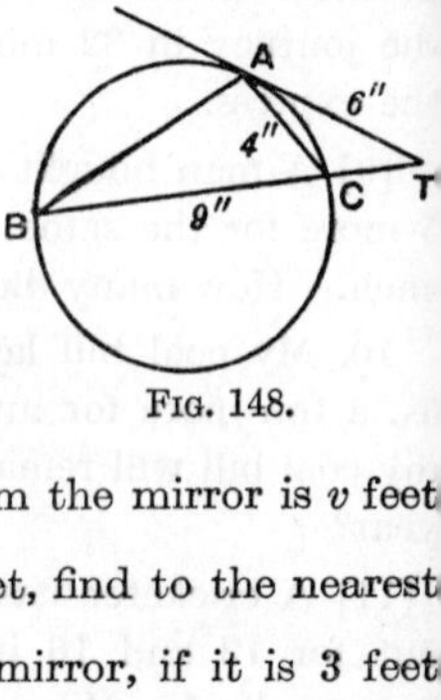

Fig. 148.

*21. If an object is at a distance of u feet from a spherical mirror of focal length f feet, the distance of the image from the mirror is v feet where $\dfrac{1}{v}+\dfrac{1}{u}=\dfrac{1}{f}$. If the focal length is 4 feet, find to the nearest inch the distance of the object from the mirror, if it is 3 feet nearer the mirror than the image is.

*22. A swimming-bath is filled by 2 pipes in 12 hours. The smaller pipe by itself takes 7 hours longer than the larger pipe by itself to fill the bath. How long does the larger pipe take to fill the bath?

*23. Two turnstiles A and B admit spectators to a football ground. It takes the average spectator $\frac{1}{5}$ second longer to pass through A than through B; B admits on an average 10 more spectators per minute than A. How many spectators can enter the ground in a quarter of an hour?

*24. When the price of petrol is reduced by x per cent., a man uses x per cent. more petrol per year. His yearly bill for petrol is then reduced from £50 to £48. Find the value of x.

*25. A hoop of radius b feet is bowled along with a velocity v feet per second and comes to a step of height h feet. The hoop will climb the step if v^2 is not less than $\dfrac{128bh}{(2b-h)^2}$, $(h < 2b)$.

If the velocity of the hoop is 8 feet per second, and if its radius is $1\frac{1}{2}$ feet, find to the nearest inch the height of the tallest step it can climb.

*26. A solid rectangular block with a square base is h feet high; its total surface area is S sq. ft. and its volume is V cu. ft. Prove that $(hS - 2V)^2 = 16h^3V$. Also find V if $h = 2$, $S = 10$. Find also the breadth of the block.

REVISION EXERCISE R. 6 (Ch. X–XI)

Solve the equations:

1. (i) $x(x-1) = x$; (ii) $(x-1)^2 = x^2$; (iii) $(x-1)^2 = x-1$.

2. $(x-1)(2y-9) = 0$, $5x = 2y + 1$.

3. $6x^2 + x = 2$.   [4] $12x^2 = 11x + 15$.   [5] $(3x-1)^2 = (2x+3)^2$.

6. $21(x+2)^2 - 40(x+2) = 21$.   7. $(x^2 + x - 4)^2 = 4$.

[8] If $y = mx + \dfrac{a}{m}$, find the value of m when $x = 0.5$, $y = 2$, $a = 2$.

Form equations with *integral* coefficients having as roots:

9. $\frac{2}{3}$, $1\frac{1}{2}$.   10. 0.4, -0.25.   [11] $-1\frac{1}{2}$, $-2\frac{1}{3}$.   [12] 0.6, 0.

13. If the roots of $ax^2 - bx - 12 = 0$ are $1\frac{1}{2}$, -4, find the values of a. b.

[14] If $x = 5$ is one root of $x^2 + 3x + c = 0$, what is the other root ?

15. If $x = 6$ is one root of $x^2 + bx = 4$, what is the other root ?

16. What are the possible values of b if both of the roots of $x^2 + bx - 12 = 0$ are integers ?

Find the values of $\dfrac{1}{a} + \dfrac{1}{\beta}$ and $a^2 + \beta^2$ if a, β are the roots of the equations:

17. $x^2 - 3x - 1 = 0$.   18. $3x^2 + 7x + 3 = 0$.   [19] $2x^2 + x = 5$.

Find the values of $\dfrac{a}{\beta} + \dfrac{\beta}{a}$ and $(a - \beta)^2$ if a, β are the roots of the equations:

[20] $x^2 + 4x = 2$.   21. $5x^2 = 10x + 1$.   22. $x + \dfrac{1}{x} = 3\frac{1}{2}$.

Copy and complete:

23. $t^2 - 9t \ldots = (t \ldots)^2$.   [24] $r^2 + r \ldots = (r \ldots)^2$.

Solve correct to 2 places of decimals:

25. $x^2 + x = 4$.   [26] $x^2 - 5x = 3$.   27. $3x^2 + 4x - 5 = 0$.

28. For what value of x has $\dfrac{x^2 + 1}{x - 1}$ the same value as it has when $x = 4$.

[29] If $(3x - 4)(2x - 1)$ and $(2x - 3)(3x - 2)$ are consecutive even numbers, what numbers are they ?

30. Find values of x and y such that $y = \frac{1}{2}(x^2 - 3)$ and $x + y = 6$.

31. If $x = 3y$, find the value of $\dfrac{3x^2 - 2y^2}{2x^2 - 3y^2}$.

[32] If $\dfrac{4x}{y} = 1\frac{1}{4}$, find the value of $\dfrac{4x + y}{4x - y}$.

Simplify:

33. $\dfrac{a^2 + 2a + 1}{a^2 - 5a - 6}$.   34. $b - \dfrac{b^2 - 5}{b + 5}$.   35. $\dfrac{(d - c)^2}{c(c - d)}$.

[36] $\dfrac{1}{m^2} - \dfrac{1}{m^2 + m}$.   [37] $\dfrac{r^3 - rs^2}{r + s}$.   [38] $\dfrac{1}{t^2 - 4} + \dfrac{1}{4 - t^2}$.

[39] $\dfrac{1}{4a - 4b} + \dfrac{1}{6b - 6a}$.   40. $\dfrac{1}{c(c - d)} - \dfrac{1}{c^2 + d^2 - 2cd}$.

Simplify:

[41] $(m-n)^3 \div (n-m)$.

42. $(p-q)^3 \div (q-p)^2$.

[43] $\dfrac{x^2+xy}{xy-xz} \times \dfrac{y^2-yz}{xz+yz}$.

44. $\dfrac{x^2+(a+1)x+a}{x^2-a^2} \times \dfrac{1}{ax+a}$.

[45] $\dfrac{x^6}{x^2+2x+1} \div \dfrac{x^2}{x^2-1}$.

46. $\dfrac{x^7-x^6}{ax-a} \div \dfrac{ax^2}{ax-x}$.

[47] $\left(\dfrac{1}{b^3}-\dfrac{1}{b}\right) \div \left(\dfrac{1}{b^2}-\dfrac{1}{b}\right)$.

48. $\left(1-\dfrac{c}{c-1}\right) \div \left(\dfrac{1}{c}-c\right)$.

[49] $\dfrac{p}{2} \div \left(1-\dfrac{2n+p}{2n-p}\right)$.

50. $\left(t-2+\dfrac{1}{t}\right) \div \left(1-\dfrac{1}{t^2}\right)$.

[51] $\dfrac{1}{y-z}+\dfrac{1}{y+z}-\dfrac{3z-y}{y^2-z^2}$.

52. $\dfrac{2}{a^2-2ab-3b^2}-\dfrac{1}{a^2-4ab+3b^2}$.

[53] $\dfrac{2c-1}{c+2}+\dfrac{1-4c}{c+4}+2$.

54. $\dfrac{1}{t(t-1)}+\dfrac{1}{t(t+1)}-\dfrac{1}{t^2-1}$.

[55] $\dfrac{x+y}{2x-3y}-\dfrac{x-y}{2x+3y}-\dfrac{11xy}{2(4x^2-9y^2)}$.

56. $\dfrac{x}{(a-b)(a-c)}-\dfrac{2x}{(b-c)(b-a)}+\dfrac{x}{(c-a)(c-b)}$.

Solve the equations:

57. $\dfrac{t-3}{t+3}+\dfrac{4}{t}=1$.

[58] $\dfrac{1}{p+3}+\dfrac{1}{p}=\dfrac{2}{p+2}$.

59. $\dfrac{1-2x}{2-5x}=\dfrac{3-x}{6-3x}$.

[60] $\dfrac{(1-3y)(4-y)}{(2-3y)(1-y)}=-2\tfrac{1}{2}$.

61. $\dfrac{z+2}{z+1}-\dfrac{z+1}{z+2}=\dfrac{7}{12}$.

[62] $\dfrac{n+2}{n+3}-\dfrac{n+1}{n+2}=\dfrac{1}{2}$.

63. $\dfrac{1}{r-5}-\dfrac{1}{r-2}=\dfrac{2}{3(r-4)}$.

[64] $\dfrac{1}{2-5x}-\dfrac{1}{1-2x}=\dfrac{2}{5-12x}$.

65. $\dfrac{y+7}{y^2-y-6}=\dfrac{y-5}{y^2-4y+3}$.

[66] $\dfrac{6}{3z-2}-\dfrac{1}{z-4}=\dfrac{2}{2z-3}$.

Solve correct to 2 places of decimals:

67. $\dfrac{2}{x} + \dfrac{3}{x-1} = \dfrac{1}{x+2}$.   [68] $\dfrac{1}{x+3} + \dfrac{2}{x-3} = \dfrac{3x-4}{x^2-4}$.

Simplify:

69. $\left(1 + \dfrac{x+y}{x-y}\right)^2 \div \left(1 + \dfrac{x-y}{x+y}\right)^2$.

[70] $\dfrac{(a^2 - 3ab - 10b^2)(a^2 + 3ab - 10b^2)}{(a^2 - 4b^2)(a^2 - 25b^2)}$.

71. $\dfrac{1}{(x+1)(x-2)} - \dfrac{6}{(x+1)(x+4)(x-2)}$.

72. $\dfrac{1}{(2x+1)(2x+3)} + \dfrac{1}{(2x+3)(2x+5)} + \dfrac{1}{(2x+5)(2x+1)}$.

73. $\dfrac{x^2 - (y-z)^2}{(x+z)^2 - y^2} \times \dfrac{y^2 - (z-x)^2}{(x+y)^2 - z^2} \times \dfrac{z^2 - (x-y)^2}{(y+z)^2 - x^2}$.

[74] $\left(1 + \dfrac{a}{b}\right)\left(\dfrac{1}{a} - \dfrac{1}{b}\right) \div \left\{\dfrac{1}{a}\left(a - \dfrac{a^3}{b^2}\right)\right\}$.

75. If $p = \dfrac{2x}{1-x}$ and $q = \dfrac{1-x}{1+x}$, express $\dfrac{p+q}{1-pq}$ in terms of x.

76. If $a = \dfrac{1}{n+2}$ and $b = \dfrac{1}{n-2}$, express $\dfrac{3-a}{2+a} + \dfrac{3+b}{2-b}$ in terms of n.

CHAPTER XII

LITERAL RELATIONS

Transformation of Formulae

Example 1. The volume V cu. in. of a circular cone of base-radius r in. and height h in. is given by the formula,

$$V = \tfrac{1}{3}\pi r^2 h.$$

Make r the subject of the formula.

$$\tfrac{1}{3}\pi r^2 h = V, \qquad \therefore \; \pi r^2 h = 3V;$$

divide each side by πh, $\qquad \therefore \; r^2 = \dfrac{3V}{\pi h};$

take the square root of each side,

$$\therefore \; r = \sqrt{\left(\dfrac{3V}{\pi h}\right)}.$$

We do not write $r = \pm\sqrt{\left(\dfrac{3V}{\pi h}\right)}$ because r is the radius in inches of the base of the cone.

Example 2. Make (i) u, (ii) z the subject of the optical formula,

$$\frac{1}{f} = \frac{1}{u} + \frac{1}{zu}.$$

(i) Multiply each side by fu, $\quad \therefore \; \dfrac{fu}{f} = \dfrac{fu}{u} + \dfrac{fu}{zu},$

$$\therefore \; u = f + \frac{f}{z}.$$

This may also be written, $u = \dfrac{fz+f}{z} = \dfrac{f(z+1)}{z}.$

(ii) Multiply each side by fuz, $\quad \therefore \; uz = fz + f.$

To make z the subject, *collect terms in z on one side of the equation, terms without z on the other side,*

$$\therefore \; uz - fz = f;$$
$$\therefore \; z(u - f) = f;$$
$$\therefore \; z = \frac{f}{u - f}.$$

EXERCISE XII. a

1. Interpret the simple interest formula, $A = P + \dfrac{PRT}{100}$.

Make (i) P, (ii) T, the subject of the formula.

Find T if $A = 504$, $P = 420$, $R = 5$.

2. If a car increases its speed from u ft. per sec. to v ft. per sec. in t seconds, at a steady rate of increase, a ft. per sec. every second, then $v = u + at$. Make a the subject of the formula.

If with the data of No. 2, the car travels s feet in this time t seconds, the following formulae can be proved:

$$(i) \ s = \frac{u+v}{2} \cdot t; \qquad (ii) \ s = ut + \tfrac{1}{2}at^2;$$

$$(iii) \ v^2 = u^2 + 2as; \qquad (iv) \ s = vt - \tfrac{1}{2}at^2.$$

Use the *appropriate* formula for the following:

3. Find u in terms of s, a, t.   **4.** Find v in terms of s, u, t.

5. Find a in terms of u, v, s.   **6.** Find t in terms of s, u, v.

[7] Find v in terms of s, a, t.   **[8]** Find u in terms of s, v, t.

9. Find a in terms of s, u, t.   **10.** Find u in terms of a, v, s.

[11] Find a in terms of s, v, t.   **[12]** Find v in terms of u, a, s.

13. Interpret the formula, $C = 2\pi r$, and make r the subject.

14. Interpret the formula, $A = \pi r^2$, and make r the subject.

[15] Interpret the formula, $V = \pi r^2 h$, and make r the subject.

16. If the radius of a sphere is r inches, its surface S sq. in., and its volume V cu. in. are given by the formulae, $S = 4\pi r^2$, $V = \tfrac{4}{3}\pi r^3$. Find r in terms of (i) S, (ii) V.

Change the following formulae to the required forms:

[17] $P = \dfrac{Wv^2}{32r}$;   subject (i) r, (ii) v.

18. $Pt = \dfrac{W}{g}(v - u)$;   subject (i) W, (ii) u.

19. $d = t\dfrac{\mu - 1}{\mu}$;   subject μ.   **[20]** $t = \dfrac{2pr}{p + 2s}$;   subject p.

21. $E = \dfrac{wa}{(w + W)b}$; subject w.　　**[22]** $a = \dfrac{b(1 + ch)}{1 - dh}$; subject h.

23. $t = \sqrt{\left(\dfrac{2s}{g}\right)}$; subject s.　　**[24]** $v = \sqrt{(2gh)}$; subject h.

25. $(D - a)(d - a) = k^2$; subject d.

26. $\dfrac{1}{n} = 1 - \dfrac{r}{100}$; subject (i) r; (ii) n.

[27] $\dfrac{1}{u} + \dfrac{1}{v} = \dfrac{1}{f}$; subject (i) f; (ii) u.

28. $\dfrac{a}{x} + \dfrac{b}{y} = \dfrac{a}{y}$; subject (i) a; (ii) x.

[29] $\dfrac{1}{f} = (\mu - 1)\left(\dfrac{1}{r} - \dfrac{1}{s}\right)$; subject (i) f; (ii) μ.

30. $v^2 - gh = g\sqrt{(c^2 + h^2)}$; subject h.

31. $A = \pi\{(r + t)^2 - r^2\}$; subject (i) r; (ii) t.

[32] $s - a = \sqrt{\left(\dfrac{ab}{t} + a^2\right)}$; subject t.

33. If V cu. in. of water are poured into a spherical bowl of radius r in., and if the depth of the water at the centre is h in., V is given by the formula, $V = \pi h^2(r - \frac{1}{3}h)$.

　(i) Express V in terms of r if $h = 2r$; compare No. 16.

　(ii) Express V in terms of r if $h = \frac{1}{2}r$, and make r the subject.

[34] From the formula $T = \frac{1}{188}(l - \frac{3}{5}b)b^2$, express l in terms of T if $b = \frac{1}{10}l$.

*35. From the formulae, $P = \dfrac{W}{7\cdot5} + 1\cdot5$, $E = \dfrac{W}{8P}$, express E in terms of P only.

*36. From the formulae, $v = u + at$, $s = \frac{1}{2}(u + v)t$, express s in terms of (i) u, a, t; (ii) u, a, v.

*37. If $T^2 = 4\pi^2\left(\dfrac{h^2 + k^2}{hg}\right)$, express k^2 in terms of T, g, h. There is a number l different from h such that $T^2 = 4\pi^2\left(\dfrac{l^2 + k^2}{lg}\right)$ is true; equate the values of k^2 obtained from the two formulae, and hence express g in terms of h, l, T.

Simple and Simultaneous Equations

Use the same methods as are used for numerical equations.

Example 3.   Solve for x, $ax + \dfrac{b}{a} = bx + \dfrac{a}{b}$, where $a \neq b$.   Collect terms in x on one side of the equation, and terms without x on the other side:

$$ax - bx = \frac{a}{b} - \frac{b}{a};$$

$$\therefore\; x(a - b) = \frac{a^2 - b^2}{ab} = \frac{(a+b)(a-b)}{ab};$$

Divide each side by $(a - b)$; this is permissible since $a - b \neq 0$;

$$\therefore\; x = \frac{a+b}{ab}.$$

Note.   If $a = b$, the given equation is satisfied by every value of x.

Example 4.   Given that $a \neq b$, find x and y from the simultaneous equations,

$$ax - by = 2bc \quad \dots\dots\dots\dots\dots\dots\dots\dots\dots\text{(i)}$$

$$\frac{ax}{b} - \frac{by}{a} = \left(\frac{a}{b} + \frac{b}{a}\right)c \quad \dots\dots\dots\dots\dots\dots\text{(ii)}$$

From (ii), $\times ab$, $a^2 x - b^2 y = (a^2 + b^2)c \quad \dots\dots\dots\dots\dots\text{(iii)}$

From (i), $\times b$, $abx - b^2 y = 2b^2 c \quad \dots\dots\dots\dots\dots\dots\text{(iv)}$

Subtracting, $(a^2 - ab)x = (a^2 - b^2)c;$

but $a - b \neq 0$ and $a \neq 0$, $\therefore\; x = \dfrac{(a+b)(a-b)c}{a(a-b)} = \dfrac{(a+b)c}{a}.$

Substitute for x in (i)

$$\therefore\; (a+b)c - by = 2bc;$$

$$\therefore\; (a-b)c = by;$$

$$\therefore\; y = \frac{(a-b)c}{b}.$$

Thus $x = \dfrac{c(a+b)}{a}, \qquad y = \dfrac{c(a-b)}{b}.$

Note.   The given form of equation (ii) implies that $a \neq 0$ and $b \neq 0$.

EXERCISE XII. b

Solve for x the following equations:

1. $\dfrac{a}{x} = \dfrac{b}{c}$.

2. $a - x = \dfrac{1}{b}$.

[3] $\dfrac{1}{x} = b + c$.

[4] $bx = b + b^2$.

5. $p(x + q) = 3pq$.

[6] $x = mx + c$.

7. $\dfrac{1}{x} = \dfrac{1}{a} + \dfrac{1}{b}$.

[8] $\dfrac{x}{2a} + \dfrac{x}{3a} = b$.

[9] $\dfrac{x + p}{x - q} = 2$.

10. $px + q = p + qx$, $p \neq q$.

[11] $ax + bx = a^2 - b^2$, $a + b \neq 0$.

12. $r(x + s) = s(x + r)$, $r \neq s$.

[13] $(x - a)^2 = x^2 + b^2$, $a \neq 0$.

14. $\dfrac{1}{x - a} + \dfrac{1}{x - b} = \dfrac{2}{x}$, $a + b \neq 0$.

[15] $\dfrac{c}{x - d} + \dfrac{d}{x - c} = \dfrac{c + d}{x}$, $cd \neq 0$.

Find x and y from the following simultaneous equations; state any inequalities assumed in the solutions.

[16] $x + y = 7c$.
$x - y = 3c$.

17. $2x - y = a$.
$x + 3y = b$.

[18] $ax + 2by = 4c$.
$2ax - by = 3c$.

19. $x + y = p + q$.
$px + qy = 2pq$.

[20] $x + cy = d$.
$x + dy = c$.

21. $ax + y = ab$.
$bx - ay = b^2$.

[22] $ax - by = a^2 + b^2$.
$x + y = 2a$.

23. $b(x - b) = ay$.
$a(x - a) = b(x - y)$.

[24] $cx + dy = 2cd$.
$dx - cy = d^2 - c^2$.

25. $ax + by = bx - ay = a^2 + b^2$.

[26] $x - p = y - q = \dfrac{px - qy}{p + q}$.

27. $qx = py$.
$px - qy = p + q$.

[28] $\dfrac{x}{a} + \dfrac{y}{b} = 2$.
$ax + by = a^2 + b^2$.

29. $\dfrac{x - a}{b} + \dfrac{y}{a} = 0$.
$\dfrac{x - b}{a} - \dfrac{y}{b} = 0$.

30. $(p - q)x + (p + q)y = (p + q)^2$, $qx - py = q^2 - pq$.

Problems involving Letters

Example 5.   The length of a field is n times its breadth; the perimeter is p yards; find the breadth.

Let the breadth be x yards.

Then the length is nx yards;

$\therefore$ the perimeter is $(2nx + 2x)$ yards; but this is p yards;

$$\therefore \ 2nx + 2x = p; \quad \therefore \ 2x(n+1) = p;$$

Divide each side by $2(n+1)$, $\therefore \ x = \dfrac{p}{2(n+1)}.$

$\therefore$ the breadth is $\dfrac{p}{2(n+1)}$ **yards.**

If you do not see how to solve a problem containing letters, invent a similar problem *with numbers*, and work that out first. Then apply the same method to the given problem.

Thus, in the above case, first solve the following:

The length of a field is 5 times its breadth; the perimeter is 400 yards; find the breadth.

Example 6.   A car is sold for £P at a gain of R per cent.   Find its cost price.

Let the cost price be £x.

Since the gain is R per cent. of the *cost* price,

$$\text{the gain} = \frac{R}{100} \text{ of } £x = £\frac{Rx}{100};$$

$\therefore$ the selling price $= £x + £\dfrac{Rx}{100}$; but this is £P;

$$\therefore \ x + \frac{Rx}{100} = P;$$

$$\therefore \ 100x + Rx = 100P;$$

$$\therefore \ x(100 + R) = 100P;$$

$$\therefore \ x = \frac{100P}{100 + R}.$$

$\therefore$ the cost price is £$\dfrac{100P}{100 + R}.$

Or as follows:

A gain of R per cent. means that if the *cost* price is £100, the selling price is £(100 + R);

∴ the cost price = $\dfrac{100}{100 + R}$ of the selling price

$$= £\dfrac{100P}{100 + R}.$$

EXERCISE XII. c

1. (i) I share 4 shillings between 2 boys so that one gets 5 times as much as the other. How much does each get?

   (ii) I share p shillings between 2 boys so that one gets n times as much as the other. How much does each get?

[2] (i) The sum of two consecutive integers is 91. What are they?

   (ii) The sum of two consecutive integers is 2N + 15. What are they?

3. A man, N years old, has a son, n years old. In how many years' time will the man be (i) just twice as old as his son, (ii) just t times as old as his son?

4. A hall is k times as long as it is wide; and its floor area is S sq. feet. What is its length?

[5] Two rods, of lengths a in. and $(a + b)$ in., are cut down by equal amounts. If the first is then just half the length of the second, how long is each?

6. In Fig. 149, AE bisects ∠CAB; if ∠DAB = $x°$, ∠DAE = $y°$, find a formula for (i) y in terms of x, (ii) x in terms of y.

7. A man starts with a salary of £P a year for his first year and receives each year an increase of £M a year. How much does he receive for his 3rd year? Find a

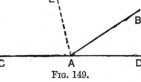

FIG. 149.

formula for the money, £S, he receives for his nth year of service. Then make (i) M, (ii) n the subject.

[8] A has £p, B has £q; how much must A give B so that they have equal amounts?

9. One tap supplies per minute k times as much water as another tap; together, they supply n gallons in t minutes. How many gallons per minute does the first tap supply?

[10] Share c shillings between 2 boys so that one gets six pence more than twice what the other gets.

11. What number exceeds n by r per cent.?

[12] N + (r per cent. of N) equals k. Find N in terms of r, k.

13. If a certain number is decreased by r per cent., the result is k; find the number.

[14] The bottom of a lidless box is a square of side c inches and the box is h inches high, external measurements. If the total external surface area is A sq. inches, find h in terms of A, c.

Express in symbols the statements in Nos. 15–19, and prove that they are correct.

15. The square of the sum of two numbers exceeds the square of their difference by four times their product.

[16] For any three consecutive integers, the square of the middle number exceeds the product of the others by 1.

17. For any three consecutive integers, the sum of the squares of the greatest and least exceeds twice the square of the middle number by 2.

[18] For any four consecutive integers, the product of the greatest and least is less by 2 than the product of the others.

19. The difference between the square of the sum of two consecutive integers and the product of the two integers is numerically equal to the difference between the cubes of the integers.

20. To a number of two digits is added the number formed by reversing the digits. Prove that the result is divisible by 11.

[21] Write down expressions for five consecutive integers, three of which are even, and prove that the sum of their squares is always divisible by 10.

22. Goods are bought for £x and sold for £y so as to produce a profit of r per cent. on the *sale* price. Express $\dfrac{y}{x}$ in terms of r.

[23] For what value of p will $\dfrac{a+p}{b-p}$ reduce to $\dfrac{4a}{3b}$?

24. Fig. 150 represents three circular arcs, centres **A**, **B**, **C**; $BC = a$, $CA = b$, $AB = c$; the units are inches. Express r in terms of a, b, c.

FIG. 150.

[25] If a man sells a bicycle for £**P** his profit is n times as much as his loss would be if he let it go for £**Q**. What did the bicycle cost him?

26. If **A** gives half his money to **B**, then **B** will have n times as much as **A**. If **B** gives c shillings to **A**, then **A** will have twice as much as **B**. How much has each?

[27] A square lawn has a paved path, d yards wide, all round it. If the area of the path is **S** sq. yards, find the length of the lawn.

28. A man rows upstream at u miles an hour and back to the same place at v miles an hour, and takes half an hour altogether. How far upstream did he go?

[29] A river flows at v miles per hour. What is the speed through the water of a steamer that can go downstream n times as fast as upstream?

*30. For a railway journey, n lb. of luggage is allowed free and the charge for the rest is a penny per w lb. How much luggage do I take, if I pay at the rate of a penny per **W** lb. on the whole of it?

*31. If I run to the station at u miles per hour I shall have p minutes to spare; but if I walk at $\dfrac{3u}{4}$ miles per hour I shall miss the train by np minutes. How far off is the station?

*32. A certain sum of money will pay a man's wages for b days and will pay a boy's wages for c days. For how long will it suffice to pay for both a man and a boy?

*33. A man spends £x on books costing y shillings each and £y on books costing x shillings each. Find the average cost per book in shillings.

*34. One train travelling uniformly does a certain journey in *b* hours and another train travelling uniformly does the same journey in the opposite direction in *c* hours. If they start at the same time, find how long it will be before they meet.

*35. In Fig. 151 a chord AB of length *l* inches cuts off from a circle of radius *r* inches a segment of height *h* inches. Prove that $l^2 + 4h^2 = 8rh$.

If $r = 4h$, find *l* in terms of *r*.

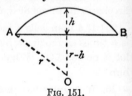

FIG. 151.

*36. A beaker when empty weighs *b* grams, when full of water it weighs *c* grams, and when full of methylated spirit *d* grams. Find the specific gravity of the methylated spirit (*i.e.* the ratio of the weight of any amount of it to the weight of the same amount of water).

Quadratic Equations

Any quadratic equation can be reduced to the form

$$ax^2 + bx + c = 0,$$

and its roots (if they exist) may be found by the method of "completing the square."

$$ax^2 + bx = -c;$$

divide each side by *a*,

$$\therefore x^2 + \frac{b}{a}x = -\frac{c}{a};$$

Add $\left(\dfrac{b}{2a}\right)^2$ to each side,

$$\therefore x^2 + \frac{b}{a}x + \left(\frac{b}{2a}\right)^2 = \frac{b^2}{4a^2} - \frac{c}{a};$$

$$\therefore \left(x + \frac{b}{2a}\right)^2 = \frac{b^2 - 4ac}{4a^2}.$$

Take the square root of each side. *This is possible if $b^2 - 4ac$ is positive or zero ; it is impossible if $b^2 - 4ac$ is negative.*

$$\therefore x + \frac{b}{2a} = \pm \frac{\sqrt{(b^2 - 4ac)}}{2a};$$

$\therefore$ either $x = -\dfrac{b}{2a} + \dfrac{\sqrt{(b^2 - 4ac)}}{2a}$ or $x = -\dfrac{b}{2a} - \dfrac{\sqrt{(b^2 - 4ac)}}{2a}$

This is written more shortly in the form

$$x = \frac{-b \pm \sqrt{(b^2 - 4ac)}}{2a}$$

and is called the *formula* for the roots of the quadratic

$$ax^2 + bx + c = 0.$$

The quadratic has **no** roots if $b^2 - 4ac$ is **negative.** If $b^2 = 4ac$, *the two roots are* equal, each being $-\dfrac{b}{2a}$.

If the roots of the quadratic, $ax^2 + bx + c = 0$, are denoted by a, β, it was proved on p. 223 that

$$a + \beta = -\frac{b}{a} \quad \text{and} \quad a\beta = \frac{c}{a}.$$

These two facts should be committed to memory; they may be verified by using the formula.

Example 7. Solve $5x^2 = 9x + 6$, expressing each root **correct** to two places of decimals.

$$5x^2 - 9x - 6 = 0.$$

The equation, $ax^2 + bx + c = 0$, is equivalent to $5x^2 - 9x - 6 = 0$, if $a = 5$, $b = -9$, $c = -6$.

$\therefore$ the roots are $\quad x = \dfrac{-(-9) \pm \sqrt{\{(-9)^2 - 4(5)(-6)\}}}{2(5)}$

$$= \frac{9 \pm \sqrt{(81 + 120)}}{10} = \frac{9 \pm \sqrt{201}}{10};$$

Also $\sqrt{201} \simeq 14 \cdot 18$,

$$\therefore x = \frac{9 \pm 14 \cdot 18}{10};$$

$$\therefore x = \frac{23 \cdot 18}{10} \quad \text{or} \quad -\frac{5 \cdot 18}{10}$$

$$= 2 \cdot 318 \quad \text{or} \quad -0 \cdot 518;$$

$$\therefore x = 2 \cdot 32 \quad \text{or} \quad -0 \cdot 52, \text{ to 2 decimal places.}$$

Do not use the formula, if you can solve the equation by the direct factor method.

Do not use the formula, if you can solve the equation *rapidly* by completing the square.

If you use the formula, *substitute first, and simplify afterwards.* Do not try to do both at once.

If you intend to use the formula, you must learn it by heart.

Example 8. If α and β are the roots of $px^2 + qx + r = 0$, find the value of $\dfrac{\alpha}{\beta} + \dfrac{\beta}{\alpha}$.

Since α, β are the roots of $x^2 + \dfrac{q}{p}x + \dfrac{r}{p} = 0$,

$$\alpha + \beta = -\frac{q}{p} \text{ and } \alpha\beta = \frac{r}{p}.$$

$$\frac{\alpha}{\beta} + \frac{\beta}{\alpha} = \frac{\alpha^2 + \beta^2}{\alpha\beta}.$$

$$(\alpha + \beta)^2 = \frac{q^2}{p^2}, \quad \therefore \; \alpha^2 + 2\alpha\beta + \beta^2 = \frac{q^2}{p^2};$$

$$\therefore \; \alpha^2 + \beta^2 = \frac{q^2}{p^2} - 2\alpha\beta = \frac{q^2}{p^2} - \frac{2r}{p}$$

$$= \frac{q^2 - 2pr}{p^2};$$

$$\therefore \; \frac{\alpha}{\beta} + \frac{\beta}{\alpha} = \frac{q^2 - 2pr}{p^2} \div \frac{r}{p} = \frac{q^2 - 2pr}{p^2} \times \frac{p}{r}$$

$$= \frac{q^2 - 2pr}{pr}.$$

Example 9. If α, β are the roots of $x^2 + 7x + p = 0$ and if $\dfrac{1+\alpha}{\alpha}$, $\dfrac{1+\beta}{\beta}$ are the roots of $3x^2 - 8x + q = 0$, find the values of p, q.

$$\alpha + \beta = -7 \quad\quad\quad\quad\quad\quad\dots\dots\dots\dots\dots\dots\dots\text{(i)}$$

and

$$\frac{1+\alpha}{\alpha} + \frac{1+\beta}{\beta} = \frac{8}{3} \quad\quad\quad\quad\dots\dots\dots\dots\dots\dots\text{(ii)}$$

From (ii), $\times \alpha\beta$,

$$\beta + \alpha\beta + \alpha + \alpha\beta = \tfrac{8}{3}\alpha\beta;$$

$$\therefore \; \tfrac{2}{3}\alpha\beta = \alpha + \beta = -7;$$

$$\therefore \; \alpha\beta = -\tfrac{21}{2};$$

$$\therefore \; p = \alpha\beta = -10\tfrac{1}{2};$$

Also

$$\frac{q}{3} = \frac{1+\alpha}{\alpha} \times \frac{1+\beta}{\beta} = \frac{1+\alpha+\beta+\alpha\beta}{\alpha\beta}$$

$$= \frac{1 - 7 - 10\tfrac{1}{2}}{-10\tfrac{1}{2}} = \frac{16\tfrac{1}{2}}{10\tfrac{1}{2}};$$

$$\therefore \; q = \tfrac{33}{21} \times 3 = 4\tfrac{5}{7}.$$

EXERCISE XII. d

Solve the following equations by whatever method is best. If the roots are irrational, give their values correct to one place of decimals.

1. $x^2 - 3x - 1 = 0$. **2.** $x^2 - 3x + 1 = 0$. **3.** $x^2 - 7x = 18$.

4. $2x^2 + 3x = 3$. **5.** $3x^2 + 5 = 8x$. **6.** $6x^2 = 2x + 1$.

[7] $x^2 + 5x - 3 = 0$. **[8]** $x^2 + 7x = 5$. **[9]** $x^2 = 8x + 7$.

[10] $2x^2 - 5x = 4$. **[11]** $2x^2 = 3x + 2$. **[12]** $5x^2 - 7x - 4 = 0$.

13. $7x^2 + x - 1 = 0$. **14.** $\dfrac{x^2}{3} - \dfrac{x}{2} = \dfrac{1}{5}$. **15.** $x + \dfrac{1}{x} = 4$.

16. $\dfrac{3x^2}{4} - x = \dfrac{1}{3}$. **17.** $x^2 + 2\cdot5x = 1\cdot8$. **18.** $(x+1)^2 = 20$.

[19] $10x - 5x^2 = 3$. **[20]** $8x^2 - 3x = 11$. **[21]** $6x^2 + 11x = 10$.

[22] $\dfrac{2x}{3} - \dfrac{5}{2x} = 1\tfrac{1}{2}$. **[23]** $10x + 11 = \dfrac{6}{x}$. **[24]** $2x^2 - 1\cdot7 = 1\cdot2x$.

25. Solve $x^2 + 2kx = l^2$. **26.** Solve $px^2 + 2qx + r = 0$.

27. (i) What are the roots of $(x-2)^2 = 7$?

(ii) Combine into a single statement $x = 5 + \sqrt{2}$ or $5 - \sqrt{2}$.

Construct equations having the following roots:

28. $1 + \sqrt{3}$, $1 - \sqrt{3}$. **29.** $\dfrac{-3 + \sqrt{2}}{2}$, $\dfrac{-3 - \sqrt{2}}{2}$.

[30] $-2 + \sqrt{5}$, $-2 - \sqrt{5}$. **[31]** $\dfrac{5 + \sqrt{3}}{2}$, $\dfrac{5 - \sqrt{3}}{2}$.

32. If $x = 3$ is a root of each of the following equations, *write down* the other root, and then find the value of p.

(i) $x^2 - 5x + p = 0$; (ii) $x^2 + 4x + p = 0$;

(iii) $x^2 + px + 12 = 0$; (iv) $5x^2 + px - 6 = 0$.

[33] Find c if $3x^2 - 8x + c = 0$ has equal roots.

[34] One root of $7x^2 + 6x + c = 0$ is double the other; find the roots; also find c.

35. One root of $4x^2 + bx + 75 = 0$ is three times the other; find the roots; also find b.

36. If a, β are the roots of $x^2 - 4x - 7 = 0$, find the values of

$\qquad$ (i) $a^2 + \beta^2$; $\qquad$ (ii) $\dfrac{a}{\beta} + \dfrac{\beta}{a}$; $\qquad$ (iii) $\dfrac{1}{a} + \dfrac{1}{\beta}$.

[37] If a, β are the roots of $2x^2 + 6x + 3 = 0$, find the values of

$\qquad$ (i) $a^2 + \beta^2$; $\qquad$ (ii) $(a+1)(\beta+1)$; $\qquad$ (iii) $\dfrac{1}{a^2} + \dfrac{1}{\beta^2}$.

38. Find the value of c if $x^2 + (c-1)x = 2c + 1$ has equal roots.

[39] Find the value of c if the sum of the roots of the equation $x^2 - (c+6)x + 2(2c-1) = 0$ is half their product.

40. If a, β are the roots of $2x^2 + 15x - 24 = 0$, and if $\dfrac{a}{\beta}$, $\dfrac{\beta}{a}$ are the roots of $px^2 + qx + 1 = 0$, find the values of p, q.

*41. If a, β are the roots of $x^2 - 6x + q = 0$ and if $\dfrac{1-a}{a}$, $\dfrac{1-\beta}{\beta}$ are the roots of $8x^2 + 10x + r = 0$, find the values of q, r.

*42. Find the two values of p such that the roots of $x^2 - 19x + 25 = 0$ are the squares of the roots of $x^2 + px - 5 = 0$.

*43. If a, β are the roots of $x + \dfrac{1}{x-c} = 1$, find in terms of c the values of $a + \beta$, $a\beta$, and $a^2 + \beta^2$. If c is not equal to -1, find its value when $5a = 3\beta$.

*44. If $2x^2 - 5x + b = 0$ has equal roots, and if the roots of $2x^2 - cx + b = 0$ differ by $\tfrac{15}{8}$, find the values of b, c.

*45. Find the equation whose roots are the squares of the roots of $2x^2 - 4x = 3$.

Solve for x the following equations:

$\qquad$ **46.** $x^2 - 5ax + 6a^2 = 0$. $\qquad\qquad$ [47] $x^2 - 3cx = 10c^2$.

$\qquad$ **48.** $x^2 - (c+d)x + cd = 0$. $\qquad\qquad$ [49] $(x-b)^2 = 4c^2$.

$\qquad$ **50.** $x^2 - 2px = q^2 - p^2$. $\qquad\qquad$ [51] $x^2 + 2x = a^2 - 1$.

$\qquad$ ***52.** $x^2 - 2(a+b)x + (a-b)^2 = 0$. $\qquad$ ***53.** $x - \dfrac{1}{x} = 2c$.

$\qquad$ ***54.** $a(x^2 + 1) = (a^2 + 1)x$. $\qquad\qquad$ ***55.** $ax^2 + (1+ab)x + b = 0$.

CHAPTER XIII

FURTHER PROCESSES

Simultaneous Linear and Quadratic Equations

Use the linear equation to eliminate one of the unknowns from the quadratic equation.

Example 1. Find x, y from the simultaneous equations,

$$2x - 3y = 1 \quad \dots\dots\dots\dots\dots\dots\text{(i)}$$

$$2x^2 - 2xy - 3y^2 = 1 \quad \dots\dots\dots\dots\dots\text{(ii)}$$

From (i), $2x = 1 + 3y$; $\therefore x = \dfrac{1 + 3y}{2} \quad \dots\dots\dots\dots\dots\dots\text{(iii)}$

Using (iii), substitute for x in (ii),

$$\therefore 2\left(\frac{1+3y}{2}\right)^2 - 2\left(\frac{1+3y}{2}\right)y - 3y^2 = 1;$$

$$\therefore \frac{2(1+6y+9y^2)}{4} - y(1+3y) - 3y^2 = 1;$$

$$\therefore 1 + 6y + 9y^2 - 2y(1+3y) - 6y^2 = 2;$$

$$\therefore 1 + 6y + 9y^2 - 2y - 6y^2 - 6y^2 = 2;$$

$$\therefore -3y^2 + 4y - 1 = 0; \quad \therefore 3y^2 - 4y + 1 = 0;$$

$$\therefore (y-1)(3y-1) = 0; \quad \therefore y - 1 = 0 \text{ or } 3y - 1 = 0;$$

$$\therefore y = 1 \text{ or } \tfrac{1}{3}.$$

Substitute in (iii). If $y = 1$, $x = \dfrac{1+3}{2} = 2$.

$$\text{If } y = \frac{1}{3}, \ x = \frac{1+1}{2} = 1.$$

$\therefore$ the solution is $\mathbf{x = 2, \ y = 1,}$ *or* $\mathbf{x = 1, \ y = \dfrac{1}{3}}.$

Before starting to solve the equations, look at them **carefully** and see which is the easier unknown to eliminate.

Eliminate whichever unknown is easier.

When you have found one unknown, the other should be found by substituting in the given *linear* equation, or its equivalent.

EXERCISE XIII. a

Solve the following simultaneous equations:

1. $x = y.$
$2x^2 - y^2 = 1.$

2. $x - 2y = 1.$
$xy = 3.$

3. $x + y = 0.$
$xy - y^2 = -8.$

4. $2x - y = 5.$
$xy = 0.$

5. $3x + y = 4.$
$xy = 1.$

6. $x + y = 1.$
$x^2 - xy = 15.$

7. $3x - 4y = 4.$
$y^2 = x.$

8. $x + y = 6.$
$x^2 + 2y^2 = 24.$

9. $3x - y = 8.$
$3x^2 - xy + 9 = y^2.$

[10] $x - y = 1.$
$xy - 2x = 4.$

[11] $x + y = 7.$
$x^2 + y^2 = 29.$

[12] $x^2 - y^2 = 40.$
$x + y = 10.$

[13] $x - 3y = 0.$
$2x^2 + 3xy - 2x = 21.$

[14] $x + 2y = -1.$
$x^2 - 2xy = 3 - 4x.$

[15] $3x - y = 9.$
$6x^2 - 17xy + 5y^2 = 171.$

16. $2x + 2y = 3.$
$x^2 - xy = \frac{1}{2}.$

17. $2x - 3y = 12.$
$x^2 - xy = 15.$

18. $3x - 2y = 7.$
$x^2 + xy + y^2 = 3.$

19. $(x + 1)(2y + 1) = 4xy,\ 3x - y = 3.$

20. $x - y = 10.$
$\dfrac{12}{y} - \dfrac{12}{x} = 5.$

21. $\dfrac{x^2 - 3y^2}{x^2 + 3y^2} = \dfrac{1}{2} = \dfrac{2x - y}{10}.$

[22] $x + 3 = 5y.$
$x^2 - y^2 = 45.$

[23] $x + 4y = -5.$
$5x^2 + 9xy + 25 = 4y^2.$

[24] $x - 3y = -1.$
$3x^2 - 7xy = 5.$

[25] $x + y = 1.$
$\dfrac{x}{y} + \dfrac{y}{x} = 2\frac{1}{2}.$

[26] $\dfrac{x^2 - y^2}{8xy} = \dfrac{1}{3} = \dfrac{x + 2y - 8}{6}.$

*27. $\dfrac{1}{x - 2y} - \dfrac{1}{x + 2y} = \dfrac{2}{3},\qquad 3x - 4y = 4.$

Obtain a linear equation from the pairs of given equations in Nos. 28–30, and then solve them:

*28. $(x - 1)(y + 2) = 15,\ xy = 12.$

*29. $(x + 2)(y - 2) = 144,\ xy = 160.$

*30. $(x + 3)(y + 2) = 25,\ (2x - 1)(y + 1) = 12.$

Graphical Solutions

Any quadratic equation, which has roots, can be solved by reading off the x-coordinates of the intersections of a suitable straight line with the graph of $y = x^2$.

Example 2. Solve graphically $5x^2 - 9x - 6 = 0$.

$$5x^2 = 9x + 6; \qquad \therefore \ x^2 = \tfrac{1}{5}(9x + 6).$$

$\therefore$ the roots of this equation are the values of x which satisfy the *simultaneous* equations, $y = x^2$, $y = \tfrac{1}{5}(9x + 6)$.

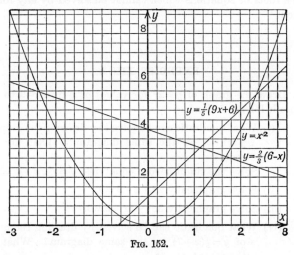

FIG. 152.

The graphs of $y = x^2$ and $y = \tfrac{1}{5}(9x + 6)$ are shown in Fig. 152.

Oral work on Fig. 152.

(i) Read off the roots of $5x^2 - 9x - 6 = 0$, as accurately as Fig. 152 permits. Compare the answer with Example 7, p. 273.

(ii) Read off the solution of the simultaneous equations,

$$y = x^2, \quad 5y = 9x + 6.$$

(iii) Fig. 152 shows the graph of $y = \tfrac{2}{3}(6 - x)$. What quadratic equation can be solved by using it? What are the roots?

(iv) Solve the simultaneous equations, $y = x^2$, $2x + 3y = 12$.

(v) By drawing a line *in pencil* in Fig. 152, or by laying your ruler across the figure, find the roots of $x^2 = x + 2$.

(vi) Repeat (v) for the following:

$\qquad$ (a) $x^2 + x = 3$; $\quad$ (b) $2x^2 + x = 4$; $\quad$ (c) $3x^2 = 4x + 12$.

(vii) By drawing a line *in pencil* or by laying your ruler across the paper, show that $x^2 - 2x + 2 = 0$ has no roots.

In Example 2, we have used graphical methods to solve equations which can be solved easily by calculation. By drawing suitable graphs it is possible to find numerical approximations for the roots of equations which cannot be solved by any formal method.

EXERCISE XIII. b

1. Draw the graph of $y = x^2$ for values of x from -3 to $+3$, and use it for the following:

$\qquad$ (i) What quadratic can be solved by drawing the graph of $y = 1 - x$ on the same diagram? What are the roots?

$\qquad$ Solve the simultaneous equations, $y = x^2$, $x + y = 1$.

$\qquad$ (ii) Solve graphically $x^2 + x - 2 = 0$.

$\qquad$ (iii) Solve graphically $3x^2 - 2x - 6 = 0$.

$\qquad$ (iv) What quadratic can be solved by drawing the graph of $y = \frac{4}{5}(x + 7)$ on the same diagram? What are the roots?

$\qquad$ Solve the simultaneous equations,
$$y = x^2, \quad 4x - 5y + 28 = 0.$$

$\qquad$ (v) Show graphically that $x^2 + x + 1 = 0$ has no roots.

[2] Draw the graph of $y = 2 + 3x - x^2$ for values of x from -1 to $+4$. Find graphically the values of x for which $2 + 3x - x^2$ is equal to $1 + \frac{1}{2}x$.

3. Draw the graphs of $y = \frac{1}{2}x^2 - \frac{1}{4}$ and $y = \frac{1}{4}(3x + 2)$ for values of x from -3 to $+3$. What quadratic equation can be solved by using these graphs? Solve it. For what range of values of x is $\frac{1}{4}(3x + 2)$ greater than $\frac{1}{2}x^2 - \frac{1}{4}$?

4. Draw the graph of $y = x^3$ for values of x from -3 to $+3$, and use it for the following:

(i) What equation in x can be solved by drawing the graph of $y = 3x + 3$ on the same diagram ?   What are the roots ?

(ii) Solve graphically $x^3 = 15 - 5x$.

(iii) What equation in x can be solved by drawing the graph of $y = 5x$ on the same diagram ?   What are the roots ?

(iv) Solve graphically $x^3 + 2x - 5 = 0$.

(v) Solve graphically $2x^3 - 7x - 4 = 0$.

(vi) Solve graphically $3x^3 + 10x + 30 = 0$.

[5] Taking 1 inch as the unit both for the x-axis and the y-axis, draw the graph of $y = \frac{1}{40}x^3$ from $x = 0$ to $x = 6$.   Use this and another suitable graph to find approximate values of the two positive roots of the equation $x^3 = 10(3x - 2)$.

[6] Draw the graph of $y = \frac{1}{10}(x^3 + 8x - 40)$ for values of x from 0 to 4.   Solve graphically the equation $x^3 + 8x = 40$.

7. Draw the graph of $y = \frac{1}{10}x(x^2 - 4)$ for values of x from -4 to $+4$ and read off answers to the following:

(i) For what positive value of x is $x^3 - 4x$ a minimum ?

(ii) What is the maximum value of $x^3 - 4x$ if x is negative ?

(iii) For what values of x is $\frac{1}{10}(x^3 - 4x)$ equal to $0 \cdot 2$?

(iv) Solve the equations (a) $x^3 - 4x = 1$; (b) $x^3 - 4x + 1 = 0$.

[8] Draw the graph of $y = \frac{1}{5}x(x+1)(x-4)$ for values of x from -3 to $+5$.   Use it to answer the following:

(i) For what value of x does $x^3 - 3x^2 - 4x$ equal 6 ?

(ii) What is the least value of $x^3 - 3x^2 - 4x$ if x is positive ?

(iii) What is the largest value of $x^3 - 3x^2 - 4x$ if x is negative ?

(iv) Solve (a) $x^3 - 3x^2 - 4x = 13$;   (b) $x^3 - 3x^2 - 4x = -4$;
     (c) $x^3 - 3x^2 - 4x + 19 = 0$;   (d) $x^3 - 3x^2 - 4x = 16$;
     (e) $x^3 - 3x^2 - 4x + 12 = 0$.

9. The base of an open cistern is a square of side x feet; its volume is 200 cu. ft. If the total area of the base and sides is A sq. ft., prove that $A = x^2 + \dfrac{800}{x}$. Represent the relation between A and x by a graph for values of x from 4 to 12. For what value of x is A least? For what positive values of x is A equal to 175?

[10] Draw the graph of $y = x + \dfrac{8}{1+x}$ for values of x from 0 to 5 and find the least value of y as x varies from 0 to 5.

*11. The graph of $y = a + bx + cx^2$, where a, b, c are constants, passes through the origin and the two points $(1, 1)$, $(2, -2)$. Find the values of a, b, c and calculate the values of x when $y = -5$. Draw the graph and find the maximum value of y.

*12. The graph of $y = x^2 + bx + c$, where b, c are constants, passes through the points $(3, 14\frac{1}{4})$, $(-7, 24\frac{1}{4})$. Find the values of b and c and draw the graph for values of x from -5 to $+2$. Find from the graph (i) the minimum value of y, (ii) the range of values of x for which y is less than $-1\frac{3}{4}$.

*13. Without making a table of values, draw rough figures of the graphs of (i) $y = (x-1)^2$; (ii) $y = (x-1)^2 - 4 = x^2 - 2x - 3$; (iii) $y = (x-1)^2 + 4 = x^2 - 2x + 5$.

Which of the equations, $x^2 - 2x - 3 = 0$, $x^2 - 2x + 5 = 0$, has no roots?

*14. Without making a table of values, draw rough figures of the graphs of (i) $y = -(x-2)^2$; (ii) $y = -(x-2)^2 + 9 = 5 + 4x - x^2$; (iii) $y = -(x-2)^2 - 9 = -13 + 4x - x^2$.

Which of the equations, $x^2 = 4x + 5$, $x^2 = 4x - 13$, has no roots?

15. Draw the graph of $y = \dfrac{4 - x^2}{5 + x}$ for values of x from -3 to $+3$. (i) What is the value of $\dfrac{4 - x^2}{5 + x}$ if $2x^2 + x = 3$? Hence use the graph to solve this equation. (ii) Solve graphically $2x^2 - x = 13$.

[16] Draw the graph of $y = \dfrac{2x^2 - 3}{x + 8}$ for values of x from -3 to $+3$.

(i) What is the value of $\dfrac{2x^2 - 3}{x + 8}$ if $2x^2 = x + 11$?   Hence use the graph to solve this equation.   (ii) Solve graphically $4x^2 - x = 14$.

17. Draw the graph of $y = x - \dfrac{2}{x}$ for values of x from -3 to $-\dfrac{1}{2}$ and from $+\dfrac{1}{2}$ to $+3$.   Use the graph (i) to solve $x - \dfrac{2}{x} = 1{\cdot}75$; (ii) to find approximately the value of $\sqrt{2}$; (iii) to solve $2x^2 + 3x - 4 = 0$.

Remainder Theorem

Example 3.   Find the quotient and remainder when $x^3 - 11x + 2$ is divided by $x - 3$.

$$
\begin{array}{r}
x^2 + 3x - 2 \\
x - 3 \overline{\smash{)}\ x^3 \qquad\ -11x + 2} \\
x^3 - 3x^2 \\
\hline
3x^2 - 11x \\
3x^2 - 9x \\
\hline
-2x + 2 \\
-2x + 6 \\
\hline
-4
\end{array}
$$

Thus the quotient is $x^2 + 3x - 2$ and the remainder is -4. This result shows that

$$x^3 - 11x + 2 \equiv (x - 3)(x^2 + 3x - 2) - 4$$

where the symbol $\equiv$ is used to mean that the left side is equal to the right side for *all* values of x.

A relation of this kind is called an **identity**.

If we merely wish to find the *remainder*, we can do so without performing the actual division.

Denote the quotient by Q and the remainder by R;

then $\qquad\qquad x^3 - 11x + 2 \equiv (x - 3)\mathsf{Q} + \mathsf{R}$

where R is a constant, *i.e.* its value does not depend on the value of x.   In this identity put $x = 3$,

$$\therefore\ 3^3 - 11.3 + 2 = 0 + \mathsf{R};$$
$$\therefore\ \mathsf{R} = 27 - 33 + 2 = -4.$$

This method can be used to find the value of the remainder whenever the divisor is of the first degree.

Example 4. Find the remainder if $2x^3 + x^2 + 3$ is divided by $x + 2$.

Denote the quotient by Q and the remainder by R;

then $$2x^3 + x^2 + 3 \equiv (x+2)Q + R$$

where R is a constant.

Put $x = -2$, then $2(-2)^3 + (-2)^2 + 3 = 0 + R$;

$$\therefore \quad R = -16 + 4 + 3 = -9.$$

$$\therefore \quad \text{the remainder is } -9.$$

The reader should check this result by actual division.

In the same way it may be shown that when the divisor is $x - k$, the remainder is obtained by substituting $x = k$ in the expression; thus in Example 4 where the divisor is $x + 2$, the remainder is obtained by substituting $x = -2$. *The value to be substituted for* x *is the value which makes the divisor zero.*

Example 5. Prove that $x + 1$ is a factor of $x^4 - 6x^2 + x + 6$.

To obtain the remainder when $x^4 - 6x^2 + x + 6$ is divided by $x + 1$, put $x = -1$ in $x^4 - 6x^2 + x + 6$.

$$\therefore \quad \text{remainder} = (-1)^4 - 6(-1)^2 - 1 + 6$$
$$= 1 - 6 - 1 + 6 = 0.$$

Since the remainder is zero, $x + 1$ is a factor.

Example 6. Factorise $x^3 + 2x^2 - 5x - 6$.

Try putting $x = 1, -1, 2, -2, 3, -3, 6, -6$ (these are the various factors of the constant term -6), and see if the result is zero in any of these cases.

If $x = 1$, $x^3 + 2x^2 - 5x - 6 = 1 + 2 - 5 - 6 = -8$;

$$\therefore \quad (x - 1) \text{ is } not \text{ a factor.}$$

If $x = -1$, $x^3 + 2x^2 - 5x - 6 = -1 + 2 + 5 - 6 = 0$;

$$\therefore \quad (x + 1) \text{ is a factor.}$$

The other factor may now be found by long division or by inspection;

$$\therefore \quad x^3 + 2x^2 - 5x - 6 = (x+1)(x^2 + x - 6)$$
$$= (x+1)(x-2)(x+3).$$

EXERCISE XIII. c

Find the remainders in the following:

1. $(x^2 - 5x + 4) \div (x - 1)$.   [2] $(x^2 + 3x + 2) \div (x + 1)$.

3. $(x^2 - 2x - 15) \div (x + 3)$.   [4] $(x^2 + 5x - 14) \div (x - 2)$.

5. $(2x^2 + 3x - 2) \div (2x - 1)$.   [6] $(3x^2 - x - 2) \div (3x + 2)$.

7. $(2x^2 - x - 3) \div (x - 1)$.   [8] $(x^3 - 1) \div (x + 1)$.

9. $(x^3 + 7x^2 + 4x - 2) \div (x + 1)$.

[10] $(x^3 - 2x^2 + 3x - 6) \div (x - 2)$.

11. $(2x^3 + 5x^2 - 5x - 6) \div (x + 3)$.

[12] $(2x^3 - x^2 - 3x - 1) \div (2x + 1)$.

[13] Prove that $x - 1$ is a factor of $3x^3 - x^2 - x - 1$ and write down the other factor.

14. Prove that $x + 1$ is a factor of $2x^3 + 3x^2 - 1$ and find the other factors.

[15] Prove that $x + 2$ is a factor of $x^3 - x^2 - 10x - 8$ and find the other factors.

16. Prove that $x - 3$ is a factor of $x^3 - x^2 - 9x + 9$ and find the other factors.

17. Prove that $x - a$ is a factor of $x^3 - a^3$ and find the other factor. What are the factors of $A^3 - B^3$?

18. Prove that $x + a$ is a factor of $x^3 + a^3$ and find the other factor. What are the factors of $A^3 + B^3$?

Factorise:

19. $x^3 - 2x^2 - 5x + 6$.   [20] $x^3 - 21x + 20$.

21. $x^3 - 4x^2 + x + 6$.   [22] $x^3 + 4x^2y - 15xy^2 - 18y^3$.

23. $2a^3 + a^2b - 13ab^2 + 6b^3$.   [24] $2 + 5x - 28x^2 - 15x^3$.

[25] For what value of a is $x - 1$ a factor of $x^2 - 7x + a$?

26. For what value of b is $x + 1$ a factor of $x^2 + bx - 5$?

27. For what value of c is $x - 1$ a factor of $x^3 + cx^2 - 5x + 6$? What are then the other factors ?

28. For what values of a, b are $x + 1$ and $x - 2$ factors of $x^3 + ax^2 + 2x + b$? What is then the other factor ?

[29] For what values of b, c are $x + 2$ and $2x - 1$ factors of $4x^3 + bx + c$? What is then the other factor ?

30. Find the values of a, b if $x^4 + ax^3 + bx^2 - 12x + 4$ vanishes both when $x = 1$ and $x = 2$. Show by factorising that for these values of a and b there is no other value of x for which the expression vanishes.

*31. Prove that $a - b$ is a factor of $a^2(b - c) + b^2(c - a) + c^2(a - b)$, and find two other factors.

*32. Prove that $x + y$ is a factor of
$$xy(x + y) + yz(y + z) + zx(z + x) + 2xyz,$$
and find two other factors.

*33. Prove that $x - y$ is a factor of $(x - y)^3 + (y - z)^3 + (z - x)^3$, and find two other factors.

*34. Solve for x and y the simultaneous equations,
$$ax + by + c = 0, \ a^2x + b^2y + c^2 = 0, \ a \neq b, \ ab \neq 0,$$
and if in addition $x + y + 1 = 0$, prove that c is equal to either a or b.

*35. Prove that $x + y + z$ is a factor of
$$(x - y - z)(y - z - x)(z - x - y) - 8xyz.$$

Further Factors and Fractions

The previous exercise has included the following identities:
$$A^3 + B^3 \equiv (A + B)(A^2 - AB + B^2)$$
$$A^3 - B^3 \equiv (A - B)(A^2 + AB + B^2).$$

In each of these it is easy to remember the first factor; the second factor can then be obtained by division or inspection; this was done for $a^3 + b^3$ on p. 214 (see Example 30).

Example 7. Factorise $27x^3 - 8y^3$.
$$\begin{aligned}27x^3 - 8y^3 &= (3x)^3 - (2y)^3 \\ &= (3x - 2y)\{(3x)^2 + (3x)(2y) + (2y)^2\} \\ &= (3x - 2y)(9x^2 + 6xy + 4y^2).\end{aligned}$$

Example 8. Factorise $(2x^2 - x - 5)^2 - (x^2 - 6x + 9)^2$.

The expression
$$\begin{aligned}&= \{(2x^2 - x - 5) + (x^2 - 6x + 9)\}\{(2x^2 - x - 5) - (x^2 - 6x + 9)\} \\ &= (2x^2 - x - 5 + x^2 - 6x + 9)(2x^2 - x - 5 - x^2 + 6x - 9) \\ &= (3x^2 - 7x + 4)(x^2 + 5x - 14) \\ &= (x - 1)(3x - 4)(x - 2)(x + 7).\end{aligned}$$

Example 9. Factorise $x^2 - y^2 + 2yz - z^2$.

$$x^2 - y^2 + 2yz - z^2 = x^2 - (y^2 - 2yz + z^2)$$
$$= x^2 - (y - z)^2$$
$$= \{x + (y - z)\}\{x - (y - z)\}$$
$$= (x + y - z)(x - y + z).$$

EXERCISE XIII. d

Factorise:

1. $b^3 - 1$.   [2] $c^3 + 27$.   [3] $8 - d^3$.   4. $8x^3 + 125y^3$.

5. $3z^3 - 24$.   [6] $a^6 + b^6$.   7. $x^6 - y^6$.   [8] $a^3b^3 - 8c^3$.

9. $(2a - 3b)^2 - (a - b)^2$.   [10] $(x + c)^2 - (y - d)^2$.

11. $(x^2 - 3x - 1)^2 - 9$.   [12] $(x^2 + 3x + 1)^2 - (2x + 3)^2$.

13. $4(x^2 - x + 3)^2 - (x^2 + 7x - 8)^2$.   [14] $x^2 - 4x + 4 - y^2$.

15. $a^2 - b^2 - c^2 - 2bc$.   [16] $x^2 - y^2 - x^2z^2 + 2xyz$.

17. $(x - 2)^3 + (x + 1)^3$.   [18] $(2x + 1)^3 - (x + 1)^3$.

19. $a^2 + ab - 2b^2 + a - b$.   [20] $x^2 + xy - 6y^2 - 2xz + 4yz$.

Simplify:

21. $\dfrac{x^3 - y^3}{x - y} - \dfrac{x^3 + y^3}{x + y}$.   [22] $\dfrac{(a^3 + b^3)(a - b)}{(a^3 - b^3)(a + b)}$.

[23] $\dfrac{x^3 + y^3}{x^3 - y^3} - \dfrac{x^2}{x^2 + xy + y^2}$.   24. $\dfrac{(a^4 - b^4)(a - b)}{(a^2 - 2ab + b^2)(a^3 + b^3)}$.

[25] $\dfrac{x^3 - y^3}{x^2y + y^3} \div \dfrac{x - y}{x^2 - y^2}$.   26. $\left(\dfrac{a^2}{b} + \dfrac{b^2}{a}\right) \div \left\{\left(\dfrac{a}{b} + 1\right)\left(\dfrac{b}{a} + 1\right)\right\}$.

[27] $(x^2 - xy + y^2)\left(\dfrac{1}{x} + \dfrac{1}{y}\right) \div \left(\dfrac{x}{y^2} + \dfrac{y}{x^2}\right)$.

28. $\left(\dfrac{2ab}{a^2 + b^2} - 1\right)\left(\dfrac{b}{a} + \dfrac{a}{b}\right) \div \left(\dfrac{a^3 - b^3}{a - b} - 3ab\right)$.

[29] Find the value when $x = -a$ of the expression

$$\frac{\{x^2 + (a + b)x + a^2\}\{x^2 + (a + b)x + b^2\}}{(x + b)\{x^2 - (a - b)x - ab\}}.$$

30. If $(1 - b)x = 1 + b$ and $(1 - c)y = 1 + c$, express $\dfrac{x - y}{1 + xy}$ in terms of b, c.

[31] If $(a - c)x = a$ and $(b - c)y = b$, express $\dfrac{x - y}{1 - xy}$ in terms of a, b, c.

[32] Simplify $\left(\dfrac{a}{b} - 1 + \dfrac{b}{a}\right)\left(\dfrac{a}{b} + 2 + \dfrac{b}{a}\right) \div \left(\dfrac{a^2}{b} + \dfrac{b^2}{a}\right).$

33. Substitute $x = a + b$ in

$$\frac{a}{x^2 + b^2 - a^2} + \frac{b}{x^2 + a^2 - b^2} - \frac{a+b}{x^2 - a^2 - b^2}$$

and simplify.

*34. If $2x = a + c$, express $(a - x)^2 + (x - c)^2 + 2x^2$ in terms of a, c.

*35. If $x(b - c) = y(c - a) = z(a - b) = 1$, simplify $2yz + 2zx + 2xy$.

*36. If $t = a + b + c$, prove that $(at + bc)(bt + ca)(ct + ab)$ is a perfect square.

*37. If $2s = a + b + c$, prove that $\dfrac{s^2 - (s - a)^2}{(s - c)^2 - (s - b)^2} = \dfrac{b + c}{b - c}.$

*38. If $x = a^2 + 2ab - b^2$, $y = b^2 + 2ab - a^2$, $z = a^2 + b^2$, prove by using factors that $x^2 + y^2 - 2z^2 = 0$.

*39. If $\dfrac{1}{x + y} + \dfrac{1}{z} = \dfrac{1}{x} + \dfrac{1}{y + z}$ and if x is not equal to z, prove that either $y = 0$ or $x + y + z = 0$.

REVISION EXERCISE R. 7 (Ch. XII–XIII)

1. Make t the subject of the formula, $l = \dfrac{gt^2}{2\pi}.$

[2] Make l the subject of $\mathbf{A} = lb - (l - 2t)(b - 2t)$.

3. Find x in terms of a, y if $y = \dfrac{x - a}{1 + ax}.$

[4] Find n in terms of h, k if $h = \dfrac{2nk}{1 + (n + 1)k}.$

5. Make t the subject of $a = 1 - \dfrac{2b}{ct - b}$, and find its value if $a = 4$, $b = 2c$.

[6] Solve for x the equation,

$$\frac{1}{a}(2x - b) + \frac{1}{b}(3x + c) = d.$$

7. Given $s = ut + \frac{1}{2}at^2$ and $v = u + at$, express s in terms of a, v, t only.

[8] If $at^2 + 2ht = b$ and $at + h = k$, express b in terms of a, h, k only.

9. If $l^2 + 4h^2 = 8rh$ (see Exercise XII c, No. 35, p. 272), express h in terms of l, r, and verify the result by using Pythagoras' theorem.

10. Express the following statement in algebraic symbols and prove that it is true: the product of the greatest and least of four consecutive odd integers is less than the product of the two middle numbers by 8.

[11] Prove that the sum of a number of 4 digits and the number formed by reversing the digits is always divisible by 11.

*12. A rectangular tank a feet long, b feet wide, c *inches* deep is half full of water. If d gallons occupy 1 cu. yard, find the depth of the water after x gallons have been drawn out.

*13. An article is bought for £x and sold for £$(x + p)$. If the profit is r per cent. of the cost price and is t per cent. of the selling price, prove that $t = \dfrac{100r}{100 + r}$.

*14. A number of two digits has x for its tens-digit and y for its units-digit; also the sum of the digits is more than 10. What are the three digits of the sum of the number and the number obtained by reversing the digits? Show that the tens-digit of this sum is always equal to the sum of the other two digits [*e.g.* $97 + 79 = 176$ and $1 + 6 = 7$.]

15. Solve for x, y the simultaneous equations:
$$x - by + b^2 = 0, \quad x - cy + c^2 = 0, \quad b \neq c.$$

[16] Solve for x, y the simultaneous equations:
$$p(x - p) = qy, \quad q(x - q) = p(x - y).$$

Find, correct to two places of decimals, the roots of
[17] $x^2 + 6x = 10$.   18. $x^2 - x = 3$.   19. $3x^2 - 4x = 5$.

Express with integral coefficients equations whose roots are
[20] $4, -1\frac{1}{2}$.   21. $\frac{3}{4}, \frac{2}{5}$.   22. $3 + \sqrt{5}, 3 - \sqrt{5}$.

23. Find c if $x^2 + 3x + c = 0$ has equal roots.

[24] Find b if one root of $9x^2 - 18x + b = 0$ is double the other; and find the roots.

25. If a, β are the roots of $2x^2 + 3x - 4 = 0$, find the value of $(a+1)(\beta+1)$ and find the equation whose roots are $a+1$ and $\beta+1$.

[26] If a, β are the roots of $3x^2 - x = 1$, find the values of $a^2 + \beta^2$ and $(a - \beta)^2$.

27. *Write down* the simplified form of

$$(3x - y)^2 + (2x - y)^2 - 2(3x - y)(2x - y).$$

Solve the simultaneous equations:

[28] $x + y = 3$.   **29.** $3x - 2y + 1 = 0$.   **[30]** $\frac{1}{2}x - \frac{1}{3}y = 1$.
    $x^2 + 3xy = 10$. $x^2 + 4y^2 = 17$. $3x^2 - 2xy - 5y^2 = 3$.

Solve graphically *and* algebraically the following simultaneous equations:

31. $y = \frac{1}{4}x^2$.   **[32]** $y = \frac{1}{5}(x^2 - 2x + 2)$.
    $9y - 3x + 1 = 0$. $4x + 15y = 14$.

[33] Draw with the same axes and scales the graphs of $y = x^3$ and $y = 2x^2 + 3x$ from $x = -2$ to $x = +3$. What equation in x can be solved from the graph and what are its roots?

34. Draw the graph of $y = \dfrac{3x^2 - 1}{x + 6}$ for values of x from -2 to $+4$. What is the value of $\dfrac{3x^2 - 1}{x + 6}$ if $3x^2 - x - 7 = 0$? Hence solve this equation graphically. Solve graphically $3x^2 - 2x = 13$.

Factorise:

35. $64x^3 - 27y^3$.   **36.** $1 - c^6$.   **[37]** $a^3 + \dfrac{1}{a^3}$.

38. $a^2 - b^2 - 6b - 9$.   **[39]** $9x^2 - 4y^2 + 36x + 24y$.
40. $a^2 - 2ab + b^2 - 2a + 2b$.   **[41]** $x^3 - 4x^2 + x + 6$.
42. $x^3 - 8x^2 + 19x - 12$.   **[43]** $2x^3 - 3x^2 - 3x + 2$.

44. Divide $a^2 + b^2 - c^2 - 2ab$ by $a - b + c$.

[45] Divide $2x^4 + 3x^3 - 13x^2 - 2x + 12$ by $x^2 + 2x - 4$.

[46] Pick out the coefficients of x^3 and x^2 in the expansion of $(3x^3 - x^2 - 5x - 2)(2x^3 - 4x^2 + x - 3)$.

47. Find the quotient and remainder if $x^3 - x^2 - 2x + 1$ is divided by $x + 1$.

Simplify:

48. $\left(x + \dfrac{1}{x} - 1\right)\left(\dfrac{1}{x} + \dfrac{1}{x^2}\right)$.   [49] $(1 - \tfrac{1}{2}x - \tfrac{1}{8}x^2)^2 - (1 - x)$.

Solve:

50. $x(x-1)(x-2) = (x-5)(x+1)^2$.

[51] $10xy = 5(2x+5y) = 2(3x+4y)$.

52. $x^2 + xy + 4y^2 = 2x - 2y = 4$.

[53] Divide $a^4 + a^2b^2 + b^4$ by $a^2 + ab + b^2$.

[54] For what value of c is $x+2$ a factor of $x^3 + cx + 16$?

55. For what values of a, b are $x+3$ and $x-2$ factors of $x^3 - ax^2 - bx - 6$?

Solve for x:

[56] $(x-a)(x-c) = (x-b)^2$.   **57.** $\dfrac{a}{x(x+a)} = \dfrac{1}{x} + \dfrac{1}{a}$.

*58. Find c if the roots of $x = c(x-1)(x-2)$ are equal.

*59. If $x + ay = b$ and $x + by = a$, $a \neq b$, express $x - cy$ in terms of a, b, c only.

*60. Find the value of c if the simultaneous equations, $3x + 4y = c$, $x^2 + y^2 = 4$, have one, and only one, solution.

*61. If $c^2 = c + 1$, prove that $c^5 = 5c + 3$.

*62. If α and β are the roots of $x^2 - 5x - 2 = 0$, and if $\alpha + \dfrac{1}{\beta}$, $\beta + \dfrac{1}{\alpha}$ are the roots of $x^2 + qx + r = 0$, find the values of q and r.

*63. If α, β are the roots of $qx = \dfrac{1}{x+p}$, find in terms of p, q the values of (i) $\dfrac{1}{\alpha} + \dfrac{1}{\beta}$;   (ii) $\dfrac{\alpha}{\beta} + \dfrac{\beta}{c}$;   (iii) $(\alpha - \beta)^2$.

CHAPTER XIV

INDICES, SURDS, AND LOGARITHMS

Fractional and Negative Indices

If m and n are positive integers

$$a^m \times a^n = a^{m+n};$$
$$a^m \div a^n = a^{m-n}, \text{ if } m > n;$$
$$(a^m)^n = a^{mn}.$$

These results are direct consequences of the definition,

$$a^m = a \times a \times a \times \ldots \text{ to } m \text{ factors.}$$

If m is not a positive integer, *e.g.* if $m = \frac{2}{3}$ or -4 or 0, the symbol a^m has not yet been defined; we now proceed to show what meaning must be given to it if the law

$$a^m \times a^n = a^{m+n}$$

remains true for *all* values of m and n.

Example 1. Find the meaning of $16^{\frac{1}{2}}$.

$$16^{\frac{1}{2}} \times 16^{\frac{1}{2}} = 16^{\frac{1}{2} + \frac{1}{2}} = 16^1 = 16;$$

$$\therefore \ 16^{\frac{1}{2}} \text{ is a } square \ root \text{ of } 16;$$

$$\therefore \ 16^{\frac{1}{2}} = 4 \ (\text{or } -4).$$

Note. Throughout this chapter we shall consider only the *positive* value of a square root.

Example 2. Find the meaning of $a^{\frac{1}{3}}$.

$$a^{\frac{1}{3}} \times a^{\frac{1}{3}} \times a^{\frac{1}{3}} = a^{\frac{1}{3} + \frac{1}{3} + \frac{1}{3}} = a^1 = a;$$

$$\therefore \ a^{\frac{1}{3}} \text{ is the } cube \ root \text{ of } a;$$

$$\therefore \ a^{\frac{1}{3}} = \sqrt[3]{a}.$$

Example 3. Find the meaning of $a^{\frac{3}{4}}$.

$$a^{\frac{3}{4}} \times a^{\frac{3}{4}} \times a^{\frac{3}{4}} \times a^{\frac{3}{4}} = a^{\frac{3}{4} + \frac{3}{4} + \frac{3}{4} + \frac{3}{4}} = a^{\frac{3}{4} \times 4} = a^3;$$

$$\therefore \ a^{\frac{3}{4}} \text{ is a } fourth \ root \text{ of } a^3;$$

$$\therefore \ a^{\frac{3}{4}} = \sqrt[4]{(a^3)}.$$

We may also proceed as follows:

By the method of Example 2,

$$a^{\frac{1}{4}} = \sqrt[4]{a};$$

but

$$a^{\frac{3}{4}} = a^{\frac{1}{4}} \times a^{\frac{1}{4}} \times a^{\frac{1}{4}} = \left(a^{\frac{1}{4}}\right)^3;$$

$$\therefore a^{\frac{3}{4}} = (\sqrt[4]{a})^3.$$

$$\therefore \mathbf{a^{\frac{3}{4}} = \sqrt[4]{(a^3)} = (\sqrt[4]{a})^3}.$$

For example, $16^{\frac{3}{4}} = \sqrt[4]{(16^3)} = \sqrt[4]{(2^4 \times 2^4 \times 2^4)}$
$$= \sqrt[4]{(2^{12})} = 2^3.$$

But it is quicker to say,

$$16^{\frac{1}{4}} = \sqrt[4]{16} = 2, \quad \therefore 16^{\frac{3}{4}} = 2^3.$$

Example 4.   Find the meaning of a^{-5}, given $a \neq 0$.

$$a^7 \times a^{-5} = a^{7-5} = a^2;$$

Divide each side by a^7, $\therefore a^{-5} = \dfrac{a^2}{a^7};$

$$\therefore \mathbf{a^{-5} = \dfrac{1}{a^5}}.$$

Example 5.   Find the meaning of a^0, given $a \neq 0$.

$$a^2 \times a^0 = a^{2+0} = a^2;$$

Divide each side by a^2, $\therefore a^0 = \dfrac{a^2}{a^2} = 1.$

$$\therefore \mathbf{a^0 = 1}.$$

By using the methods of Examples 2–4, it may be proved that, if p, q are integers and q is positive,

$$\mathbf{a^{\frac{1}{q}} = \sqrt[q]{a}};$$

$$\mathbf{a^{\frac{p}{q}} = \sqrt[q]{a^p} = (\sqrt[q]{a})^p}, \qquad \mathbf{a \neq 0};$$

$$\mathbf{a^{-p} = \dfrac{1}{a^p}}, \qquad \mathbf{a \neq 0}.$$

If m is positive, $0^m = 0$; no meaning is given to the symbol 0^m if m is negative or zero.

Example 6.   Evaluate $(\frac{27}{8})^{-\frac{2}{3}}$.

Since $a^{-1} = \frac{1}{a}$, $\left(\frac{27}{8}\right)^{-1} = \frac{8}{27}$;

$$\therefore \ (\tfrac{27}{8})^{-\frac{2}{3}} = (\tfrac{8}{27})^{\frac{2}{3}}$$
$$= (\sqrt[3]{\tfrac{8}{27}})^2 = (\tfrac{2}{3})^2$$
$$= \tfrac{4}{9}.$$

EXERCISE XIV a

[Nos. 1–50 are intended for oral work.]

1. Find from first principles the simplest forms for
   (i) $a^2 \times a^4$;   (ii) $b^6 \div b^2$;   (iii) $(c^2)^3$.

2. Write down the simplest forms for
   (i) $a^2 \div a^6$;   (ii) $b \div b^4$;   (iii) $c^4 \div c^4$.

3. Write down the squares of x^3, x^4, x^5.

4. Write down the cubes of y^3, y^4, y^5.

Express as powers of x:

5. The square roots of x^8, x^9, x.

6. The cube roots of x^{12}, x^{10}, x^{11}, x.

7. $\left(x^{1\frac{1}{2}}\right)^2$.   8. $\left(x^{1\frac{1}{3}}\right)^3$.   9. $\left(x^{\frac{5}{6}}\right)^4$.

10. $\sqrt{x}$; $\sqrt[3]{x}$.   11. $\sqrt[4]{x}$; $\sqrt[4]{x^3}$; $\sqrt[4]{x^2}$.   12. $\sqrt[3]{x^4}$; $\sqrt[4]{x^6}$.

Express with positive indices:

13. a^{-2}; b^{-1}.   14. $c^{-\frac{1}{2}}$; $d^{-\frac{1}{3}}$.   15. $\left(\frac{1}{e}\right)^{-2}$; $\left(\frac{f}{g}\right)^{-3}$; $\left(\frac{h}{k}\right)^{-1}$.

Express with root signs:

16. $a^{\frac{1}{5}}$; $b^{\frac{2}{3}}$.   17. $2^{\frac{3}{2}}$; $3^{-\frac{3}{2}}$.   18. $10^{0.75}$; $10^{1\frac{1}{3}}$; $10^{-\frac{1}{2}}$.

Write down the values of:

19. $9^{\frac{1}{2}}$.   3   20. $8^{\frac{1}{3}}$.   2   21. $8^{\frac{2}{3}}$.   4   22. $81^{\frac{1}{4}}$.   3

23. $27^{\frac{2}{3}}$.   9   24. $32^{\frac{3}{5}}$.   8   25. $9^{1\frac{1}{2}}$.   27   26. $27^{1\frac{1}{3}}$.   81

27. $16^{1\frac{1}{4}}$.   32   28. $4^{3\frac{1}{2}}$.   128   29. $125^{\frac{2}{3}}$.   25   30. $32^{1\frac{3}{5}}$.   256

31. 3^{-2}.   1/9   32. 4^{-1}.   1/4   33. 5^0.   1   34. 2^{-3}.   1/8

35. 1^{-1}.   1   36. 10^0.   1   37. 5^{-1}.   1/5   38. 10^{-4}.   1/1000

39. $9^{-\frac{1}{2}}$.　40. $8^{-\frac{1}{3}}$.　41. $27^{-\frac{2}{3}}$.　42. $32^{-\frac{4}{5}}$.

43. $(\frac{1}{3})^{-2}$.　44. $(\frac{3}{4})^{-1}$.　45. $(\frac{2}{3})^{-3}$.　46. $(1\frac{1}{2})^{-4}$.

47. $(\frac{1}{9})^{-\frac{1}{2}}$.　48. $(\frac{4}{25})^{-\frac{1}{2}}$.　49. $1^{-\frac{2}{3}}$.　50. $(\frac{125}{64})^{-\frac{2}{3}}$.

Find the values of:

51. $(2\frac{1}{4})^{-1\frac{1}{2}}$.　52. $32^{0\cdot4}$.　[53] $(0\cdot1)^{-1}$.　[54] $16^{-0\cdot5}$.

55. $(0\cdot25)^{-1\cdot5}$.　56. $(0\cdot027)^{-\frac{2}{3}}$.　[57] $(3\frac{3}{8})^{-1\frac{1}{3}}$.　[58] $(0\cdot0001)^{-\frac{3}{4}}$.

59. $(0\cdot4)^{2}\times(0\cdot125)^{\frac{1}{3}}\div(2\frac{1}{2})^{-3}$.　　60. $\sqrt{2}\times\sqrt[3]{2}\times\sqrt[6]{2}$.

[61] $(\frac{4}{9})^{\frac{1}{2}}\times4^{0}\times(1\frac{1}{3})^{-1}$.　　　[62] $(\frac{27}{64})^{-\frac{2}{3}}\times(\frac{9}{64})^{\frac{1}{2}}\div(\frac{3}{8})^{-1}$.

63. $(0\cdot1)^{-3}\times(\frac{1}{9})^{0}\times(\frac{25}{36})^{-1\frac{1}{2}}\div(0\cdot5)^{-4}$.

[64] $(0\cdot04)^{-\frac{1}{2}}\times(2\frac{1}{4})^{-1}\times(0\cdot125)^{\frac{1}{3}}\times(1\frac{1}{3})^{-2}$.

65. $2^{m}\times3^{n}\times6^{m-n}$.　　　[66] $4^{n+1}\times8^{1-n}\times16^{n-3}$.

67. $12^{2n}\div(18^{n}\times4^{\frac{1}{2}n})$.　　[68] $20^{2n+1}\times100^{2-n}\div64^{\frac{1}{3}n}$.

Example 7. Simplify $4x^{\frac{2}{3}}\div\left(6x^{\frac{1}{6}}\right)$.

$$\frac{4x^{\frac{2}{3}}}{6x^{\frac{1}{6}}}=\tfrac{2}{3}x^{\frac{2}{3}-\frac{1}{6}}$$
$$=\tfrac{2}{3}x^{\frac{1}{2}}.$$

Example 8. Simplify $(9y^{-6})^{-\frac{3}{2}}$.

$$(9y^{-6})^{-\frac{3}{2}}=9^{-\frac{3}{2}}y^{-6\times-\frac{3}{2}}$$
$$=\frac{1}{9^{\frac{3}{2}}}y^{9}=\frac{1}{(\sqrt{9})^{3}}y^{9}$$
$$=\tfrac{1}{27}y^{9}.$$

Example 9. Expand $\left(x^{\frac{1}{2}}+3-2x^{-\frac{1}{2}}\right)\left(x^{\frac{1}{2}}-2+x^{-\frac{1}{2}}\right)$.

By ordinary multiplication, the expression equals

$x^{\frac{1}{2}}\left(x^{\frac{1}{2}}-2+x^{-\frac{1}{2}}\right)+3\left(x^{\frac{1}{2}}-2+x^{-\frac{1}{2}}\right)-2x^{-\frac{1}{2}}\left(x^{\frac{1}{2}}-2+x^{-\frac{1}{2}}\right)$

$=\left(x-2x^{\frac{1}{2}}+1\right)+\left(3x^{\frac{1}{2}}-6+3x^{-\frac{1}{2}}\right)-\left(2-4x^{-\frac{1}{2}}+2x^{-1}\right)$

$=x-2x^{\frac{1}{2}}+1+3x^{\frac{1}{2}}-6+3x^{-\frac{1}{2}}-2+4x^{-\frac{1}{2}}-2x^{-1}$

$=x+x^{\frac{1}{2}}-7+7x^{-\frac{1}{2}}-2x^{-1}.$

EXERCISE XIV. b

Simplify:

1. $a^{\frac{1}{3}} \times a^{\frac{1}{6}}$.

2. $b^{\frac{3}{4}} \times b^{\frac{1}{4}}$.

3. $c^3 \times c^{-\frac{5}{2}}$.

4. $d^{\frac{1}{2}} \times d^{-\frac{1}{2}}$.

5. $e^{-2} \times e^{\frac{2}{3}}$.

6. $f^{-\frac{1}{3}} \times f^{-\frac{1}{6}}$.

7. $n^{\frac{3}{4}} \div n^{\frac{5}{8}}$.

8. $p^{1\frac{1}{4}} \div p^{\frac{3}{4}}$.

9. $r^{\frac{1}{3}} \div r^{1\frac{1}{3}}$.

10. $s^3 \div s^{-3}$.

11. $t^{\frac{1}{3}} \div t^{-\frac{1}{6}}$.

12. $x^{\frac{1}{3}} \times x^{\frac{2}{3}} \times x^{-1}$.

[13] $a^{\frac{2}{3}} \times a^{\frac{1}{3}}$.

[14] $b^{\frac{2}{3}} \times b^{-\frac{1}{6}}$.

[15] $c^{\frac{1}{3}} \times c^{-\frac{1}{3}}$.

[16] $d^{\frac{3}{4}} \div d^{\frac{1}{4}}$.

[17] $e \div e^{-1}$.

[18] $f^{-\frac{1}{3}} \div f^{\frac{2}{3}}$.

19. $(2\frac{1}{2}a)^{-1}$.

20. $(2\frac{1}{4}b^3)^{\frac{1}{2}}$.

[21] $(4c^{-4})^{-\frac{1}{2}}$.

22. $(27d^{-12})^{-\frac{2}{3}}$.

23. $\left(x^{\frac{1}{2}}y^{-\frac{1}{2}}\right)^{-2}$.

[24] $(1\frac{1}{2}s^{-2}t)^{-1}$.

25. $\left(\dfrac{8a^3}{b^3}\right)^{-\frac{1}{3}}$.

26. $\left(\dfrac{c^{-1}}{3d^2}\right)^{-2}$.

[27] $\dfrac{(4e)^{-\frac{1}{2}}}{(2e)^{-2}}$.

28. $\sqrt{(16x^{-4})}$.

29. $\sqrt[3]{(125y^{-1\frac{1}{2}})}$.

[30] $\sqrt[4]{(81z^{-6})}$.

31. $\dfrac{\sqrt{p^5}}{p^{-1\cdot5}}$.

32. $\dfrac{r^{\frac{1}{2}}s^{-1}}{\sqrt{(r^{-3}s^{-4})}}$

[33] $\dfrac{6xy^2}{\sqrt[3]{(8x^{-3})}}$.

Expand:

34. $x^{\frac{1}{2}}\left(x^{\frac{1}{2}} - 2x^{-\frac{1}{2}} + x^{-\frac{3}{2}}\right)$.

35. $\left(y^{\frac{1}{3}} - 2z^{\frac{1}{3}}\right)\left(2y^{-\frac{1}{3}} + z^{-\frac{1}{3}}\right)$.

[36] $a^{\frac{1}{6}}\left(a^{\frac{1}{3}} - a^{-\frac{2}{3}} + 3a^{-\frac{5}{3}}\right)$.

[37] $\left(b^{\frac{1}{2}} - c^{\frac{1}{4}}\right)\left(b^{\frac{1}{2}} + 3c^{\frac{1}{4}}\right)$.

38. $\left(x^{\frac{1}{3}} - 1\right)\left(x^{\frac{2}{3}} + x^{\frac{1}{3}} + 1\right)$.

39. $\left(3y^{\frac{1}{2}} - 2\right)\left(2y - y^{\frac{1}{2}} + y^{-\frac{1}{2}}\right)$.

[40] $\left(z^{\frac{1}{2}} + z^{-\frac{1}{2}}\right)\left(z^{\frac{1}{2}} - 1 + z^{-\frac{1}{2}}\right)$.

[41] $(t + 1 + t^{-1})(t - 1 + t^{-1})$.

42. $\left(2a^{\frac{1}{2}} + 3a^{\frac{1}{4}} + 1\right)\left(a^{\frac{1}{2}} - a^{\frac{1}{4}} + 1\right)$.

43. $\left(b^{\frac{2}{3}} + c^{\frac{2}{3}}\right)\left(b^{\frac{4}{3}} - b^{\frac{2}{3}}c^{\frac{2}{3}} + c^{\frac{4}{3}}\right)$.

[44] $\left(2x^{\frac{2}{3}} - 2 + x^{-\frac{1}{3}}\right)\left(x^{\frac{1}{3}} + 2 + x^{-\frac{1}{3}}\right)$.

[45] $\left(y^{\frac{1}{2}} - y^{\frac{1}{4}}z^{-\frac{1}{4}} + z^{-\frac{1}{2}}\right)\left(y^{\frac{1}{2}} + y^{\frac{1}{4}}z^{-\frac{1}{4}} + z^{-\frac{1}{2}}\right)$.

Simplify:

46. $\left(3x^{\frac{4}{3}} - 6x^{\frac{2}{3}} + 9\right) \div \left(3x^{\frac{1}{3}}\right)$.

47. $(a - b) \div \left(a^{\frac{1}{2}} - b^{\frac{1}{2}}\right)$.

[48] $\left(y^{\frac{1}{2}} - y^{\frac{1}{4}}z^{-\frac{1}{4}} + z^{-\frac{1}{2}}\right) \div \left(y^{\frac{1}{4}}z^{-\frac{1}{4}}\right)$.

[49] $(c + 1) \div \left(c^{\frac{1}{3}} + 1\right)$.

*50. $\dfrac{1}{1 - a^{p-q}} - \dfrac{1}{a^{q-p} - 1}$.

*51. $\dfrac{(b + 2c)^{\frac{1}{2}}(b - 2c)^{-\frac{1}{3}}}{(b^2 - 4c^2)^{\frac{1}{6}}}$.

*52. $\dfrac{x^n}{(x+y)^m} - \dfrac{x^{n+1}}{(x+y)^{m+1}}$.

*53. $\dfrac{1}{(y+z)^{-2}} \div (y^{-2} - z^{-2})$.

Surds

It can be proved that numbers such as $\sqrt{3}$, $\sqrt[3]{5}$, π, etc. cannot be expressed exactly as the *ratio* of two integers; they are therefore called *irrational* numbers; whereas numbers which can be reduced to the form $\dfrac{p}{q}$, where p and q are integers, are called *rational*.

If the root of any rational number is not itself rational, it is called a *surd*, thus $\sqrt{(\tfrac{3}{4})}$ and $\sqrt[3]{5}$ are surds, but $\sqrt[3]{8}$ is not a surd because $\sqrt[3]{8} = 2$.

Although a number such as 9 has two square roots, $+3$ and -3, we shall use the symbol $\sqrt{9}$ to denote the *positive* square root of 9, and in general $\sqrt{x}$ denotes the positive square root of x.

EXERCISE XIV. c (Oral)

If $a = 4$, $b = 9$, $c = 16$, $d = 25$, evaluate the following pairs of expressions and note which pairs are unequal.

1. $\sqrt{a} \times \sqrt{b}$; $\sqrt{(ab)}$.   2. $\sqrt{b} + \sqrt{c}$; $\sqrt{(b+c)}$.
3. $\sqrt{d} - \sqrt{c}$; $\sqrt{(d-c)}$.   4. $\sqrt{b} \div \sqrt{d}$; $\sqrt{(b \div d)}$.
5. $\sqrt{(100a)}$; $10\sqrt{a}$.   6. $\sqrt{(36d)}$; $6\sqrt{d}$.

Operations with Surds. The examples in the last exercise illustrate that, when $\sqrt{a}$ and $\sqrt{b}$ are rational,

$$\sqrt{a} \times \sqrt{b} = \sqrt{(ab)} \quad \text{and} \quad \frac{\sqrt{a}}{\sqrt{b}} = \sqrt{\left(\frac{a}{b}\right)};$$

but $\sqrt{a} + \sqrt{b}$ is *not equal* to $\sqrt{(a+b)}$ unless $a = 0$ or $b = 0$; and $\sqrt{a} - \sqrt{b}$ is *not equal* to $\sqrt{(a-b)}$ unless $b = 0$.

We shall now *assume* that the fundamental laws of algebra are the same for irrational as for rational numbers; then

$$(\sqrt{a} \times \sqrt{b})^2 = \sqrt{a} \times \sqrt{b} \times \sqrt{a} \times \sqrt{b} = \sqrt{a} \times \sqrt{a} \times \sqrt{b} \times \sqrt{b}$$
$$= a \times b = ab;$$

take the square root of each side, then

$$\sqrt{a} \times \sqrt{b} = \sqrt{(ab)}.$$

Similarly,
$$\left(\frac{\sqrt{a}}{\sqrt{b}}\right)^2 = \frac{\sqrt{a} \times \sqrt{a}}{\sqrt{b} \times \sqrt{b}} = \frac{a}{b};$$

$$\therefore \quad \frac{\sqrt{a}}{\sqrt{b}} = \sqrt{\left(\frac{a}{b}\right)}.$$

Example 10 (i). Given that $\sqrt{5} = 2 \cdot 236$ to 4 figures, evaluate to 3 figures (i) $\sqrt{45}$; (ii) $\dfrac{1}{\sqrt{5}}$.

(i) $\sqrt{45} = \sqrt{(9 \times 5)} = \sqrt{9} \times \sqrt{5} = 3\sqrt{5}$

$\rightleftharpoons 3 \times 2 \cdot 236 = 6 \cdot 71$ to 3 figures.

(ii) $\dfrac{1}{\sqrt{5}} = \dfrac{\sqrt{5}}{\sqrt{5} \times \sqrt{5}} = \dfrac{\sqrt{5}}{5}$

$\rightleftharpoons \dfrac{2 \cdot 236}{5} = 0 \cdot 447$ to 3 figures.

Note. The fact, $\sqrt{5} \times \sqrt{5} = 5$, is the definition of $\sqrt{5}$, and it should be written down immediately, instead of saying

$$\sqrt{5} \times \sqrt{5} = \sqrt{25} = 5.$$

Example 10 (ii) illustrates the fact that fractions with surds in the denominator can often be dealt with more easily if replaced by equivalent fractions with rational denominators. This process is called *rationalising the denominator*.

Example 11. Simplify (i) $\sqrt{15} \times \sqrt{20}$; (ii) $\dfrac{12}{\sqrt{18}}$.

(i) $\sqrt{15} \times \sqrt{20} = \sqrt{(15 \times 20)} = \sqrt{(2^2 \, . \, 3 \, . \, 5^2)}$

$= 2 \, . \, 5\sqrt{3} = 10\sqrt{3}.$

(ii) $\dfrac{12}{\sqrt{18}} = \dfrac{12}{\sqrt{9} \times \sqrt{2}} = \dfrac{12}{3\sqrt{2}}$

$= \dfrac{4 \times \sqrt{2}}{\sqrt{2} \times \sqrt{2}} = \dfrac{4\sqrt{2}}{2}$

$= 2\sqrt{2}.$

EXERCISE XIV. d

Express the following surds so that the integer under the square root sign is as small as possible:

1. $\sqrt{8}$.   2. $\sqrt{90}$. $3\sqrt{10}$ [3] $\sqrt{12}$. $2\sqrt{3}$ [4] $\sqrt{18}$. $3\sqrt{2}$

5. $\sqrt{50}$.   6. $\sqrt{27}$. $3\sqrt{3}$ [7] $\sqrt{48}$. $4\sqrt{3}$ [8] $\sqrt{20}$. $2\sqrt{5}$

9. $\sqrt{80}$. $4\sqrt{5}$ 10. $\sqrt{540}$.   [11] $\sqrt{28}$. $2\sqrt{7}$ [12] $\sqrt{720}$. $12\sqrt{5}$

Express the following as the square roots of integers:

13. $3\sqrt{2}$.   14. $5\sqrt{10}$.   15. $6\sqrt{6}$.   16. $\frac{1}{2}\sqrt{48}$.

[17] $2\sqrt{3}$.   [18] $3\sqrt{7}$.   [19] $4\sqrt{5}$.   [20] $\frac{1}{3}\sqrt{135}$.

Express the following with rational denominators:

21. $\dfrac{1}{\sqrt{2}}$.   22. $\dfrac{2}{\sqrt{6}}$.   23. $\dfrac{6}{\sqrt{27}}$.   24. $\sqrt{\left(\dfrac{4}{3}\right)}$.

[25] $\dfrac{6}{\sqrt{3}}$.   [26] $\dfrac{10}{\sqrt{12}}$.   [27] $\dfrac{15}{\sqrt{50}}$.   [28] $5\sqrt{\left(\dfrac{2}{5}\right)}$.

Evaluate to 3 significant figures the following, given that $\sqrt{2}\simeq1\cdot414$, $\sqrt{5}\simeq2\cdot236$.

29. $\dfrac{10}{\sqrt{2}}$.   30. $\dfrac{5}{\sqrt{20}}$.   [31] $\dfrac{3}{\sqrt{5}}$.   [32] $\dfrac{1}{\sqrt{50}}$.

Simplify the following:

33. $\sqrt{2}\times\sqrt{8}$.   34. $\sqrt{10}\times\sqrt{20}$.   35. $3\sqrt{2}\times\sqrt{6}$.

[36] $\sqrt{6}\times\sqrt{3}$.   [37] $2\sqrt{5}\times5\sqrt{2}$.   [38] $3\sqrt{8}\times2\sqrt{8}$.

39. $\sqrt{2}\times\sqrt{(\tfrac{1}{2})}$.   40. $(\sqrt{3})^3$.   41. $2\sqrt{45}\times\tfrac{1}{3}\sqrt{10}$.

42. $\sqrt{2}\div\sqrt{(\tfrac{1}{2})}$.   43. $\sqrt{15}\div\sqrt{20}$.   44. $\sqrt{(\tfrac{2}{3})}\div\sqrt{(\tfrac{1}{12})}$.

[45] $\sqrt{6}\div\sqrt{12}$.   [46] $\sqrt{3}\div\sqrt{(\tfrac{3}{4})}$.   [47] $2\{\sqrt{(\tfrac{1}{2})}\}^3$.

48. $\sqrt{6}\times\sqrt{8}\times\sqrt{12}$.   49. $\sqrt{20}\times\sqrt{15}\div\sqrt{6}$.

50. $\sqrt{(1\tfrac{1}{2})}\times\sqrt{(1\tfrac{1}{3})}\times\sqrt{(1\tfrac{1}{4})}$.

Example 12.   Simplify $\sqrt{12}+\sqrt{75}-12\sqrt{(\tfrac{1}{3})}$.

$$\sqrt{12}=\sqrt{4}\times\sqrt{3}=2\sqrt{3};\qquad\sqrt{75}=\sqrt{25}\times\sqrt{3}=5\sqrt{3};$$

$$12\sqrt{\left(\frac{1}{3}\right)}=12\times\frac{1}{\sqrt{3}}=12\times\frac{\sqrt{3}}{\sqrt{3}\times\sqrt{3}}=\frac{12\sqrt{3}}{3}=4\sqrt{3};$$

$$\therefore\ \text{expression}=2\sqrt{3}+5\sqrt{3}-4\sqrt{3}$$
$$=3\sqrt{3}.$$

Example 13.   Expand $(2\sqrt{10}+3\sqrt{6})(3\sqrt{5}-2\sqrt{3})$.

By ordinary multiplication, the expression equals
$$6\sqrt{50}-4\sqrt{30}+9\sqrt{30}-6\sqrt{18}$$
$$=30\sqrt{2}+5\sqrt{30}-18\sqrt{2}$$
$$=12\sqrt{2}+5\sqrt{30}.$$

Example 14.   Expand $(5\sqrt{2}+4\sqrt{3})(5\sqrt{2}-4\sqrt{3})$.

Since $(a+b)(a-b)$ equals a^2-b^2,
$$\text{the expression}=(5\sqrt{2})^2-(4\sqrt{3})^2$$
$$=25\times2-16\times3=50-48$$
$$=2.$$

Example 15. Express with a rational denominator, $\dfrac{6\sqrt{2}}{4\sqrt{2}+\sqrt{5}}$.

$$\frac{6\sqrt{2}}{4\sqrt{2}+\sqrt{5}}=\frac{6\sqrt{2}(4\sqrt{2}-\sqrt{5})}{(4\sqrt{2}+\sqrt{5})(4\sqrt{2}-\sqrt{5})}$$

$$=\frac{6(8-\sqrt{10})}{(4\sqrt{2})^2-(\sqrt{5})^2}=\frac{6(8-\sqrt{10})}{32-5}$$

$$=\frac{6(8-\sqrt{10})}{27}$$

$$=\frac{2(8-\sqrt{10})}{9}.$$

EXERCISE XIV. e

Simplify:

1. $\sqrt{2}+\sqrt{8}$.   2. $\sqrt{12}-\sqrt{3}$.   3. $2\sqrt{20}-\sqrt{80}$.

[4] $\sqrt{3}+\sqrt{27}$.   [5] $\sqrt{45}-\sqrt{20}$.   [6] $3\sqrt{18}-2\sqrt{32}$

7. $\sqrt{2}-\dfrac{1}{\sqrt{2}}$.   8. $\dfrac{1}{2}\sqrt{5}-\sqrt{\left(\dfrac{1}{5}\right)}$.   9. $\sqrt{\left(\dfrac{3}{2}\right)}-\sqrt{\left(\dfrac{2}{3}\right)}$

[10] $\sqrt{3}+\sqrt{\left(\dfrac{1}{3}\right)}$.   [11] $\dfrac{1}{\sqrt{2}}-\dfrac{1}{\sqrt{8}}$.   [12] $\sqrt{\left(\dfrac{10}{3}\right)}-\sqrt{\left(\dfrac{5}{6}\right)}$

13. $\sqrt{20}+2\sqrt{45}-\sqrt{125}$.   14. $\sqrt{\left(\dfrac{4}{5}\right)}+\sqrt{\left(\dfrac{1}{5}\right)}-\dfrac{5}{\sqrt{20}}$.

[15] $2\sqrt{27}+\sqrt{12}-2\sqrt{48}$.   [16] $6\sqrt{\left(\dfrac{1}{3}\right)}+\sqrt{\left(\dfrac{4}{3}\right)}-\dfrac{1}{\sqrt{3}}$.

17. $\sqrt{2}(1+\sqrt{2})$.   18. $\sqrt{6}(\sqrt{3}-\sqrt{2})$.

19. $2\sqrt{2}(\sqrt{8}+3\sqrt{2})$.   [20] $\sqrt{5}(5-\sqrt{20})$.

[21] $\sqrt{15}(\sqrt{6}+\sqrt{5})$.   [22] $3\sqrt{3}(\sqrt{75}-2\sqrt{12})$.

23. $(\sqrt{3}+2)(\sqrt{3}-1)$.   24. $(3+2\sqrt{2})(5-3\sqrt{2})$.

25. $(5\sqrt{2}-3)^2$.   26. $(8+3\sqrt{7})(8-3\sqrt{7})$.

27. $(2\sqrt{3}+5\sqrt{2})^2$.   28. $(5\sqrt{6}-7\sqrt{2})(2\sqrt{6}+3\sqrt{2})$.

[29] $(2\sqrt{10}-\sqrt{5})(2\sqrt{2}+1)$.   [30] $(5\sqrt{6}-3\sqrt{2})^2$.

31. $(5\sqrt{7}+2\sqrt{5})(5\sqrt{7}-2\sqrt{5})$.   32. $(\sqrt{a}+\sqrt{b})(\sqrt{a}-\sqrt{b})$.

[33] $(3\sqrt{5}-2\sqrt{11})(3\sqrt{5}+2\sqrt{11})$.   [34] $(\sqrt{x}-\sqrt{y})^2$.

[35] $(3\sqrt{6}+2\sqrt{5})(2\sqrt{15}-3\sqrt{2})$.   [36] $\{3\sqrt{(\tfrac{1}{2})}+2\sqrt{(\tfrac{1}{3})}\}^2$.

Express the following with rational denominators:

37. $\dfrac{1}{\sqrt{2}+1}$.

38. $\dfrac{6}{\sqrt{3}-1}$.

39. $\dfrac{1}{3\sqrt{2}-3}$. $\dfrac{3\sqrt{2}+3}{11}$

40. $\dfrac{\sqrt{2}}{\sqrt{6}-\sqrt{2}}$.

41. $\dfrac{\sqrt{2}+1}{\sqrt{2}-1}$. $\dfrac{(\sqrt{2}+1)^2}{} = 3+2\sqrt{2}$

42. $\dfrac{3\sqrt{5}-2}{2\sqrt{5}-4}$.

[43] $\dfrac{1}{3-\sqrt{5}}$. $\dfrac{3+\sqrt{5}}{4}$

[44] $\dfrac{10}{\sqrt{5}-\sqrt{3}}$.

[45] $\dfrac{\sqrt{7}-\sqrt{5}}{\sqrt{7}+\sqrt{5}}$.

Simplify:

46. $\dfrac{1}{\sqrt{3}+1}+\dfrac{1}{\sqrt{3}-1}$.

47. $\dfrac{\sqrt{5}+2}{\sqrt{5}-2}-\dfrac{\sqrt{5}-2}{\sqrt{5}+2}$.

48. b^2+2b if $b=\sqrt{5}-1$.

49. $\dfrac{c-1}{c+1}$ if $c=\dfrac{\sqrt{6}+\sqrt{2}}{\sqrt{6}-\sqrt{2}}$.

[50] $\dfrac{\sqrt{2}}{\sqrt{7}-1}-\dfrac{\sqrt{2}}{\sqrt{7}+1}$.

[51] $\dfrac{2\sqrt{7}+5}{2\sqrt{7}-5}+\dfrac{2\sqrt{7}-5}{2\sqrt{7}+5}$.

[52] x^2-6x if $x=3-\sqrt{11}$.

[53] $\dfrac{1}{(2\sqrt{2}-\sqrt{3})^2}-\dfrac{1}{(2\sqrt{2}+\sqrt{3})^2}$.

*54. $\dfrac{2\sqrt{10}}{\sqrt{10}-\sqrt{5}}-\dfrac{5}{2\sqrt{2}-\sqrt{3}}$.

*55. $\dfrac{3(1+\sqrt{2})}{(\sqrt{5}-\sqrt{2})^2}-\dfrac{2\sqrt{2}}{3\sqrt{5}-6}$.

56. If $y=\dfrac{z+1}{z-1}$ and $z=x^2-1$, find the value of y when $x=1+\sqrt{7}$.

[57] If $a=\sqrt{7}+\sqrt{5}$ and $b=\sqrt{7}-\sqrt{5}$, find the values of ab, a^2+b^2, $a^4+b\cdot$.

58. Find the value of x to 3 figures if $x+x\sqrt{3}=10$.

[59] Find the value of y to 3 figures if $y+y\sqrt{\frac{1}{2}}=1$.

*60. Find x in terms of c if $(x+c)^2=3x^2$.

$x=\dfrac{10}{1+\sqrt{3}}$

$=\dfrac{10(\sqrt{3}-1)}{2}$

$= 5(\sqrt{3}-1)$

$= 5\times0.732$

$= 3.660$

Theory of Logarithms

The use of logarithms forms part of the Arithmetic course; the following section deals with the theory, but an exercise in computation is added for purposes of revision.

If $x = 10^m$, then m is called the logarithm of x to base 10, and we write
$$m = \log_{10} x.$$

Thus the logarithm of a number x to base 10 is the power to which 10 must be raised to give the number; in short, *a logarithm is always an index*.

The definition may be expressed also in the form:
$$\log_{10}(10^m) = m;$$

and in particular, $\log_{10} 1 = 0$, since $10^0 = 1$,

and $\qquad\qquad \log_{10} 10 = 1$, since $10^1 = 10$.

Properties of Logarithms

(i) $\log_{10}(xy) = \log_{10} x + \log_{10} y.$

Let $\log_{10} x = m$ and $\log_{10} y = n$.

Then $\qquad\qquad x = 10^m \quad$ and $\quad y = 10^n;$
$$\therefore\ xy = 10^m \times 10^n = 10^{m+n};$$
$$\therefore\ \log_{10} xy = m + n = \log_{10} x + \log_{10} y.$$

(ii) $\log_{10}\left(\dfrac{x}{y}\right) = \log_{10} x - \log_{10} y.$

With the same notation as before,
$$\frac{x}{y} = 10^m \div 10^n = 10^{m-n};$$
$$\therefore\ \log_{10}\left(\frac{x}{y}\right) = m - n = \log_{10} x - \log_{10} y.$$

(iii) $\log_{10}(x^p) = p \log_{10} x.$

Let $\log_{10} x = m, \quad \therefore\ x = 10^m;$
$$\therefore\ x^p = (10^m)^p = 10^{mp};$$
$$\therefore\ \log_{10}(x^p) = mp = p \log_{10} x.$$

From this result, we have the following:
$$\log_{10}\left(\frac{1}{x^q}\right) = \log_{10}(x^{-q}) = -q \log_{10} x;$$

and $\qquad \log_{10}(\sqrt[n]{x}) = \log_{10}\left(x^{\frac{1}{n}}\right) = \frac{1}{n} \log_{10} x.$

For convenience, we denote in this section $\log_{10} x$ by $\log x$, unless there is some special reason, as in Example 17, for emphasising that the base is 10.

Example 16. Simplify $\dfrac{\log 125}{\log 25}$.

$$\log 125 = \log (5^3) = 3 \log 5,$$
$$\log 25 = \log (5^2) = 2 \log 5;$$
$$\therefore \text{ expression} = \frac{3 \log 5}{2 \log 5} = \frac{3}{2}.$$

Example 17. Simplify $\log_{10} \frac{27}{32} - \log_{10} \frac{125}{9} + 2 \log_{10} \frac{1}{45}$.

$$\text{The expression} = \log_{10} \frac{3^3}{2^5} + \log_{10} \frac{3^2}{5^3} + \log_{10} \left(\frac{1}{3^2 \cdot 5} \right)^2$$
$$= \log_{10} \frac{3^3 \cdot 3^2}{2^5 \cdot 5^3 \cdot 3^4 \cdot 5^2} = \log_{10} \frac{3}{10^5}$$
$$= \log_{10} 3 - \log_{10} 10^5 = -5 + \log_{10} 3.$$

EXERCISE XIV. f

Express the following in the form $\log x$:

1. $\log 2 + \log 4.$ 2. $\log 12 - \log 3.$ 3. $3 \log 2.$

4. $-\log 4.$ 5. $2 \log 5 + \log 1.$ 6. $\frac{1}{2} \log 16.$

7. $\frac{4}{3} \log 27.$ 8. $2 + \log_{10} 3.$ 9. $1 - \log_{10} 2.$

[10] $\log 4 + 2 \log 3.$ [11] $5 \log 2 - \log 8.$ [12] $\frac{1}{3} \log 125.$

[13] $\frac{3}{4} \log 16.$ [14] $2 \log_{10} 3 + 1.$ [15] $3 \log_{10} 5 - 2.$

Write down the values of x for the following equations:

16. $\log_{10} x = 3.$ 17. $\log_{10} x = 1.$ 18. $\log_{10} x = -1.$

19. $\log_{10} x = \frac{1}{2}.$ 20. $\log_{10} x = -2.$ 21. $\log_{10} x = -\frac{1}{2}.$

Given $\log_{10} 2 \simeq 0 \cdot 30103$ and $\log_{10} 3 \simeq 0 \cdot 47712$, obtain approximate values of the logarithms to base 10 of the following:

22. 20.   23. 81.   24. 5.   25. 0·2.   26. 0·12.

[27] 18.   [28] 15.   [29] 0·5.   [30] 2·5.   [31] 0·125.

Simplify:

32. $\dfrac{\log 8}{\log 2}$.　　33. $\dfrac{\log 27}{\log 9}$.　　34. $\dfrac{\log 5}{\log \sqrt{5}}$.　　35. $\dfrac{\log 2}{\log \frac{1}{4}}$.

[36] $\dfrac{\log 9}{\log 3}$.　　[37] $\dfrac{\log 216}{\log 36}$.　　[38] $\dfrac{\log \sqrt{8}}{\log \sqrt[3]{2}}$.　　[39] $\dfrac{\log \frac{1}{9}}{\log \sqrt{3}}$

40. $\log 27 - \log 3$.　　41. $\log 2 - \log \sqrt{2}$.　　42. $\log 1 \times \log 10$.

[43] $\log (x^2) - 2 \log (xy) + \log (y^2)$.　　[44] $\log z + \log \dfrac{1}{z}$.

45. $\log_{10} 125 + \log_{10} 32 - \log_{10} 4$.

46. $\log_{10} 7 \cdot 5 + \log_{10} 28 - \log_{10} 0 \cdot 21$.

[47] $\log_{10} 1 \cdot 5 + \log_{10} 0 \cdot 8 - \log_{10} 30$.

[48] $\log_{10} 2 \cdot 4 + \log_{10} 75 - \log_{10} 450$.

49. $\log_{10} \frac{81}{32} + 3 \log_{10} \frac{5}{3} + \log_{10} \frac{1}{9} + \log_{10} 768$.

[50] $2 \log_{10} \frac{2}{9} + 1\frac{1}{2} \log_{10} \frac{9}{25} - 5 \log_{10} \frac{2}{3}$.

Express the following in a form which does not involve the logarithmic notation, the logarithmic base being 10:

51. $\log x + \log y = 3$.　　[52] $\log x + 2 \log y = 2$.

53. $3 \log x - 2 \log y = 1$.　　[54] $x \log 5 = \log 6$.

55. $x \log 2 = -1$.　　[56] $x \log 5 - y \log 6 = 2$.

57. $\log x + \log y = \log 3$.　　[58] $\log x - 3 \log y = \log 5$.

59. $2 \log y + 3 \log x = 0 \cdot 7$.　　[60] $\log y = 1 \cdot 6 \log x + 0 \cdot 58$.

Example 18.　Find the value of x correct to 3 figures if

$$(0 \cdot 716)^x = 0 \cdot 415.$$

$$x \log 0 \cdot 716 = \log 0 \cdot 415;$$
$$\therefore \ x = \frac{\log 0 \cdot 415}{\log 0 \cdot 716} = \frac{\bar{1} \cdot 6180}{\bar{1} \cdot 8549}$$
$$= \frac{-0 \cdot 3820}{-0 \cdot 1451} = \frac{3 \cdot 820}{1 \cdot 451}.$$

The value of this fraction may now be found by long division, or may be computed by logarithms in the ordinary way;

$$\therefore \ x = 2 \cdot 63, \text{ to 3 figures.}$$

$$\begin{array}{r} 0 \cdot 5821 \\ 0 \cdot 1617 \\ \hline 0 \cdot 4204 \end{array}$$

Example 19.   After how many years will £160 amount to £500 at $3\frac{1}{2}$ per cent. compound interest?

By the compound interest formula, £P at r per cent. per annum compound interest amounts in n years to $£P\left(1 + \dfrac{r}{100}\right)^n$.

$$\therefore 160\left(1 + \frac{3\cdot5}{100}\right)^n = 500;$$

$$\therefore (1\cdot035)^n = \tfrac{500}{160};$$

$$\therefore n \log 1\cdot035 = \log 500 - \log 160;$$

$$\therefore n \times 0\cdot0149 = 2\cdot6990 - 2\cdot2041;$$

$$\therefore n = \frac{0\cdot4949}{0\cdot0149}.$$

$$\begin{aligned}&\overline{1}\cdot6945\\&\overline{2}\cdot1732\\&\overline{1\cdot5213}\end{aligned}$$

Hence by long division or computing by logarithms,

$$n = 33\cdot2;$$

$\therefore$ the length of time is 33 years, to the nearest year.

Note. Since the denominator $0\cdot0149$ is given only to 3 significant figures, the value of n can only be found reliably to 2 figures.

EXERCISE XIV. g

[Give answers correct to 3 figures unless otherwise stated.]

Evaluate:

1. $(38\cdot64)^{\frac{2}{3}}$.
2. $(0\cdot8172)^{\frac{3}{4}}$.
3. $(201\cdot8)^{-\frac{1}{2}}$.

[4] $(0\cdot5718)^{\frac{4}{9}}$.
[5] $(79\cdot46)^{-\frac{1}{3}}$.
[6] $(0\cdot6153)^{-\frac{1}{4}}$.

[7] $\dfrac{1}{\sqrt[5]{10}}$.
[8] $(18\cdot07)^{-0\cdot4}$.
[9] $(0\cdot3927)^{-1\cdot6}$.

10. $(0\cdot0876)^{-\frac{2}{3}}$.
11. $\dfrac{1}{\sqrt[3]{(0\cdot735)^{-\frac{1}{2}}}}$.
12. $\dfrac{1}{(0\cdot1)^{0\cdot2}}$.

13. $\dfrac{18 \times 1\cdot43 \times 10^7}{(0\cdot16)^3 \times \sqrt{0\cdot525}}$.
[14] $173 \times \sqrt[3]{\left(\dfrac{37\cdot8}{2\cdot46}\right)}$.

15. $\dfrac{x\sqrt[3]{(x-y)}}{z}$ if $x = 4\cdot143$, $y = 3\cdot791$, $z = 0\cdot6952$.

[16] $\sqrt{\left\{45\cdot08 \times \dfrac{144 \times 14\cdot7}{0\cdot0809} \times \left(1 + \dfrac{16}{273}\right)\right\}}$.

[17] $\sqrt{(u^2 + 2as)}$ if $u = 77\cdot5$, $a = -32\cdot2$, $s = 26$.

18. $\dfrac{-b + \sqrt{(b^2 - 4ac)}}{2a}$ if $a = 2 \cdot 074$, $b = 8 \cdot 163$, $c = 3 \cdot 572$.

19. $\pi l(R^2 - r^2)$ if $l = 0 \cdot 726$, $R = 0 \cdot 817$, $r = 0 \cdot 629$, $\pi = 3 \cdot 1416$.

[20] $\dfrac{1}{47} \sqrt{\left\{ \dfrac{84 \cdot 15}{319 \cdot 6} + \dfrac{2 \cdot 718}{5 \cdot 623} \right\}}$.

[21] $0 \cdot 0004796 \sqrt{\left(\dfrac{32 \cdot 14^3}{0 \cdot 36 \times 9\frac{2}{3}} \right)}$.

22. $\pi r \sqrt{(h^2 + r^2)}$ if $h = 20 \cdot 3$, $r = 12 \cdot 7$, $\log \pi = 0 \cdot 4971$.

23. $\sqrt{\left\{ \dfrac{1 \cdot 63 x^5}{(p + 0 \cdot 4x)^3} \right\}}$ if $x = 23 \cdot 2$, $p = 15 \cdot 68$.

[24] If $gt^2 = 4\pi^2 l$, find t when $l = 75$, $g = 981$, $\pi = 3 \cdot 1416$.

25. If $\frac{4}{3} \pi k r^3 = 0 \cdot 872$, find r when $k = 2 \cdot 74$, $\pi = 3 \cdot 1416$.

[26] If $x^3 \times (0 \cdot 02137)^2 = 1$, find x.

[27] If $x^3 = y^3 + z^3$, find x when $y = 0 \cdot 827$, $z = 0 \cdot 619$.

28. If $x^5(1 + \sqrt[3]{10}) = \sqrt[4]{10}$, find x.

Evaluate:

29. $5 \cdot 29 e^{kt}$ if $e = 2 \cdot 718$, $k = 3$, $t = 0 \cdot 2$.

[30] $35 \cdot 2 \, e^{c\pi}$ if $e = 2 \cdot 718$, $c = 0 \cdot 465$, $\pi = 3 \cdot 1416$.

31. $p \dfrac{r^t - 1}{r - 1}$ if $p = 26 \cdot 67$, $r = 1 \cdot 055$, $t = 20$; (to 2 figures).

32. $\dfrac{\log n - \log 273}{\log 2 \cdot 718}$ if $n = 373$.

[33] $\log 2 \div \log \left(1 + \dfrac{r}{100} \right)$ if $r = 2\frac{1}{2}$.

[34] $\dfrac{2 \cdot 303}{\mu} \log_{10} \left(\dfrac{P}{W} \right)$ if $\mu = 0 \cdot 65$, $P = 27 \cdot 3$, $W = 16$.

35. $\dfrac{1}{13} \left(\dfrac{a}{b} - \dfrac{1}{9} \log_{10} c \right)$ if $a = 343$, $b = 51 \cdot 2$, $c = 0 \cdot 426$.

36. $\log \left(\dfrac{Ar}{100P} + 1 \right) \div \log \left(1 + \dfrac{r}{100} \right)$ if $P = 150$, $A = 1720$, $r = 6$.

[37] $5 \cdot 25 k^3 d^{-4}$ if $k = 2 \cdot 085$, $d = 0 \cdot 2173$.

38. $G^{\frac{3}{4}}(0 \cdot 41H)^{-\frac{1}{4}}$ if $G = 250$, $H = 12 \cdot 5$.

Evaluate:

[39] $27 \cdot 36 H^{\frac{3}{4}} p^{-\frac{1}{2}}$ if $H = 10$, $p = 160$.

40. $\dfrac{0 \cdot 022 v^2 l}{g d^{1 \cdot 2}}$ if $v = 8 \cdot 55$, $l = 54 \cdot 6$, $g = 32 \cdot 2$, $d = 2 \cdot 66$.

[41] $3 \cdot 55 \times 10^4 D^{0 \cdot 7} T^{0 \cdot 6}$ if $D = \frac{7}{8}$, $T = \frac{1}{80}$.

42. $\dfrac{100 A}{r} \left\{ 1 - \left(1 + \dfrac{r}{100} \right)^{-n} \right\}$ if $r = 3\frac{1}{2}$, $A = 200$, $n = 6$; (to 2 figures).

Find the values of x given by the following equations:

43. $2^x = 10$.   44. $5^x = \sqrt{10}$.   45. $(0 \cdot 847)^x = 0 \cdot 307$.

[46] $3^x = 100$.   [47] $7^x = 140$.   [48] $(6 \cdot 23)^x = 0 \cdot 618$.

[49] If $pv^n = 13{,}800$, find the value of n if $p = 7 \cdot 62$, $v = 82 \cdot 3$.

[50] Find the least integral value of n such that $(1 \cdot 01)^n$ exceeds $2 \cdot 5$.

51. Find the least integral value of n such that $(0 \cdot 95)^n$ is less than $0 \cdot 1$.

[52] Find the least integral value of n such that $(0 \cdot 88)^n$ is less than $0 \cdot 08$.

53. Find the integral value of n such that $10{,}000{,}000$ lies between 3^n and 3^{n+1}.

[54] If $3^x = 4^y$, find the ratio $x : y$.

55. If $y = cx^n$ where c, n are constants, and if for $x = 2$, $y = 10 \cdot 6$, and for $x = 3$, $y = 6 \cdot 2$, find the values of c, n.

56. After how many years will £210 amount to £450 at 3 per cent. per annum compound interest?

[57] After how many years will a sum of money be doubled if invested at $2\frac{1}{2}$ per cent. per annum compound interest?

58. After how many years will a sum of money be increased by 60 per cent., if invested at $4\frac{1}{2}$ per cent. per annum compound interest?

REVISION EXERCISE R. 8 (Ch. XIV)

1. Find n if (i) $y^n \times y^n = y$; (ii) $y^n \times y^n = \dfrac{1}{y}$; (iii) $y^n \times y^n = 1$.

2. Write down the values of 6^{-2}, 5^{-1}, $16^{-\frac{1}{2}}$, 3^0.

3. Write down the values of $4^{-\frac{3}{2}}$, $16^{-\frac{3}{4}}$, $100^{2 \cdot 5}$, $1^{-\frac{1}{2}}$.

[4] If $x = 16$, $y = 9$, write down the values of

(i) $x^{\frac{1}{2}} + y^{\frac{1}{2}}$; (ii) $(x+y)^{\frac{1}{2}}$; (iii) $\left(\dfrac{x}{y}\right)^{-\frac{1}{2}}$.

[5] Find the value of n if (i) $3^n = 9$; (ii) $9^n = 3$; (iii) $(\frac{1}{3})^n = \sqrt{3}$.

6. Express without using fractional or negative indices:

(i) $y = ax^{-2}$; (ii) $pv^{-1} = c$; (iii) $z = x^{-\frac{1}{2}}y^{\frac{3}{2}}$.

7. Express as powers of 4, (i) $\frac{1}{4}$; (ii) 2; (iii) 8; (iv) 1.

[8] Simplify (i) $(a^3 b^{\frac{1}{2}})^{\frac{2}{3}}$; (ii) $c^3(c^{-1} + c^{-2})$.

9. Multiply $x^{\frac{2}{3}} + 2 + 3x^{-\frac{2}{3}}$ by $x^{\frac{2}{3}} - 2 + 3x^{-\frac{2}{3}}$ and evaluate the result if $x = 8$.

10. Find the value of x if $2 \times 4^{x-1} = 8^{-x}$.

[11] If $a^2 x = 1$ and $a^3 = y$, express x in the form y^n.

12. If $(ax)^{-\frac{1}{2}} = b$ and $b^{\frac{2}{3}} = a$, express x in terms of a only.

Find without using tables the values of:

13. $\sqrt{7 \cdot 5} \times \sqrt{120}$.   [14] $\sqrt{72} \div \sqrt{200}$.   [15] $\sqrt[3]{6 \cdot 75} \div \sqrt[3]{0 \cdot 128}$.

16. $(2^2 \times 3^2)^{-\frac{5}{3}} \times 2^{-\frac{2}{3}} \times 3^{\frac{7}{3}}$.   **17.** $(0 \cdot 00243)^{-\frac{3}{5}} \times (3 \cdot 375)^{-\frac{1}{3}}$.

[18] $(2 \cdot 5)^{\frac{1}{2}} \times (\frac{4}{15})^{-\frac{1}{2}} \div (1 \cdot 5)^{\frac{3}{2}}$.   [19] $(0 \cdot 00032)^{\frac{3}{5}} \div (0 \cdot 015625)^{-\frac{2}{3}}$.

[20] The horse-power of the engines required to drive a ship of T tons at a speed of v knots is $0 \cdot 0042 v^3 \sqrt[3]{T^2}$. Find correct to 2 figures the horse-power if a ship of 30,700 tons is to have a maximum speed of $25 \cdot 4$ knots.

21. If $\frac{4}{3}\pi r^3 = 5$, find correct to 3 figures the value of $4\pi r^2$ [log $\pi = 0 \cdot 4971$].

[22] Find correct to 3 figures the value of $a^{\frac{2}{5}}b^{-1}c^{-3}$ if $a = 0\cdot0376$, $b = 16\cdot92$, $c = 0\cdot3947$.

23. If $z = 3\cdot58x^{0\cdot6}y^{-0\cdot6}$, express x in the form cy^pz^q, giving c correct to 3 figures.

24. Given that $\log_{10} 2 = 0\cdot301030$, calculate the value of $\log_{10} 2\cdot5$ correct to 5 figures.

Simplify:

25. $\log x^3 \div \log \left(\dfrac{1}{x}\right).$ [26] $\log y^3 - \log \left(\dfrac{1}{y^3}\right).$

27. $\sqrt[3]{x} \times \sqrt[6]{x}.$ [28] $\sqrt[3]{y^2} \div \sqrt[6]{y}.$ 29. $(3\sqrt{3} - \sqrt{12})^2.$

30. $\dfrac{12}{\sqrt{2}}.$ [31] $\dfrac{\sqrt{18}}{\sqrt{2}}.$ 32. $\dfrac{3 - \sqrt{8}}{3 + \sqrt{8}}.$

[33] $(1 + \sqrt{2} - \sqrt{3})(1 + \sqrt{2} + \sqrt{3}).$

34. $(\sqrt{3} + \sqrt{5} - 2\sqrt{2})(\sqrt{3} + \sqrt{5} + 2\sqrt{2}).$

[35] Given that $\log_{10} 12 = 1\cdot079181$ and $\log_{10} 18 = 1\cdot255272$, calculate correct to 5 figures the values of $\log_{10} 2$, $\log_{10} 3$, $\log_{10} 5$.

Evaluate the following:

[36] $\log_{10} (100\sqrt[3]{10} \div \sqrt{10}).$

37. $\log_{10} \sqrt{44} + \log_{10} \sqrt{275} - \log_{10} 11.$

[38] $4b - b^2$ if $b = 2 - \sqrt{3}.$ 39. $c + \dfrac{1}{c}$ if $c = \dfrac{7 - 3\sqrt{5}}{7 + 3\sqrt{5}}.$

40. Find x, y if $\dfrac{\log x}{\log 5} = \dfrac{\log 36}{\log 6} = \dfrac{\log 64}{\log y}.$

[41] Simplify $\dfrac{a - b}{a\sqrt{b} - b\sqrt{a}}.$ [42] If $8^x = 16^y$, find the value of $\dfrac{x}{y}.$

43. $y = ax^n$ is satisfied by $x = 2$, $y = 3\cdot45$ and by $x = 5$, $y = 9\cdot82$, find n and a correct to 3 figures.

44. If $\log_{10} \mathsf{V} = 2 \log_{10} 3 + \log_{10} 5 + 0\cdot4971$, evaluate V correct to 3 figures.

[45] If $a = 10^x$, $b = 10^y$, $c = 10^z$, express $\log_{10} \left(\dfrac{10\sqrt{b}}{a^3c}\right)$ in terms of x, y, z.

CHAPTER XV

RATIO, PROPORTION, AND VARIATION

Ratio. If two parcels weigh respectively 5 lb. and 8 lb., the weight of the first is $\frac{5}{8}$ of the weight of the second, and their weights are said to be in the *ratio* of 5 to 8, written $5:8$. In general, the ratio of any two numbers x and y is measured by the fraction $\frac{x}{y}$ and is often written $x:y$. Any two quantities *of the same kind* can be compared in this way by expressing the first as a fraction of the second. For example, the ratio of x yards to y feet is found by expressing each length *in the same unit*; the lengths are x yd., $\frac{1}{3}y$ yd., or $3x$ ft., y ft., or $36x$ in., $12y$ in., and their ratio is represented by any one of the equal fractions $\frac{x}{\frac{1}{3}y}, \frac{3x}{y}, \frac{36x}{12y}$. Ratios should always be expressed in as simple a form as possible; they are reduced in the same way as fractions.

Two quantities of different kinds cannot be compared. There is no ratio between say 20 miles and 6 hours.

If x, y, z are three numbers, the relation

$$x:y:z = 7:3:15$$

means that

$$\frac{x}{7} = \frac{y}{3} = \frac{z}{15},$$

and we say that x, y, z are *proportional* to 7, 3, 15.

These equations are equivalent to $\frac{x}{y} = \frac{7}{3}, \frac{y}{z} = \frac{3}{15}, \frac{x}{z} = \frac{7}{15}$.

Similarly $x:y:z:u:v = a:b:c:d:e$, means that $\frac{x}{a} = \frac{y}{b} = \frac{z}{c} = \frac{u}{d} = \frac{v}{e}$, and x, y, z, u, v are said to be *proportional* to a, b, c, d, e.

Example 1. If $x : y = 9 : 5$, find the ratio $(4x - 3y) : (5x - 2y)$.

Any two numbers in the ratio $9 : 5$ can be expressed in the form $9k, 5k$.

Put $x = 9k$, then $y = 5k$.

$$\therefore \frac{4x - 3y}{5x - 2y} = \frac{36k - 15k}{45k - 10k} = \frac{21k}{35k} = \frac{3}{5};$$

$$\therefore (4x - 3y) : (5x - 2y) = 3 : 5.$$

Example 2. If $x : y = 9 : 8$ and $y : z = 6 : 7$, find the three least positive integers to which x, y, z are proportional.

$$\frac{x}{9} = \frac{y}{8} \quad \text{and} \quad \frac{y}{6} = \frac{z}{7}.$$

The L.C.M. of the denominators 8, 6 of y in the two equations is 24;

thus
$$\frac{x}{27} = \frac{y}{24} \quad \text{and} \quad \frac{y}{24} = \frac{z}{28};$$

$$\therefore x : y : z = 27 : 24 : 28.$$

EXERCISE XV. a

Express the following ratios in their simplest forms:

1. $2x$ yards : $9x$ feet.   **[2]** $15y$ shillings : £$2z$.

3. $1\frac{1}{4}b$ hours : $45c$ minutes.   **[4]** $8\frac{3}{4}$ inches : $8\frac{1}{6}$ inches.

If $a : b = 4 : 3$ and $x : y = 9 : 10$, find the following ratios:

5. $a^2 : b^2$.   **[6]** $ax : by$.   **7.** $\dfrac{a}{x} : \dfrac{b}{y}$.   **[8]** $\dfrac{1}{a} : \dfrac{1}{b}$.

Find the ratio of $a : b$ in the following:

9. $4a = 3b$.   **[10]** $a = b - \frac{1}{3}b$.   **11.** $9a^2 = 4b^2$.

[12] $3a - 2b = a + 6b$.   **13.** $(a + b) : (a - b) = 7 : 3$.

14. a exceeds b (i) by 20 per cent., (ii) by r per cent.

Find $x : y : z$ in its simplest form in the following:

15. $x : y = 10 : 21$ and $y : z = 28 : 9$.

[16] $x = 3y$, $y = 5z$.   **17.** $6x = 9y = 10z$.

If $a : b = 11 : 7$, find the following ratios:

18. $(a + b) : (a - b)$.   **[19]** $(5a - 4b) : (2a + 5b)$.

[20] $(a^2 - b^2) : (a^2 - 2b^2)$.   **21.** $(a + b)^2 : (2a - b)(a + 3b)$.

If $a : b : c = 7 : 3 : 5$, find the following ratios:

22. $b : (a + c)$.　　　　　　[23] $(a - b) : (a + 3c)$.

[24] $(a + b + c) : (2a + b - c)$.　　25. $(a^2 - b^2 - c^2) : (ab + bc)$.

26. Two numbers are in the ratio $p : q$. If the first is b, find the second. If the second is c, find the first.

27. The ratio of the radii of two spheres is $3 : 4$. What is the ratio of (i) the areas of their surfaces, (ii) their volumes?

[28] The ratio of the heights of two circular cylinders is $5 : 4$ and the ratio of their diameters is $2 : 3$. Find the ratio of their volumes.

Find the ratios in which the following expressions are changed if x and y are each increased in the ratio $4 : 3$.

29. $\dfrac{x^2}{y^2}$.　　　[30] $\dfrac{x^3}{y}$.　　　　[31] $x^2 - 2y^2$.　　　32. $\dfrac{x^3 - y^3}{xy}$.

Find the two possible values of the ratio $x : y$ in the following:

33. $x^2 - 8xy + 15y^2 = 0$.　　　　[34] $10x^2 = 7xy + 12y^2$.

35. $(x + 3y)^2 : (x - y)^2 = 9 : 4$.

36. If $(a + b) : (a - b) = 7 : 3$, find $(2a - b) : (2a + b)$.

[37] If $(p + 5q) : (3p + q) = 4 : 3$, find $(2p + 3q) : (p - 2q)$.

38. If $4x - 2y - 7z = 0$ and $3x + 8y - 29z = 0$, find $x : y : z$.

[39] If $3p - 2q + 4r = p + 2q - 3r = 0$, find $p : q : r$.

40. If $(x + 2y) : (x - 2y) = a : 1$, find the ratio $(5x + 4y) : (3x + 2y)$ in terms of a. Find also the value of a if $x : y = 7 : 3$.

[41] If $(2x - y) : (3x + y)$ equals $(k - 1) : (k + 1)$, express in terms of k (i) $x : y$, (ii) $(x + y) : (x + 2y)$.

42. If the ratio of $\dfrac{a}{2c} - 1$ to $\dfrac{b}{2c} - 1$ is equal to the ratio of b to a, and if a is not equal to b, express a in terms of b, c.

[43] If the ratio of $a - b$ to $c + a$ is equal to the ratio of b^2 to c^2, and if $b + c$ is not zero, express c in terms of a, b.

44. If the ratio of $\dfrac{3a}{b} - 1$ to $\dfrac{3a}{c} - 1$ is equal to the ratio of c^2 to b^2, and if b is not equal to c, express a in terms of b, c.

Equal Ratios

Example 3. If $\dfrac{a}{b} = \dfrac{c}{d}$, prove that $\dfrac{2a - 5c}{2b - 5d} = \dfrac{a}{b}$.

Let $\dfrac{a}{b} = k$, then $\dfrac{c}{d} = k$; $\therefore$ $a = bk$ and $c = dk$.

$$\therefore \quad \frac{2a - 5c}{2b - 5d} = \frac{2bk - 5dk}{2b - 5d} = k$$

$$= \frac{a}{b}.$$

Example 4. If $\dfrac{a}{b} = \dfrac{c}{d} = \dfrac{e}{f}$, prove that

$$\frac{4a - 7c}{4b - 7d} = \sqrt{\left(\frac{a^2 - 5ce}{b^2 - 5df}\right)}.$$

Let $\dfrac{a}{b} = k$, then $\dfrac{c}{d} = k$ and $\dfrac{e}{f} = k$;

$$\therefore \quad a = bk, \quad c = dk, \quad e = fk;$$

$$\therefore \quad \text{left side} = \frac{4bk - 7dk}{4b - 7d} = k,$$

$$\text{and right side} = \sqrt{\left(\frac{b^2 k^2 - 5df k^2}{b^2 - 5df}\right)}$$

$$= \sqrt{(k^2)} = k;$$

$$\therefore \quad \text{left side} = \text{right side}.$$

Note. If k is negative, the negative value of the square root in the enunciation must be taken.

EXERCISE XV. b

1. If $\dfrac{a}{b} = \dfrac{3}{5}$ evaluate (i) $\dfrac{a + b}{b}$; (ii) $\dfrac{a - b}{a}$; (iii) $\dfrac{a + 3b}{3a - b}$.

If $\dfrac{a}{b} = \dfrac{c}{d}$, prove the relations, Nos. 2–5:

2. $\dfrac{a + c}{b + d} = \dfrac{a - c}{b - d}$.

[3] $\dfrac{3a + 5c}{3b + 5d} = \dfrac{2a - 7c}{2b - 7d}$.

[4] $\dfrac{a^2}{a^2 - b^2} = \dfrac{c^2}{c^2 - d^2}$.

5. $\dfrac{2a^3 - c^3}{2b^3 - d^3} = \dfrac{a^2 c + 3ac^2}{b^2 d + 3bd^2}$.

If $\dfrac{a}{b}=\dfrac{c}{d}=\dfrac{e}{f}$, prove the relations, Nos. 6–9:

6. $\dfrac{a-c+e}{b-d+f}=\dfrac{3a+e}{3b+f}.$

[7] $\dfrac{a^3-c^3}{b^3-d^3}=\left(\dfrac{c+e}{d+f}\right)^3.$

8. $\dfrac{\sqrt{(ac-2e^2)}}{\sqrt{(bd-2f^2)}}=\dfrac{c+e}{d+f}.$

[9] $\dfrac{a^4+ce^3}{c^4-a^2e^2}=\dfrac{b^4+df^3}{d^4-b^2f^2}.$

10. Find numerical values of x, y, z if
$$\frac{a}{10}=\frac{b}{9}=\frac{a-b}{x}=\frac{a+b}{y}=\frac{3a-2b}{z}.$$

[11] Find numerical values of x, y if
$$\frac{a}{6}=\frac{b}{8}=\frac{c}{9}=\frac{a+b-c}{x}=\frac{3a-b-c}{y}.$$

If $\dfrac{a}{b}=\dfrac{c}{d}=\dfrac{e}{f}$, complete the following:

12. $\dfrac{a}{b}=\dfrac{a-c+e}{\ldots}=\dfrac{\ldots}{f-b-d}=\dfrac{ax-ey}{\ldots}.$

[13] $\dfrac{a^2}{b^2}=\dfrac{ce}{\ldots}=\dfrac{\ldots}{(f-b)(f-d)}.$

14. If $\dfrac{a}{b}=\dfrac{b}{c}$, prove that $\dfrac{a^2+b^2}{(a+c)^2}=\dfrac{b^2}{b^2+c^2}.$

[15] If $\dfrac{a}{b}=\dfrac{b}{c}$, prove that $\dfrac{a^2+ab+b^2}{a}=\dfrac{b^2+bc+c^2}{c}.$

[16] If $\dfrac{a}{b}=\dfrac{b}{c}$, prove that $\left(\dfrac{a-b}{b-c}\right)^2=\dfrac{a}{c}.$

17. If $\dfrac{a}{b}=\dfrac{b}{c}=\dfrac{c}{d}$, prove that $\dfrac{ab+bc+ca}{bc+cd+db}=\left(\dfrac{a}{d}\right)^{\frac{2}{3}}.$

18. If $\dfrac{a}{pq}=\dfrac{b}{p^2}=\dfrac{c}{qr}$, express $p:q:r$ in terms of a, b, c.

Variation

If a train travels uniformly at 48 miles per hour,

> in 5 minutes it travels 4 miles;
> in 10 minutes it travels 8 miles;
> in 15 minutes it travels 12 miles; and so on.

If the time is doubled, the corresponding distance is also doubled; if the time is halved, the distance is halved; etc.

We therefore say that the distance is *directly proportional* to the time, or that the distance *varies directly* as the time.

Suppose that in x minutes the train travels y miles, then

$$y = \tfrac{4}{5}x.$$

The corresponding travel graph is represented by **OA** in Fig. 153; it is a straight line through the origin.

Fig. 153 contains also the travel graphs **OP**, **OQ**, **OR** of three other trains and the travel graph **OS** of an aeroplane. The reader should interpret each of these graphs and state (i) what speed each represents, (ii) what relation connects x and y.

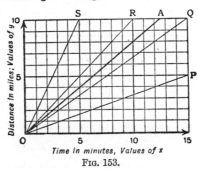

Fig. 153.

For each graph in turn, we see that

$$\frac{y}{x} = c \quad \text{or} \quad y = cx,$$

where c has some definite numerical value which measures the *slope* of the graph.

Thus for **OA**, $c = \tfrac{4}{5}$; and for **OP**, $c = \tfrac{1}{3}$; and for **OS**, $c = 2$; etc.

These graphs illustrate the fact that if the result of plotting values of y against values of x gives a straight line through the origin, then y varies directly as x; this is often written in the form, $y \propto x$, and it then follows that $y = cx$ where c is a constant.

To illustrate a different form of variation, suppose that a se of open cubical tin boxes of various sizes are made from ti sheeting and consider the relation between the area of sheetin, used, A sq. in., and the height of the box, h in.

For example, if the box is 3 in. high, the area of each face i 9 sq. in.; but there are 5 faces; ∴ the area of sheeting used i 45 sq. in. The reader should check the results in the followin, table:

h	2	3	4	5	6	7	8
A	20	45	80	125	180	245	320

It is obvious that A does not vary directly as h, e.g. A is no doubled if h is doubled. But if we tabulate corresponding value of A and h^2, as follows:

A	20	45	80	125	180	245	320
h^2	4	9	16	25	36	49	64

we see that $\dfrac{A}{h^2} = 5$ (a constant); and we then say that

$$A \text{ varies directly as the square of } h,$$

or more shortly that A varies as h^2; this is written

$$A \propto h^2.$$

If values of A are plotted against values of h^2, we obtain a straight line through the origin.

If $A \propto h^2$, the result of multiplying h by 3 is to multiply A by 3^2; the result of dividing h by 10 is to divide A by 10^2.

More generally y is said to vary directly as the nth power of x, written $y \propto x^n$,

if $\dfrac{y}{x^n}$ is constant,

that is, if $y = cx^n$,

where c is a constant

Example 5. The time of a complete oscillation of a simple pendulum varies as the square root of the length of the pendulum. If a pendulum 9 ft. long makes a complete oscillation in 3·3 sec., find the time of oscillation of a pendulum 4 ft. long.

Suppose that the time of oscillation of a pendulum, l ft. long, is t sec.; then $t \propto \sqrt{l}$.

Since $\dfrac{t}{\sqrt{l}}$ is constant, the time of oscillation, t seconds, when $l = 4$ is given by

t	3·3	?
l	9	4

$$\frac{t}{\sqrt{4}} = \frac{3 \cdot 3}{\sqrt{9}};$$

$$\therefore \ t = \frac{3 \cdot 3 \times 2}{3} = 2 \cdot 2;$$

$\therefore$ the time of oscillation of a pendulum 4 ft. long is 2·2 sec.

Inverse Variation. Suppose a number of rectangular mats are made of different shapes, but all of the same area 36 sq. in.

Then if a mat is l in. long and b in. broad,

$$lb = 36,$$

$$\therefore \ l = 36 \times \frac{1}{b} \quad \text{or} \quad l \div \frac{1}{b} = 36, \text{ a constant.}$$

It is evident that if b increases, l decreases in such a way that when b is doubled, l is halved, and so on. We then say that

l *varies inversely as* b,

or that l varies as $\dfrac{1}{b}$,

and we write

$$l \propto \frac{1}{b}.$$

The reader should construct a table giving corresponding values of l and b and show that the result of plotting values of l against values of $\dfrac{1}{b}$ is *a straight line through the origin*.

As another example of inverse variation, consider a numbe of circular cylinders, all having the same volume, 10 cu. in.

Then if the height is h in. and the base-radius is r in.,

$$\pi r^2 h = 10,$$

$$\therefore \ h = \frac{10}{\pi} \times \frac{1}{r^2} \quad \text{or} \quad h \div \frac{1}{r^2} = \frac{10}{\pi}, \text{ a constant;}$$

and we say that h *varies inversely as the square of* r, or that varies as $\frac{1}{r^2}$, and we write $h \propto \frac{1}{r^2}$.

More generally y is said to vary inversely as the nth power of x

written $$y \propto \frac{1}{x^n},$$

if $$y \div \frac{1}{x^n} \text{ is constant,}$$

that is, if $$y = \frac{c}{x^n},$$

where c is a constant.

Example 6. The number of beats per minute of a pendulum varies inversely as the square root of its length. If a pendulum 9 ft. long makes 36 beats per minute, find how many beats per minute a pendulum 4 ft. long makes; and find a general formula.

Suppose that a pendulum l ft. long makes n beats per minute, then $n \propto \dfrac{1}{\sqrt{l}}$ or $n = \dfrac{c}{\sqrt{l}}$ where c is a constant.

Since $n\sqrt{l}$ is constant, the value of n when $l = 4$ is given by $n\sqrt{4} = 36\sqrt{9}$; $\therefore \ n = 54$;

n	36	?
l	9	4

$\therefore$ a pendulum 4 ft. long makes 54 beats per minute.

For the general formula, $n\sqrt{l} = 36\sqrt{9} = 108$;

$$\therefore \ n = \frac{108}{\sqrt{l}}.$$

EXERCISE XV. c (Oral)

1. The table shows the weights of various square pieces of in cut from the same sheet:

Side of square in cm. . .	l	1	2	2·5	4	10
Weight of piece in grams . .	w	0·4	1·6	2·5	6·4	40

(i) What is the variation relation between w and l?

(ii) *Write down* the weights corresponding to $l = 20$, $l = \frac{1}{2}$.

(iii) What formula connects w and l?

2. The table shows the capacities of water-cans of fixed shape:

Breadth of can in inches . .	b	4	5	6	8
Capacity of can in pints . .	P	3·2	6·25	10·8	25·6

(i) What is the variation relation between P and b?

(ii) *Write down* the capacity of cans 10 in., 3 in. broad.

(iii) What formula connects P and b?

3. Copy and complete the following table showing the times taken to travel 24 miles at various speeds:

Speed in m.p.h. . .	v	2	3	4	6	8	12
Time in hours . . .	t						

(i) How is the value of t altered if v is trebled, if v is divided by 4?

(ii) What is the variation relation between t and v?

(iii) What is the formula for t in terms of v?

[4] Rectangular blocks of cast-iron, of fixed weight 500 gm and of equal density, are made in various shapes, but the base of each block is square.

(i) What is the variation relation between the height h cm and the side of the square base, x cm. ?

(ii) If the height is 8 cm., when the side of the base is 3 cm. find a formula for h in terms of x.

(iii) Find the height if the side of the base is 6 cm., and find the side of the base if the height is 4·5 cm.

(iv) How does x vary with h ?

5. A varies as the square of x. *Write down* the effect on **A** of (i) multiplying x by 5, (ii) dividing x by 8, and the effect on x of (i) multiplying **A** by 9, (ii) dividing **A** by 36. What kind of graph is obtained by plotting values of **A** against values of x^2 ?

6. t varies as the square root of s. *Write down* the effect on t of (i) multiplying s by 25, (ii) dividing s by 9, and the effect on s of (1) multiplying t by 9, (ii) dividing t by 4.

7. If $y=3$ when $x=5$, *write down without simplifying* the value of y when $x=7$ if (i) $y \propto x$, (ii) $y \propto x^2$, (iii) $y \propto \sqrt{x}$, (iv) $y \propto \dfrac{1}{x}$.

Complete the following, Nos. 8–13:

8. If $A \propto r^2$, $r \propto$ .... .   [9] If $V \propto r^3$, $r \propto$ .... .

10. If $t \propto \sqrt{l}$, $l \propto$ .... .   [11] If $b \propto \dfrac{1}{l}$, $l \propto$ .... .

12. If $n \propto \dfrac{1}{\sqrt{p}}$, $p \propto$ .... .   [13] If $y \propto \dfrac{1}{x^2}$, $x \propto$ .... .

Write down the variation relation between the following pairs of quantities, Nos. 14–18:

14. The area S sq. in. of the surface of a sphere of radius r in., (i) with S in terms of r, (ii) with r in terms of S.

[15] The time y days for which a fixed sum of money is sufficient to pay the wages of n men, each receiving 10s. a day.

[16] The weight w lb. of water which a jug of fixed shape of h in. can hold.

17. The cost p shillings of gilding a spoon of given shape l in. long.

18. The thickness t in. of a circular lead disc of radius r in., of fixed weight (i) with t in terms of r, (ii) with r in terms of t.

19. Two bottles are of the same shape; one is 6 in. high and holds a pint; the other is 15 in. high. What can it hold?

[20] Plaster-cast models are made of a statue. A model which is 15 cm. high weighs 50 gm. What is the weight of a model 24 cm. high?

21. A solid sphere of radius 4 in. weighs 32 lb. Find the weight of a solid sphere of the same material of radius 3 in.

EXERCISE XV. d

1. If $y \propto x^2$ and if $y = 4$ when $x = 4$, find y if $x = 3$ and find x if $y = 9$. Find also y in terms of x.

[2] If $V \propto x^3$ and if $V = 108$ when $x = 3$, find V when $x = 6$ and find x if $V = 4000$. Find also V in terms of x.

3. If $y \propto x^3$ and if $y = 50$ when $x = 5$, find y when $x = 1$ and find x when $y = 6\frac{1}{4}$. Find also y in terms of x.

4. If $y \propto \sqrt{x}$ and if $y = 0.4$ when $x = 4$, find y if $x = 100$ and find x if $y = 1.4$. Find also y in terms of x.

[5] If $y \propto \dfrac{1}{x}$ and if $y = 12$ when $x = 6$, find y if $x = 8$ and find x if $y = \frac{1}{2}$. Find also y in terms of x.

6. If $y \propto \dfrac{1}{x^2}$ and if $y = 9$ when $x = 10$, find y if $x = 6$ and find x if $y = 4$. Find also y in terms of x.

7. If r varies inversely as the square root of h, and if $r = 6$ when $h = 4$, find r when $h = 9$ and find h when $r = 8$. Find also r in terms of h.

[8] If y varies inversely as $\sqrt{x}$, and if $y = 5$ when $x = 16$, find y if $x = 100$ and find x if $y = 60$. Find also y in terms of x.

9. If a stone falls s ft. in t sec. from rest, $s \propto t^2$. If it falls 64 ft. in 2 sec., find how far it falls in (i) 3 sec., (ii) $\frac{3}{4}$ sec. Find also s in terms of t.

[10] The air-resistance to a shell varies as the square of its speed. If the resistance is 22·4 lb. when the speed is 800 ft. per sec., find the resistance when the speed is 1000 ft. per sec.

11. The volume of a sphere varies as the cube of its diameter. If the volume of a sphere of diameter 2 in. is 4·188 cu. in. approximately, find, correct to 3 figures, the volume of a sphere of diameter 4 in.

[12] If a light beam is supported at each end and carries a fixed load at its mid-point, the sag at the middle varies as the cube of the length of the beam. For a beam 5 ft. long the sag is $2\frac{1}{2}$ in.; find the sag for the same load if this beam is cut down to 4 ft.

[13] When the velocity, v ft. per sec., of a stream of water is determined by a water-pressure gauge, recording a height h in., h varies as the square of v. If a speed of 4 ft. per sec. causes a height of 3 in., find the height caused by a speed of 12 ft. per sec.

14. The distance of the horizon from an observer varies as the square root of the height of the observer. At a height of 24 ft. the distance is 6 miles; find the distance at a height of 54 ft. If the distance is d miles at a height of h feet, express d in terms of h.

[15] The time of oscillation of a pendulum varies as the square root of its length. If one complete oscillation of a pendulum 8 ft. long takes 3·1 sec., find the time for a pendulum 10 ft. long.

16. The length of a pendulum varies inversely as the square of the number of beats it makes per minute. If a pendulum 9 ft. long makes 36 beats per minute, find the length of a pendulum which makes 27 beats per minute.

[17] For wires of fixed length and material the electrical resistance varies inversely as the square of the diameter of the cross-section. If the resistance is 0·5 ohm when the diameter is 1·2 cm., find the resistance of a wire of the same length and material of diameter 1·5 cm.

[18] If $y \propto x^3$, find the ratio in which y is increased if x is increased in the ratio 3 : 2.

19. If $y \propto \dfrac{1}{x^2}$, find the ratio in which y is changed if x is increased in the ratio 5 : 3.

20. If $A \propto r^2$ and $V \propto r^3$, find the percentage increases in A and V if r is increased by 20 per cent.

21. If the surface of a soap bubble increases by 21 per cent., find the percentage increase in (i) its diameter, (ii) its volume.

[22] In what ratios (correct to 3 figures) must the diameter of a sphere be increased to double (i) its surface, (ii) its volume?

[23] If $S \propto r^2$ and $V \propto r^3$, prove that $\dfrac{V^2}{S^3}$ is constant and state how V varies with S.

24. The pressure of a given mass of gas, kept at constant temperature, is measured for various volumes (v cu. cm.) by finding the height of a column of mercury (p cm.) which exerts the same pressure, as follows:

v . .	50	40	35	30	20
p . .	79	101	113	135	197

Plot values of p against values of $\dfrac{1}{v}$ and hence show that, apart from experimental errors, $p \propto \dfrac{1}{v}$, and obtain the value of c such that $p = \dfrac{c}{v}$.

Functions of Two or More Variables

Suppose we wish to compare the weights of a number of cylindrical metal bolts. The weight of any particular bolt depends on several quantities which can alter independently: the radius of the circular cross-section r in., the length l in., and the density of the material composing it, ρ lb. per cu. in.

Since the volume of the bolt is $\pi r^2 l$ cu. in., the weight W lb. of the bolt is given by the formula,

$$\mathsf{W} = \pi \rho r^2 l,$$

and we say that W varies directly as ρ and as l and as the square of r. This is called *joint variation*.

For example, if ρ is halved, if r is multiplied by 3, and if l is multiplied by 5, W is multiplied by $\frac{1}{2} \times 3^2 \times 5$.

Similarly, if ρ is increased by 20 per cent., if r is decreased by 25 per cent., and if l is increased by 60 per cent., the multiplying factors for ρ, r, l are $\frac{120}{100}$, $\frac{75}{100}$, $\frac{160}{100}$;

∴ W is multiplied by $\frac{6}{5} \times (\frac{3}{4})^2 \times \frac{8}{5}$, $= \frac{27}{25}$ or $\frac{108}{100}$;

∴ the weight increases by 8 per cent.

Suppose next we wish to compare the *densities* of a number of cylindrical metal bolts, we make ρ the subject of the formula, $\mathsf{W} = \pi \rho r^2 l$. Then

$$\rho = \frac{1}{\pi} \cdot \frac{\mathsf{W}}{r^2 l}.$$

And we say that ρ varies directly as W and inversely as the square of r and inversely as l. This is another type of *joint variation*.

For example, if W is trebled, if r is halved, and if l is multiplied by 5, ρ is multiplied by $\dfrac{3}{(\frac{1}{2})^2 \times 5}$, or $\dfrac{12}{5}$.

Similarly if, when r is increased by 25 per cent. and l is decreased by 70 per cent., W is reduced by 40 per cent., the multiplying factors for r, l, W are $\frac{125}{100}$, $\frac{30}{100}$, $\frac{60}{100}$;

∴ ρ is multiplied by $\dfrac{\frac{3}{5}}{(\frac{5}{4})^2 \times (\frac{3}{10})}$, $= \frac{32}{25}$ or $\frac{128}{100}$;

∴ the density increases by 28 per cent.

Example 7. The volume of a given mass of gas varies directly as the absolute temperature and inversely as the pressure. At absolute temperature 360° and at pressure 736 mm., the volume is 450 c.c.; find a general formula and find its volume at absolute temperature 312° and pressure 960 mm.

If the volume is v c.c. at absolute temperature $\mathsf{T}°$ and pressure p mm., then

$$v \propto \frac{\mathsf{T}}{p} \quad \text{or} \quad v = k \times \frac{\mathsf{T}}{p},$$

where k is constant. When $v = 450$, $\mathsf{T} = 360$, and $p = 736$,

$$\therefore \ 450 = k \times \frac{360}{736};$$

$$\therefore \ k = \frac{450 \times 736}{360} = 920;$$

$$\therefore \ v = \frac{920\mathsf{T}}{p}.$$

$\therefore$ when $\mathsf{T} = 312$ and $p = 960$,

$$v = \frac{920 \times 312}{960} = 299;$$

$$\therefore \text{ the volume is 299 c.c.}$$

If a function of a variable consists of *two or more terms*, it does not vary directly or inversely as any power of that variable, although the separate terms may do so.

For example, suppose that when a train is running along the level at v miles an hour, the distance s yards in which the train can be stopped is given by the formula,

$$s = av + bv^2,$$

where a, b are constants, then s is the sum of two terms one of which varies as v, and the other as v^2, and we say that the distance *varies* **partly** *as the velocity* and **partly** *as the square of the velocity*.

Similarly the formula,

$$y = a + \frac{b}{x},$$

where a, b are constants, is described by the phrase,

y is **partly** *constant and* **partly** *varies inversely as x.*

Example 8. The volume of a segment of a sphere varies partly as the radius and the square of the height jointly, and partly as the cube of the height. Find the formula for the volume V cu. in. of a segment of a sphere of radius r in., height of segment h in., given that the volume of a sphere of radius r in. is $\frac{4}{3}\pi r^3$ cu. in.

If V is expressed in terms of r and h, there are two terms, one of which varies as rh^2 and the other as h^3;

$$\therefore \; \text{V} = arh^2 + bh^3,$$

where a, b are constants.

Now a hemisphere is a segment such that $h = r$;

$$\therefore \; \text{if } h = r, \; \text{V} = \tfrac{2}{3}\pi r^3; \qquad \therefore \; \tfrac{2}{3}\pi r^3 = ar^3 + br^3;$$
$$\therefore \; a + b = \tfrac{2}{3}\pi.$$

Also the complete sphere is a segment such that $h = 2r$;

$$\therefore \; \text{if } h = 2r, \; \text{V} = \tfrac{4}{3}\pi r^3; \qquad \therefore \; \tfrac{4}{3}\pi r^3 = ar(2r)^2 + b(2r)^3;$$
$$\therefore \; 4a + 8b = \tfrac{4}{3}\pi.$$

Solving for a, b, we have $a = \pi$, $b = -\tfrac{1}{3}\pi$;

$$\therefore \; \text{V} = \pi rh^2 - \tfrac{1}{3}\pi h^3 = \pi h^2(r - \tfrac{1}{3}h).$$

EXERCISE XV. e (Oral)

1. A rectangular brass slab has a square base, side x in., and is h in. high; its weight W lb. is given by the formula $\text{W} = \tfrac{3}{10}x^2h$.

   (i) How is W altered if x is trebled and h is halved?

   (ii) How is W altered if x is increased by 20 per cent. and h increased by 25 per cent.?

   (iii) How is W altered if x is decreased by 25 per cent. and h is increased by 60 per cent.?

   (iv) How does h vary with W and x?

   (v) How does x vary with W and h?

Express the following statements by symbols:

2. The volume of a cone varies directly as the height and the square of the base-radius. (V, h, r.)

3. The electrical resistance of a wire varies directly as its length and inversely as the square of its diameter. (R, l, d.)

4. The cost of the fuel consumed by a coasting steamer between two ports varies as the cube of the distance and inversely as the square of the time of the journey.   (**C**, *d*, *t*.)

5. The resistance to the motion of a train of given weight is partly constant and partly varies as the square of the velocity. (**R**, *v*.)

6. The force necessary to stop a tramcar in a certain distance varies directly as its weight and the square of its velocity and inversely as the distance.   (**F**, **W**, *v*, *d*.)

7. The time taken to repair a road varies directly as the length of the road and the square root of its breadth and inversely as the number of men employed.   (*t*, *l*, *b*, *n*.)

Copy and fill in the given table for the values of a function **Z** of *x* and *y*, *all the working being done mentally*, in the following cases:

Values of *y*.		Values of *x*.		
		3	6	12
	2			
	10		3	
	50			

8. **Z** ∝ *xy*.   **[9]** **Z** ∝ *xy²*.

[10] **Z** ∝ $\dfrac{x}{y}$.   **11.** **Z** ∝ $\dfrac{x^3}{y^2}$.

EXERCISE XV. f

1. If **W** varies jointly as *h* and the square of *r*, find the percentage change in **W** if *h* increases by 20 per cent. and *r* increases by 50 per cent. If **W** = 15 when *h* = 3 and *r* = 2½, find **W** when *h* = 1 and *r* = 10; find also **W** in terms of *h*, *r*.

[2] If *z* varies directly as *x* and inversely as *y*, find the percentage change in *z* if *x* increases by 20 per cent. and *y* increases by 25 per cent. If *z* = 9 when *x* = 12 and *y* = 2, find *z* when *x* = 20 and *y* = 15; find also *z* in terms of *x*, *y*.

3. If t varies directly as x and inversely as the square root of y, find the percentage change in t if x increases by 12 per cent. and y decreases by 36 per cent. If $t = 12$ when $x = 6$ and $y = 4$, find t when $x = 15$ and $y = 9$; find also t in terms of x and y.

[4] If z varies directly as the square of x and inversely as the square root of y, find the percentage change in z if x increases by 20 per cent. and y decreases by 19 per cent. If $z = 3$ when $x = 6$ and $y = 16$, find z when $x = 12$ and $y = 25$; find also z in terms of x and y.

5. The weight W lb. of a metal bar varies jointly as its length, l in., and the square of its diameter, d in. If W $= 140$ when $d = 3\frac{1}{2}$ and $l = 48$, find l in terms of W and d.

[6] If p varies directly as the cube of t and inversely as the square root of n, and if $p = 16$ when $t = 2$ and $n = 9$, find n in terms of p and t.

7. y is partly constant and partly varies as x. When $x = 2$, $y = 16$ and when $x = 7$, $y = 31$. Find y in terms of x.

[8] W varies partly as x and partly as the square of x. When $x = 2$, W $= 14$ and when $x = 4$, W $= 44$. Find W in terms of x.

9. y varies partly as x and partly inversely as x. When $x = 3$, $y = 10$ and when $x = 4$, $y = 11$. Find y in terms of x.

10. If objects are allowed to slide down a smooth sloping plank, the time of descent varies directly as the length of the plank and inversely as the square root of the height of the top of the plank above its foot. For a plank 30 ft. long with the upper end 25 ft. above the lower end, the time of descent is 1·5 seconds. Find the general formula.

11. In a certain machine the effort P lb. required to raise a load W lb. is partly constant and partly varies as the load. For loads of 40 lb., 56 lb., the necessary efforts are 11 lb., 13 lb. respectively; find the general formula.

[12] The cost of a school dinner is partly constant and partly varies as the number of pupils. For 470 pupils the cost is £22, 16s.; for 442 pupils the cost is at the rate of 1s. per head. Find the cost for 450 pupils.

13. The resistance to the motion of a car is partly constant and partly varies as the square of the velocity. At speeds of 20 m.p.h., 30 m.p.h., the resistances are 60 lb. weight, 85 lb. weight respectively. Find the resistance when the car is travelling at 40 m.p.h.; find also the general formula.

[14] The distance in which a train can be stopped varies partly as the velocity and partly as the square of the velocity. At speeds of 20 m.p.h., 40 m.p.h., the stopping distances are 100 yd., 280 yd. respectively. Find the speed of the train if it can be stopped in just a quarter of a mile.

15. On a certain building estate, the ground rents for plots of land vary partly as the frontage and partly as the frontage and depth jointly. The ground rent for a plot with 30 ft. frontage and 100 ft. depth is £38, and for a plot with 36 ft. frontage and 140 ft. depth is £60. Find the general formula; find also the ground rent for a plot with 24 ft. frontage and 90 ft. depth.

[16] The sum of the first n whole numbers 1, 2, 3, 4, . . . varies partly as n and partly as n^2. What is the sum for $n=2$ and for $n=3$? Hence find the general formula.

17. The values of silver coins vary jointly as their thicknesses and the squares of their diameters. If two silver coins have values in the ratio 25 : 14 and thicknesses in the ratio 8 : 7, and if the diameter of the first is $1\frac{3}{8}$ in., find the diameter of the second.

18. The electrical resistance of a wire varies directly as its length and inversely as the square of its diameter. Two pieces of wire of the same metal have diameters in the ratio 3 : 2, and resistances in the ratio 8 : 3. If the length of the first is 42 ft., find the length of the second.

*19. If $x \propto y^2$ and if $1+y \propto \sqrt{z}$, find x in terms of z if $z=9$ and $y=5$ when $x=1$.

*20. If $P \propto \dfrac{v^2}{x}$ and $x \propto vt$, find how P varies (i) with v, t, (ii) with x, t.

*21. If $A \propto BC^2$ and $B \propto xy^2$ and $C \propto \dfrac{y}{x}$, find how A varies with x, y.

*22. A mass w lb. is fastened to one end of a string l ft. long, and the other end is held in the hand. If the mass is whirled round in a horizontal circle at speed v ft. per sec., the tension T lb. weight in the string varies directly as w and the square of v, and inversely as l. When the mass of the body is $1\frac{1}{2}$ lb. and the string is 3 ft. long and the speed is 40 ft. per sec., the tension is 25 lb. weight. Find the general formula.

*23. The heat, h calories, developed in a wire by an electric current varies directly as the time, t sec., and as the square of the voltage, V volts, and inversely as the resistance, R ohms. If $V = 100$ and $R = 50$, the heat developed is 48 calories per second; find how much heat is developed in 1 minute in a wire of resistance 2 ohms, if the voltage is 20 volts.

*24. The illumination of a small object by a lamp varies directly as the candle-power and inversely as the square of its distance from the lamp. If an electric lamp of 32 candle-power is replaced by a lamp of 18 candle-power, find the ratio in which the distance of the object from the lamp must be changed to be illuminated as before.

*25. The horse-power required to propel a ship of given pattern varies jointly as the cube of the speed and the cube root of the square of the ship's displacement. Ship A, displacement 1000 tons, can be driven at 10 knots; ship B, displacement 8000 tons, can be driven at 12 knots. Find the ratio of the horse-power of the engines of B to that of A.

*26. The weight that can be carried by a cylindrical iron column varies directly as the fourth power of the diameter and inversely as the square of its length. (i) If the length is doubled, in what ratio must the diameter be changed to carry the same weight? (ii) If the diameter is decreased by 40 per cent. and if the weight to be carried is increased by 125 per cent., find the necessary percentage change in the length.

*27. The formula, $d = k\dfrac{Wl^3}{B}$, where k is constant, is used to calculate the deflection at the mid-point of a girder. If W is increased by 50 per cent. and B increased by 20 per cent., find the percentage change in l if d remains unaltered.

REVISION EXERCISE R. 9 (Ch. XV)

[1] If $\dfrac{x}{4} = \dfrac{y}{3}$, evaluate $\dfrac{3x - 2y}{3x + 2y}$.

2. If $\dfrac{5x + y}{3} = \dfrac{x + 5y}{2}$, evaluate $\dfrac{3x - 5y}{2x - 3y}$.

[3] Find $x : y$ if $10x^2 + 29xy - 21y^2 = 0$.

4. Find $(x + y) : (x + 2y)$ if $10x^2 + 9y^2 = 21xy$.

5. The ratio of the radii of two circles is $a : b$ and the ratio of their areas is $(a - k) : (b - k)$, find k in terms of a, b.

[6] The incomes of two men are in the ratio $a : b$, and their expenditures are in the ratio $p : q$. If each man saves £C a year, find their annual incomes.

7. The ratio of the volumes of two circular cylinders is $a : b$ and the ratio of their radii is $r : s$. Find the ratio of their heights.

8. If the ratio $c : d$ equals the ratio $\left(\dfrac{1}{x} + \dfrac{1}{c}\right) : \left(\dfrac{1}{x} + \dfrac{1}{d}\right)$, and if c is not equal to d, express x in terms of c, d.

[9] If $\dfrac{a}{b} = \dfrac{c}{d}$, prove that $\dfrac{ac}{bd} = \dfrac{7a^2 - 5c^2}{7b^2 - 5d^2}$.

10. If $\dfrac{a}{b} = \dfrac{c}{d}$, prove that $\dfrac{a - c}{b - d} = \sqrt{\left(\dfrac{a^2 - 4c^2}{b^2 - 4d^2}\right)}$.

[11] If $\dfrac{a}{b} = \dfrac{c}{d} = \dfrac{e}{f}$, prove that $\dfrac{a^3 - a^2c}{b^3 - b^2d} = \dfrac{c^3 + e^3}{d^3 + f^3}$.

12. If $\dfrac{a}{b} = \dfrac{c}{d} = \dfrac{e}{f}$, prove that $\sqrt{\left(\dfrac{a^2 - ce}{b^2 - df}\right)} = \sqrt[3]{\left(\dfrac{ace}{bdf}\right)}$.

13. If $\dfrac{x^3}{b^2c} = \dfrac{y^3}{c^2a} = \dfrac{z^3}{a^2b}$, prove that $a : b : c = yz^2 : zx^2 : xy^2$.

[14] If y varies inversely as x, and if $y = 3$ when $x = 5$, find y in terms of x.

15. A cube of aluminium, edge x cm., weighs y grams. What variation relation connects y with x? If $y = 325$ when $x = 5$, find y in terms of x.

16. Complete: (i) If $s \propto t^2$, then $t \propto \ldots$.

(ii) If $y \propto \dfrac{1}{\sqrt[3]{x}}$, then $x \propto \ldots$.

17. If $x \propto \sqrt{y}$ and $y \propto \dfrac{1}{z}$, find the percentage change in x when z is increased in the ratio $25 : 16$.

[18] If p varies directly as t and inversely as v, and if $p = 240$ when $t = 400$ and $v = 60$, find p in terms of t, v.

[19] If $x \propto \dfrac{1}{y}$ and $x \propto z^2$, find the percentage change in y when z is increased by 25 per cent.

20. If z varies as x^2 and inversely as the square root of y, and if $z = 8$ when $x = 6$ and $y = 2\frac{1}{4}$, find y in terms of x, z.

21. The cost of boring a well, x feet deep, partly varies as x and partly as x^2. A well of this kind costs £90 if the depth is 30 feet and costs £140 if the depth is 40 feet. How deep is the well if the cost is £200?

22. The sag at the centre of a plank of given width, supported at its ends, varies as the fourth power of the length and inversely as the square of the thickness. If a plank 5 feet long and $\frac{1}{2}$ inch thick sags $\frac{1}{4}$ inch, what will be the sag of a plank of the same material and width $7\frac{1}{2}$ feet long, $\frac{3}{4}$ inch thick?

[23] The error in the speedometer of a car is partly constant and partly varies as the speed. The readings of the speedometer are 45 m.p.h., 60 m.p.h., when the actual speeds are 45 m.p.h., $57\frac{1}{2}$ m.p.h. Find the speedometer reading when the actual speed is 60 m.p.h.

24. z varies as $\dfrac{x}{y^2}$, and y varies inversely as x. If $z = \frac{1}{3}$, $x = 2$, $y = \frac{1}{4}$ are simultaneous values, express (i) y in terms of x, (ii) z in terms of x. If the value of x is increased by 10 per cent., find the ratio in which the value of z is changed.

[25] If $V \propto r^3$ and if $r \propto \dfrac{1}{\sqrt{t}}$, find correct to three figures the percentage change in V if t is increased by 20 per cent.

CHAPTER XVI

PROGRESSIONS

Series. If we write down in succession a set of numbers in accordance with some law, the set of numbers is called a *series*, and each of the numbers is called a **term** of the series; for example, the series whose nth term is $(n+2)^2$ is 9, 16, 25, 36, 49, ... because $(n+2)^2 = 9$ if $n=1$, $(n+2)^2 = 16$ if $n=2$, and so on.

Arithmetical Progressions. Start from the number 4 and count upwards by threes; we obtain the series,

$$4, 7, 10, 13, 16, 19, 22, 25, 28, 31, \ldots.$$

To obtain, say, the *sixth* term, we start with 4 and add on *five* threes: $4 + 5 \times 3 = 19$.

Similarly, to obtain the nth term, we start with 4 and add on $(n-1)$ threes:

$$\therefore \text{ the } n\text{th term} = 4 + (n-1) \times 3$$
$$= 3n + 1.$$

If we start with the number 30 and count downwards by sevens, we obtain the series,

$$30, 23, 16, 9, 2, -5, -12, -19, -26, \ldots.$$

To obtain, say, the *ninth* term, we start with 30 and subtract *eight* sevens: $30 - 8 \times 7 = -26$.

Similarly, to obtain the nth term, we start with 30 and subtract $(n-1)$ sevens:

$$\therefore \text{ the } n\text{th term} = 30 - (n-1) \times 7$$
$$= 37 - 7n.$$

If a series is formed by starting with any number and counting upwards or downwards by some fixed amount, it is called an **arithmetical progression** or more shortly an **A.P.**; and the number obtained by subtracting any term from the term which follows it is called the **common difference** of the A.P.

e.g. 4, 7, 10, 13, 16, ... is an A.P., common difference 3;

30, 23, 16, 9, 2, ... is an A.P., common difference -7;

$2\frac{1}{4}$, $1\frac{1}{2}$, $\frac{3}{4}$, 0, $-\frac{3}{4}$, $-1\frac{1}{2}$, ... is an A.P., common difference $-\frac{3}{4}$.

333

Notation. Suppose the first term of an A.P. is a, and that the common difference is d, then the terms of the series are

$$a,\ a+d,\ a+2d,\ a+3d,\ \dots.$$
$$\therefore \text{ the nth term} = a+(n-1)d.$$

Example 1. A man starts with a salary of £250 a year and receives annual increases of £20 a year. How much does he receive for the nth year of service?

His salary for successive years is as follows:

$$£250,\ £270,\ £290,\ £310,\ \dots.$$

Since 250, 270, 290, 310, ... form an A.P. with common difference 20,

$$\text{the } n\text{th term} = 250+(n-1)\times 20$$
$$= 20n+230;$$

$\therefore$ for the nth year he receives £$(20n+230)$.

Example 2. Find the first term and the common difference of an A.P., if the fourth term is 23 and the tenth term is 110.

Denote the first term by a and the common difference by d:

then
$$a+3d=23,$$
$$a+9d=110;$$

$\therefore$ by subtraction, $6d=87;$ $\therefore$ $d=14\frac{1}{2};$

$$\therefore\ a=23-3d=23-43\frac{1}{2}$$
$$=-20\frac{1}{2}.$$

$\therefore$ the first term is $-20\frac{1}{2}$, and the common difference is $14\frac{1}{2}$.

Arithmetic Mean. If three numbers are in A.P., the middle term is called *the arithmetic mean* of the first and last term.

For example, since 13, 19, 25 are in A.P., the arithmetic mean of 13 and 25 is 19; it is the *average* of the two numbers.

In general, if x, y, z are in A.P., the common difference is $y-x$ and is also $z-y$,

$$\therefore\ y-x=z-y;$$
$$\therefore\ 2y=z+x;$$
$$\therefore\ y=\tfrac{1}{2}(z+x).$$

Therefore the arithmetic mean of x, z is $\tfrac{1}{2}(x+z)$.

Example 3. Find five numbers between 17 and 32 which form with 17 and 32 an A.P.

If the numbers 17, p, q, r, s, t, 32 are in A.P., the first term is 17 and the 7th term is 32; denote the common difference by d.

Since the 7th term $= 17 + 6d$, $17 + 6d = 32$;

$$\therefore\ 6d = 32 - 17 = 15;$$
$$\therefore\ d = 2\tfrac{1}{2}.$$

$\therefore$ the A.P. is 17, $19\tfrac{1}{2}$, 22, $24\tfrac{1}{2}$, 27, $29\tfrac{1}{2}$, 32.

This process is called *inserting 5 arithmetic means between* **17** *and* **32**.

EXERCISE XVI. a

Write down the first 3 terms and the 10th term of the following series:

1. nth term $= 4n - 5$.　　　　　[2] nth term $= 16 - 6n$.

3. nth term $= 3(n - 1)^2$.　　　　[4] nth term $= \dfrac{n}{n+2}$.

5. nth term $= 5 \times 2^{n-1}$.　　　　[6] nth term $= (-1)^n$.

Write down the simplest form of the nth term of each of the following series, and check your answer by putting $n = 4$:

7. 5, 6, 7, 8, 9, ...　　　　　　[8] 7, 9, 11, 13, 15, ...

9. 50, 46, 42, 38, 34, ...　　　[10] 13, 8, 3, -2, -7, ...

11. 3^3, 5^3, 7^3, 9^3, 11^3, ...　　[12] 1×3, 3×5, 5×7, 7×9, ...

13. $\tfrac{1}{2}$, $\tfrac{2}{3}$, $\tfrac{3}{4}$, $\tfrac{4}{5}$, ...　　　　[14] 3, $\tfrac{3}{2}$, $\tfrac{3}{4}$, $\tfrac{3}{8}$, $\tfrac{3}{16}$, ...

15. The nth term of a series is $7n - 25$. (i) How many terms of the series are negative? (ii) Is 66 a term of the series? If so, which term? (iii) Is the series an A.P.? If so, what is the common difference?

[16] The nth term of a series is $19 - 4n$. (i) How many terms of the series are positive? (ii) Is -49 a term of the series? If so, which term? (iii) Is the series an A.P.? If so, what is the common difference?

17. The nth term of a series is $9n + 7$. What is the result of subtracting the kth term from the $(k+1)$th term?

Find the nth term of each of the following series in A.P.:

[18] $2\frac{1}{2}$, $3\frac{1}{4}$, 4, $4\frac{3}{4}$, ...   19. 5, $4\frac{1}{3}$, $3\frac{2}{3}$, 3, ...

[20] $\dfrac{a}{2}$, a, $\dfrac{3a}{2}$, $2a$, ...   21. $b - c$, $b + c$, $b + 3c$, ...

Find the common difference and the second term for the following series in A.P.:

22. 1st term 5; 4th term 14.   [23] 1st term 8; 10th term 71.

24. 1st term 10; 8th term -11.   [25] 1st cerm 11; 6th term 9.

26. 7th term 23; 11th term 37.

[27] 10th term 17; 16th term 8.

28. 5th term $4\frac{1}{2}$; 11th term -3.   [29] 5th term x; 8th term y.

30. nth term $27 - 14n$.   [31] nth term $11n - 17$.

Find the number of terms of the following series in A.P.:

32. 6, 11, 16, ..., 66.   [33] 7, 4, 1, ..., -26.

34. 4, 3·9, 3·8, ..., 1·2.   [35] 35, 42, 49, ..., 182.

36. Write down the arithmetic means of (i) 13, 25; (ii) 8, -14; (iii) $x + 3y$, $x - 3y$.

[37] Insert 3 arithmetic means between (i) 17, 29; (ii) x, y.

38. Insert 5 arithmetic means between (i) 60, 15; (ii) $a - b$, $a + b$.

[39] A marble rolls down a sloping groove: the distances it travels in successive seconds are 3 cm., 9 cm., 15 cm., 21 cm., etc. How far does it travel in the nth second?

40. A swimming-bath has a plane sloping floor, and the depth of water is indicated by posts at equal distances apart down the bath. The reading on the first post is 14 ft. and on the second is 13 ft. 8 in.; what is the reading on the fifth post? on the nth post? How many posts are there altogether if the reading on the last post is 4 ft.?

41. The temperature of the water in a boiler is rising at a steady rate; readings taken every 20 minutes are as follows: 82° F., 88° F., 94° F., etc. The last reading was 190° F.; how many readings were taken?

[42] The last term of an A.P. containing n terms is l; the common difference is d. What are the first two terms?

43. The first and last terms of an A.P. are a, l respectively. If there are n terms, find the common difference.

Sum of Numbers in A.P.

Example 4. An instrument for a jazz band is composed of a set of 11 thin metal tubes; their lengths in inches are as follows:

$$6, \ 7\tfrac{1}{2}, \ 9, \ 10\tfrac{1}{2}, \ 12, \ 13\tfrac{1}{2}, \ 15, \ 16\tfrac{1}{2}, \ 18, \ 19\tfrac{1}{2}, \ 21.$$

What is the total length of metal tubing required for the set?

If there are only a few numbers, the quickest and simplest method is to add up in the ordinary way. But if the number of terms is large and if, as here, they form an A.P., it is easier to use a different method.

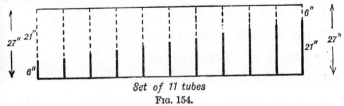

Set of 11 tubes
FIG. 154.

Fig. 154 represents a set of 11 tubes ranging from 6 inches to 21 inches. Suppose sets are manufactured as follows:

Take 11 tubes, each 27 inches long, and cut off in succession from them portions of lengths, as required:

$$6, \ 7\tfrac{1}{2}, \ 9, \ 10\tfrac{1}{2}, \ 12, \ 13\tfrac{1}{2}, \ 15, \ 16\tfrac{1}{2}, \ 18, \ 19\tfrac{1}{2}, \ 21 \text{ inches.}$$

Then there remain tubes whose lengths in order are:

$$21, \ 19\tfrac{1}{2}, \ 18, \ 16\tfrac{1}{2}, \ 15, \ 13\tfrac{1}{2}, \ 12, \ 10\tfrac{1}{2}, \ 9, \ 7\tfrac{1}{2}, \ 6 \text{ inches;}$$

these make up exactly a second set.

But the total length of 11 tubes, each 27 inches long, is 11×27 inches, and these tubes form exactly 2 sets.

∴ the length of tubing for each set is $\dfrac{11 \times 27}{2}$ inches.

The argument used in this Example illustrates the fact that if an A.P. is written down first forwards and then backwards, we obtain by addition a series of *equal* terms:

$$\text{S} = 6 + 7\tfrac{1}{2} + 9 + 10\tfrac{1}{2} + 12 + 13\tfrac{1}{2} + 15 + 16\tfrac{1}{2} + 18 + 19\tfrac{1}{2} + 21,$$

and $\quad \text{S} = 21 + 19\tfrac{1}{2} + 18 + 16\tfrac{1}{2} + 15 + 13\tfrac{1}{2} + 12 + 10\tfrac{1}{2} + 9 + 7\tfrac{1}{2} + 6;$

∴ $\quad 2\text{S} = 27 + 27 + 27 + \ \dots\dots \ (11 \text{ terms}) \ \dots\dots \ + 27 + 27$

$$= 27 \times 11.$$

$$\therefore \ \text{S} = \frac{27 \times 11}{2}.$$

Thus the average of a set of numbers in A.P. is equal to the average of the first term and last term; and therefore the sum of a series in A.P. can be found by multiplying this average by the number of terms:

sum of numbers in A.P. $= \frac{1}{2}$(first term + last term) × number of terms.

EXERCISE XVI. b (Oral)

Find the sum of the following series in A.P.:

1. 5, 7, 9, 11, ..., 21 (9 terms).

2. 100, 93, 86, 79, ..., 23 (12 terms).

[3] 8, 11, 14, 17, ..., 65 (20 terms).

[4] 15, 11, 7, 3, ..., −45 (16 terms).

5. Find the 15th term of the A.P., 20, 17, 14, 11, ..., and then find the sum of the first 15 terms.

6. Find the 100th term of the A.P., $3\frac{1}{2}$, $4\frac{3}{4}$, 6, $7\frac{1}{4}$, ..., and then find the sum of the first 100 terms.

[7] Find the 36th term of the A.P., 5, 5·2, 5·4, 5·6, ..., and then find the sum of the first 36 terms.

[8] What is the nth term of the A.P., 4, 5, 6, 7, ... ? What is the sum of the first n terms?

9. What is the nth term of the A.P., 1, 3, 5, 7, ... ? What is the sum of the first n terms?

10. The sum of the A.P., $3 + ... + 59$, is 465. What is the average of these numbers? Hence find the number of terms. Find also the common difference.

11. The sum of 12 terms of the A.P., $4 + ...$ is 246. What is the average of these numbers? Hence find the last term. Find also the common difference.

12. The sum of 20 terms of an A.P. is 1280 and the last term is 121. What is the average of the 20 terms? Hence find the first term. Find also the common difference.

Summation by Formula

Suppose the first term of an A.P. is a and that the common difference is d, then the terms of the series are

$$a, a+d, a+2d, a+3d, \ldots.$$

Denote the sum of n terms by S.

If the nth term (*i.e.* the last term) is l,

$$l = a + (n-1)d.$$

Since the common difference is d, the last term but one is $l-d$, the last term but two is $l-2d$, and so on.

$$\therefore \; S = a + (a+d) + (a+2d) + \ldots + (l-2d) + (l-d) + l,$$

and if we write the series backwards, we obtain

$$S = l + (l-d) + (l-2d) + \ldots + (a+2d) + (a+d) + a;$$

$\therefore$ adding

$$2S = (a+l) + (a+l) + (a+l) + \ldots + (a+l) + (a+l) + (a+l)$$

where there are n brackets;

$$\therefore \; 2S = n(a+l);$$

$$\therefore \; S = \frac{n}{2}(a+l).$$

Further, $l = a + (n-1)d$, $\quad \therefore \; a + l = 2a + (n-1)d;$

$$\therefore \; S = \frac{n}{2}\{2a + (n-1)d\}.$$

Example 5. Find the sum of 40 terms of the A.P.,

$$31, 30\tfrac{1}{3}, 29\tfrac{2}{3}, 29, 28\tfrac{1}{3}, \ldots.$$

With the previous notation, we have

$$a = 31, \; d = -\tfrac{2}{3}, \; n = 40;$$

$$\therefore \; S = \frac{n}{2}\{2a + (n-1)d\}$$

$$= 20\{62 + 39 \times (-\tfrac{2}{3})\}$$

$$= 20(62 - 26) = 20 \times 36$$

$$= 720.$$

$\therefore$ the sum of 40 terms is 720.

EXERCISE XVI. c

Sum the following series in A.P.:

1. 7, 8, 9, 10, ..., 100 terms.

[2] 10, 13, 16, 19, ..., 12 terms.

3. 22, 19, 16, 13, ..., 20 terms.

[4] 16, 12, 8, 4, ..., 15 terms.

5. 7, $7\frac{3}{4}$, $8\frac{1}{2}$, $9\frac{1}{4}$, ..., 33 terms.

[6] 3, -5, -13, -21, ..., 10 terms.

[7] 5·3, 7·2, 9·1, 11, ..., 25 terms.

8. 3·4, 2·8, 2·2, 1·6, ..., 16 terms.

[9] $\frac{1}{3}$, $\frac{1}{2}$, ..., 25 terms.   10. $\frac{1}{2}$, $\frac{1}{3}$, ..., 55 terms.

[11] 1, 3, 5, 7, ..., $2n$ terms.

12. 2, 4, 6, 8, ..., $(n-1)$ terms.

[13] First term 10, last term 30; 8 terms.

14. First term 7, last term -13; 10 terms.

[15] First term 3·5, last term 8; 16 terms.

[16] 101, 103, 105, ..., 199.

17. 0·7, 0·71, 0·72, ..., 1·69.

18. The first term of an A.P. is 7 and the 4th term is 22; **find the sum of the first 16 terms.**

[19] The 7th term of an A.P. is 5 and the 16th term is 11; **find the sum of the first 30 terms.**

[20] The 3rd term of an A.P. is 6 and the 8th term is 9; **find the sum of the first 50 terms.**

21. Find the simplest form for the nth term in the series:
$$\frac{1}{1}, \quad \frac{1+3}{1+4}, \quad \frac{1+3+5}{1+4+7}, \quad \frac{1+3+5+7}{1+4+7+10}, \quad \dots.$$

22. The first and last terms of an A.P. are 21, 193; the common difference is 2. Find the sum of the series.

23. The nth term of a series is $3n + 1$; find the sum of the first n terms.

[24] How many terms are taken of the series 1, 2, 3, 4, 5, ... if their sum is 120?

25. How many terms of the series 3, $4\frac{1}{2}$, 6, $7\frac{1}{2}$, ... must be taken to give a sum of 156?

26. A man saves £80 his first year of work, and each year afterwards saves £15 more than in the preceding year. How much does he save in the first 10 years?

[27] A man starting business loses £240 the first year, £160 the second year, £80 the third year; if the same improvement continues, what is his total gain or loss after 12 years?

[28] A clerk's commencing salary is £100 a year; he is offered a choice between a yearly rise of £5 and a rise of £22 every 4 years. Calculate the total sum he will receive in the course of 33 years under each arrangement.

29. I lay aside each year £20 more than I laid aside the year before, starting with £100 in the first year. How many years will it take me to lay aside £5800?

30. A shop sells various sizes of tin kettles, and the prices of successive sizes rise by equal amounts. The smallest costs 2s. and the largest 8s.; it costs £2, 10s. to buy one of every kind. How many kinds are there? What is the cost of the smallest but one?

[31] From a piece of wire 5 ft. long, 25 pieces are cut off, each 0·1 in. longer than the preceding piece. If the wire is exactly used up, find the length of the first piece cut off.

32. Find the sum of all positive integers less than 100 which are not divisible by 5.

33. Find n if the sum of n terms of the series 2, 5, 8, 11, ... is equal to the sum of n terms of the series 47, 45, 43, 41, ...

Geometrical Progressions. Start with any number, say 7, and multiply it by any other number, say 3; then multiply again by 3, and so on; the series obtained in this way,

$$7, \ 21, \ 63, \ 189, \ 567, \ ...,$$

is called a **geometrical progression,** or more shortly a **G.P.**

The terms in a G.P. can be written more simply by using the index notation; thus the series just constructed may be written

$$7, \ 7.3, \ 7.3^2, \ 7.3^3, \ 7.3^4, \ \dotfill \text{(i)}$$

and it is then evident that the nth term is

$$7.3^{n-1}.$$

Again, start with -18 and multiply in succession by $\frac{2}{3}$; we then obtain the G.P.,

$$-18, \ -12, \ -8, \ -\tfrac{16}{3}, \ -\tfrac{32}{9}, \ ...,$$

but this is recognised more easily as a G.P. if written

$$-18, \ -18(\tfrac{2}{3}), \ -18(\tfrac{2}{3})^2, \ -18(\tfrac{2}{3})^3, \ \dotfill \text{(ii)}$$

If the multiplying factor is negative, the terms are alternately positive and negative:

For example, start with 12 and multiply in succession by $-\frac{1}{2}$, we then obtain the G.P.,

$$12, \ -6, \ 3, \ -\tfrac{3}{2}, \ \tfrac{3}{4}, \ ...$$

or $\qquad 12, \ -12(\tfrac{1}{2}), \ 12(\tfrac{1}{2})^2, \ -12(\tfrac{1}{2})^3, \ 12(\tfrac{1}{2})^4. \ \dotfill \text{(iii)}$

By definition, the *ratio* of each term of a G.P. to the term preceding it is *constant*, and this ratio is called the **common ratio** of the G.P.

Thus the common ratios of (i), (ii), (iii) are respectively $3, \ \frac{2}{3}, \ -\frac{1}{2}$.

Notation. Suppose the first term of a G.P. is a, and that the common ratio is r, then the terms of the series are

$$a, \ ar, \ ar^2, \ ar^3, \ ...$$

$\therefore$ **the nth term $= ar^{n-1}$.**

Example 6. Express as simply as possible the nth terms of the following geometrical progressions:

$$\text{(i)} \quad 24, \ 18, \ \tfrac{27}{2}, \ \tfrac{81}{8}, \ \tfrac{243}{32}, \ \dots .$$

$$\text{(ii)} \quad -54, \ 36, \ -24, \ 16, \ -\tfrac{32}{3}, \ \dots .$$

(i) The common ratio $=\frac{18}{24}=\frac{3}{4}$;

$$\therefore \text{ the } n\text{th term} = 24\left(\frac{3}{4}\right)^{n-1} = 2^3 \cdot 3 \cdot \frac{3^{n-1}}{2^{2n-2}}$$

$$= \frac{3^n}{2^{2n-5}}.$$

(ii) The common ratio $= -\frac{36}{54} = -\frac{2}{3}$;

$$\therefore \text{ the } n\text{th term} = -54\left(-\frac{2}{3}\right)^{n-1} = -2 \cdot 3^3(-1)^{n-1}\frac{2^{n-1}}{3^{n-1}}$$

$$= (-1)^n \frac{2^n}{3^{n-4}}.$$

Example 7. The 3rd term of a G.P. is 360 and the 6th term is 1215. Find the first term and the common ratio.

Denote the first term by a and the common ratio by r:

then
$$ar^2 = 360;$$

and
$$ar^5 = 1215.$$

$$\therefore \frac{ar^5}{ar^2} = \frac{1215}{360};$$

$$\therefore r^3 = \frac{27}{8};$$

$$\therefore r = \sqrt[3]{\frac{27}{8}} = \frac{3}{2}.$$

Substituting for r, $a(\frac{3}{2})^2 = 360;$

$$\therefore a = \frac{360 \times 4}{9} = 160.$$

$\therefore$ the first term is 160, and the common ratio is $\frac{3}{2}$.

Geometric Mean. If three numbers are in G.P., the middle term is called *the geometric mean* of the first and last term.

For example, since 6, 30, 150 are in G.P., the geometric mean of 6 and 150 is 30.

Since 6, -30, 150 are also in G.P. (common ratio -5), -30 is also a geometric mean of 6 and 150, but it is customary to consider only positive values.

In general, if x, y, z are in G.P., the common ratio is $\dfrac{y}{x}$ and is also $\dfrac{z}{y}$,

$$\therefore \frac{y}{x} = \frac{z}{y};$$
$$\therefore y^2 = xz;$$
$$\therefore y = \pm \sqrt{(xz)};$$

and we say that **the geometric mean of x, z is** $+\sqrt{(xz)}$.

Thus the geometric mean of two numbers is the positive square root of their product.

Example 8. Find three numbers between $3\frac{3}{4}$ and 60 which form with $3\frac{3}{4}$ and 60 a G.P.

If the numbers $3\frac{3}{4}$, b, c, d, 60 are in G.P., the first term is $\frac{15}{4}$ and the 5th term is 60; denote the common ratio by r.

Since the 5th term is $\frac{15}{4}r^4$,　$\frac{15}{4}r^4 = 60$;

$$\therefore r^4 = \frac{60 \times 4}{15} = 2^4;　\therefore r = \pm 2;$$

$\therefore$ the G.P. is $\frac{15}{4}$, $\frac{15}{2}$, 15, 30, 60,　or　$\frac{15}{4}$, $-\frac{15}{2}$, 15, -30, 60.

This process is called *inserting 3 geometric means between* $3\frac{3}{4}$ *and* 60.

EXERCISE XVI. d

Write down the first two terms and 5th term of the following series:

1. nth term $= 3^{n-1}$.

2. nth term $= 50(\frac{2}{5})^n$.

[3] nth term $= 3(-2)^{n-1}$.

[4] nth term $= \dfrac{5^{n-1}}{n+1}$.

5. nth term $= a(-r)^{n-1}$.

[6] nth term $= ar^{2n-1}$.

Find the simplest form for the nth term of each of the following series. If the series is a G.P., state its common ratio:

7. 7, 14, 28, 56, ...

8. 27, -18, 12, -8, ...

[9] 5, 5^3, 5^5, 5^7, ...

[10] 12, -36, 108, -324, ...

11. $\frac{2}{3}$, $\frac{4}{6}$, $\frac{6}{12}$, $\frac{8}{24}$, $\frac{10}{48}$, ... 12. 2^2, 6^2, 18^2, 54^2, ...

[13] $\frac{1}{4}$, $\frac{1}{6}$, $\frac{1}{9}$, $\frac{2}{27}$, ... [14] $\frac{1}{4}$, $\frac{1}{6}$, $\frac{1}{8}$, $\frac{1}{10}$, ...

15. x^2, $-x$, 1, $-\dfrac{1}{x}$, ... [16] b^2c^3, b^3c^2, b^4c, b^5, ...

Write down, using the index notation, the 8th term and the nth term of a G.P. whose first two terms are as follows:

17. 5, 10. 18. 10, 5. 19. 6, -8. 20. x, y.

[21] 6, 9. [22] 1, -1. [23] 3, $-\frac{1}{3}$. [24] a^3, ab.

25. The nth term of a G.P. is $100(\frac{1}{2})^n$; how many terms of the G.P. are greater than 1?

[26] The nth term of a G.P. is $3 \cdot 2^{n-1}$; how many terms of the G.P. are less than 100?

Find the common ratio and the second term of the following series in G.P.:

27. 1st term 5; 5th term 405.

28. 4th term 15; 7th term -960.

[29] 3rd term 18; 7th term $3\frac{5}{9}$.

[30] 1st term 24; 4th term -81.

31. Find the geometric mean of (i) 12 and 75; (ii) 2 and $\frac{1}{2}$.

[32] Insert two geometric means between 54 and 16.

33. Insert two geometric means between 6 and $\frac{2}{9}$.

[34] Insert three geometric means between 162 and 1250.

35. The first term of a G.P. is 8 and the common ratio is $0\cdot7$; using logarithms, find the least value of n such that the nth term is less than $0\cdot01$.

[36] The value of a machine depreciates every year by 10 per cent. of its value at the beginning of that year. Its value when new is £300; use logarithms to find its value after 8 years to the nearest £.

*37. The sum of the first two terms of a G.P. is c, and the sum of the last two terms is d; there are n terms in all. Find the common ratio.

*38. The first and last terms of a G.P. are a and l; there are n terms in all. Find the product of all the terms.

Sum of Numbers in G.P.

Example 9.   Find the sum of the first 7 terms of the G.P.,

$$2, \ 6, \ 18, \ 54, \ \dots \ .$$

Since the common ratio is 3, the required sum S is given by

$$S = 2 + 2 \cdot 3 + 2 \cdot 3^2 + 2 \cdot 3^3 + 2 \cdot 3^4 + 2 \cdot 3^5 + 2 \cdot 3^6.$$

If we multiply each side by 3, each term is changed into the term which used to follow it; thus

$$3S = 2 \cdot 3 + 2 \cdot 3^2 + 2 \cdot 3^3 + 2 \cdot 3^4 + 2 \cdot 3^5 + 2 \cdot 3^6 + 2 \cdot 3^7.$$

Therefore if we subtract, all the terms except the first term in the first equation and the last term in the second equation disappear.

$$\therefore \ S - 3S = 2 - 2 \cdot 3^7 ;$$
$$\therefore \ -2S = 2 - 2 \cdot 3^7 ;$$
$$\therefore \ S = 3^7 - 1 = 2186.$$

Summation by Formula.   Suppose the first term of a G.P. is a and that the common ratio is r; then the terms of the series are

$$a, \ ar, \ ar^2, \ ar^3, \ \dots \ .$$

Denote the sum of n terms by S, then

$$S = a + ar + ar^2 + ar^3 + \dots + ar^{n-2} + ar^{n-1}.$$

Multiply each side by the common ratio r; each term is then changed into the term which used to follow it;

$$\therefore \ rS = ar + ar^2 + ar^3 + ar^4 + \dots + ar^{n-1} + ar^n.$$

$\therefore$ if we subtract, all terms except the first term in the first equation and the last term in the second equation disappear;

$$\therefore \ S - rS = a - ar^n ;$$
$$\therefore \ S(1 - r) = a(1 - r^n) ;$$
$$\therefore \ S = \frac{a(1 - r^n)}{1 - r}.$$

This is the more convenient form for S if r is less than 1; but if r is greater than 1, the numerator and denominator would each be negative; in this case we write $S = \dfrac{a(r^n - 1)}{r - 1}.$

$$\therefore \ S = \frac{a(1 - r^n)}{1 - r} = \frac{a(r^n - 1)}{r - 1}.$$

EXERCISE XVI. e

Find the sums of the geometrical progressions in Nos. 1–6
without using the formula. Multiply out the answers.

1. 3, 6, 12, ..., 9 terms.   [2] 5, 20, 80, ..., 6 terms.

3. 4, -12, 36, ..., 8 terms.   [4] 1, $\frac{1}{2}$, $\frac{1}{4}$, ..., 10 terms.

5. 75, 15, 3, ..., 7 terms.   [6] 54, -18, 6, ..., 8 terms.

Find the sums of the geometrical progressions in Nos. 7–16,
leaving the answers in index form.

7. 6, 24, 96, ..., 10 terms.   [8] 8, -24, 72, ..., 12 terms.

9. 2, $1\frac{1}{3}$, $\frac{8}{9}$, ..., 20 terms.   [10] 10, 5, $2\frac{1}{2}$, ..., 15 terms.

11. $2\cdot5$, -1, $0\cdot4$, ..., 14 terms.   [12] 144, -108, 81, ..., 16 terms.

[13] 1, $-a^2$, a^4, ..., 15 terms.   **14.** 2^2, 4^2, 8^2, ..., $(n-1)$ terms.

[15] $2b$, $6b^2$, $18b^3$, ..., $(n-1)$ terms.   **16.** c^2, c, 1, ..., $2n$ terms.

Use logarithms to find approximate values of the following:

17. $10\{1 + 1\cdot04 + 1\cdot04^2 + ... + 1\cdot04^{10}\}$.

[18] $12(1 + 0\cdot9 + 0\cdot9^2 + ... + 0\cdot9^8)$.

19. $3 + 2^{\frac{1}{4}} \cdot 3^{\frac{3}{4}} + 2^{\frac{1}{2}} \cdot 3^{\frac{1}{2}} + 2^{\frac{3}{4}} \cdot 3^{\frac{1}{4}} + ...$, 12 terms.

[20] $500 - 400 + 320 - 256 + ...$, 9 terms.

21. $64 - 48 + 36 - 27 + ...$, 10 terms.

22. How many terms of the G.P., 4, 6, 9, ..., must be taken to
give a sum greater than 8000?

23. The nth term of a series is $2^{n-1} + 2n$. Find the sum of
the first k terms.

24. A pendulum is set swinging; its first oscillation is through
36°, and each succeeding oscillation is $\frac{5}{6}$ of the one before it.
Find approximately by using logarithms the total angle through
which it swings in 20 oscillations.

[25] An elastic ball, dropped from a height of 16 feet, takes
1 second to reach the ground; the first bounce up and down
takes $1\frac{1}{2}$ sec., and each following one takes $\frac{3}{4}$ of the time the previous
bounce took. Find approximately by using logarithms the time
that elapses before the ball hits the ground for the tenth time.

26. Find the sum of all integral powers of 2 between 100 and
1,000,000. Give the answer in index form.

*27. Sum to n terms: $9 + 99 + 999 + 9999 + \dots$.

*28. Find in index form the value of the nth bracket and the sum of the first n brackets of the series,

$$(1) + (2 + 4) + (8 + 16 + 32) + (64 + 128 + 256 + 512) + \dots.$$

*29. If a man receives £A yearly for n years, the first payment being made in 1 year's time and if compound interest is reckoned at r per cent. per annum, show that the present value of this annuity is £P where $P = AR^{-1} + AR^{-2} + \dots + AR^{-n}$ and $R = 1 + 0.01r$; and find P in terms of A, r, n.

*30. What lump sum was paid on January 1st, 1930, in order to secure a payment of £100 a year for ten years, the first payment being made on January 1st, 1931, allowing 5 per cent. per annum compound interest? ($\log 1.05 = 0.0211893$.)

REVISION EXERCISE R. 10 (Ch. XVI)

1. Of the series (i) 5, 2, 0.8, ...; (ii) $a + b$, $3a + 2b$, $5a + 3b$, ...; (iii) $2\frac{1}{2}$, $5\frac{1}{4}$, $8\frac{1}{8}$, $11\frac{1}{16}$, ...; one is an A.P., one is a G.P., and one is neither. Which is which? Find expressions for the nth term of each series.

2. Insert three arithmetic means between 1 and n.

3. Insert two geometric means between 54 and 2.

[4] Prove that the sum of n terms of 1, 4, 7, 10, 13, ... is $\frac{3}{2}\{(n - \frac{1}{6})^2 - \frac{1}{36}\}$.

5. If $2p - 1$ and $2q - 1$ are positive odd numbers, and $p < q$, find the sum of all the odd numbers starting with $2p - 1$ and ending with $2q - 1$.

6. Sum the G.P., $1 - 3 + 9 - \dots + 531,441$.

[7] Find the sum of all the positive terms of the A.P., 35, $33\frac{1}{2}$, 32, ...

[8] The first term of an A.P. is 24 and the third term is 4; how many terms must be taken to give a sum of 20?

9. The third and fourth terms of an A.P. are respectively 15 and $13\frac{1}{2}$; how many must be taken to make the sum zero?

10. The third term of a G.P. is 40 and the sixth term is 625. Find the first term.

[11] The sum of 11 terms of an A.P. is 22 and the common difference is $\frac{2}{5}$. Find the first term.

12. The sum of n terms of an A.P. for all values of n is $3n^2 - 5n$. Find the first term and the common difference.

[13] The sum of n terms of a G.P. is $3^n - 1$ for all values of n. Find the first 3 terms.

14. A clerk is engaged at a salary of £150 a year, to be increased by £10 a year at the end of each year. Find the total amount he receives for the first 12 years.

[15] A contractor undertakes to bore a well at 30 shillings for the first 10 feet, 35 shillings for the next 10 feet, 40 shillings for the next 10 feet, and so on.   What is the depth of the well if the cost is £105?

16. A contractor knows that a certain piece of work can be done by 15 men in 19 weeks; he employs 15 men for the first week and at the beginning of each subsequent week increases by x the number of men employed, and the work is completed in 10 weeks. Assuming that the amount of work done in any week is proportional to the number of men employed throughout that week, find the value of x.

17. How many terms of the A.P., 7, 13, 19, ... must be taken to give a sum greater than 1000?

[18] How many terms of the G.P., 27, 45, 75, 125, ... must be taken to give a sum greater than 10,000?

19. The houses in a row are numbered consecutively from 1 to 49.   Show that there is a value of x such that the sum of the numbers of the houses preceding the house numbered x is equal to the sum of the numbers of the houses following it, and find this value of x.

[20] The sum of the first 10 terms of an A.P. is $\frac{3}{8}$ of the sum of the next 10 terms.   The 10th term is 78, find the 20th term.

21. The sum of the 5th and 13th terms of an A.P. is 58, and the 21st term is $2\frac{1}{2}$ times the 8th term. Find the sum of the first 15 terms.

[22] The sum of the first 2 terms of a G.P. is 6 and the sum of the first 4 terms is $7\frac{1}{2}$, and the common ratio is positive. Find the 1st term and the 6th term.

23. The sum of the first 3 terms of a G.P. is 336, and the sum of the 5th, 6th, 7th terms is 21. Find the two possible values of the 3rd term.

[24] The first terms of an A.P. and G.P. are each $\frac{2}{3}$; the common difference of the A.P. and the common ratio of the G.P. are each x; also the sums of the first 3 terms of the two series are equal. Find the two possible values of x and the sum of the first 20 terms of each of the two possible A.P. series.

25. If $a + b + \ldots + l$ is a G.P., prove that its sum is $\dfrac{bl - a^2}{b - a}$.

[26] In an A.P. the 8th term is twice the 4th term; prove that the 9th term is 3 times the 3rd term.

27. The first and last terms of an A.P. are x, y; there are n terms in all. Find the second term.

*28. In an A.P. of n terms, the sum of the first two terms is b and the sum of the last two terms is c; find the sum of n terms.

*29. If a^2, b^2, c^2 are in A.P., prove that $\dfrac{1}{b + c}$, $\dfrac{1}{c + a}$, $\dfrac{1}{a + b}$ are also in A.P.

*30. A man deposits £100 annually to accumulate at 4 per cent. per annum compound interest. How much will he have standing to his credit just after the tenth deposit? $(\log 1 \cdot 04 = 0 \cdot 0170333.)$

*31. A Corporation borrows £10,000 and repays it by 30 equal annual payments, the first being made one year after the loan has been raised. Allowing compound interest at 5 per cent. per annum, calculate the amount of each annual payment. $(\log 1 \cdot 05 = 0 \cdot 0211893.)$

TESTS IN MANIPULATION

TESTS 19–24 (Ch. I–IX)

Test 19

1. If $nr^2h = 270$, find n when $r = 3$ and $h = 6$.
2. Simplify $\frac{1}{3}(3a - 6) - \frac{1}{5}(5a - 12)$.　　3. Divide $x^6 - x^2$ by $-x^2$.

Solve the equations:

4. $5(x - 5) - 3(x - 4) + 1 = 0$.　　　　5. $2x + 1 = 3y - 1 = 0$.
6. $c = 3 - 2d,\ d = 12 - 2c$.

Factorise:

7. $a^2 - 7a - 18$.　　8. $25 - 4b^2$.　　9. $1 - 2t - 3t^2$.
10. Copy and complete, $x^2 + 10x \ldots = (x \ldots)^2$.

Test 20

Simplify:

1. $6xy^2 \div \frac{1}{3}y$.　　　　　　2. $(n + 2)(n - 7) - (n - 3)^2$.
3. $\dfrac{1 + a}{3} - \dfrac{1 + a}{2} + \dfrac{2 - a}{4}$.　　　4. $(c - 3c^2) \div (-c) - 2c$.

Solve the equations:

5. $0 \cdot 2(t - 0 \cdot 1) = 0 \cdot 3(t - 0 \cdot 2)$.　　6. $\dfrac{x}{2} + \dfrac{2x}{3} - \dfrac{3x}{4} = 1$.
7. $2x - y - 3 = 3y - x + 4 = 5x - 8y - 4$.

Factorise:

8. $x^2 - 15xy + 36y^2$.　　9. $1 + n - 6n^2$.　　10. $2t^2 + 9t - 5$.

351

Test 21

Simplify:

1. $\dfrac{6x^6}{(-2x)^3}$.

2. $2(a-1)(a+2) - (a-3)^2$.

3. $\dfrac{3b-1}{10} - \dfrac{2b-4}{15}$.

4. $\dfrac{x^2-1}{x^2-x}$.

Solve the equations:

5. $\dfrac{2t-7}{5} - \dfrac{t-2}{2} = 1$.

6. $2r + s + 10 = 0$.
$3r - 2s + 1 = 0$.

Factorise:

7. $a^2 - 8a + 16$.

8. $2b^2 - 8$.

9. $ax - cx + cy - ay$.

10. Copy and complete, $x^2 - 5x \ldots = (x \ldots)^2$.

Test 22

Simplify:

1. $2(a^2 - 11ab - 2b^2) - 3(3ab - 2a^2 + b^2) - 4(b^2 - 5ab + 2a^2)$.

2. $x - (40$ per cent. of $x)$.   3. $(c-d)(d-c) - (c+d)(d+c)$.

4. $\dfrac{3x-y}{xy} - \dfrac{2y-z}{yz} + \dfrac{z-2x}{zx}$.

Solve the equations:

5. $\dfrac{x+1}{3} - \dfrac{x-4}{7} = \dfrac{x+4}{5}$.

6. $\frac{1}{5}p + \frac{1}{3}q = 1$,
$2p + 3q = -1$.

7. Multiply $3x^2 - x + 2$ by $3x^2 + x - 2$.

Factorise:

8. $x^2 - 2xy - 15y^2$.

9. $20 - z - z^2$.

10. $ax - 4x - 4b + ab$.

Test 23

1. Find the value of $\dfrac{1}{x} - \dfrac{1}{y}$ if $x = -1\frac{1}{2}$ and $y = -4\frac{1}{2}$.

Simplify:

2. $x^2(2x)^3 \div (8x^6)$.

3. $\dfrac{c}{3bc} + \dfrac{a}{6ab}$.

4. $(x - 2y)(x + 8y) - (x - 3y)^2$.

5. $\dfrac{a - b}{a - c} \times \dfrac{b - c}{b - a} \times \dfrac{c - a}{c - b}$.

Solve the equations:

6. $5\left(\dfrac{1}{x} - 2\right) = \dfrac{1}{2x} - 1$.

7. $\frac{1}{3}x + \frac{1}{5}(y - x) + 1\frac{1}{2} = 0$,
   $7x + 3y = 0$.

Factorise:

8. $1 + a^2b^2 - a^2 - b^2$.

9. $3x^2 + 12x - 63$.

10. Divide $x^3 + 1$ by $x - 2$.

Test 24

1. If $x = \frac{2}{3}(y - 9)$, express y in terms of x.

2. Find the value of $\dfrac{15}{x}$ if $x = -2, \frac{1}{2}, 0\cdot2, -0\cdot1$

Simplify:

3. $3(2b - 3c) - 2\{4c - 2[c - 3(b - c)] - 3b\}$.

4. $\dfrac{2x^2 - 3xy}{x^2y} - \dfrac{2xy + y^2}{xy^2}$.

5. $(a + \frac{1}{4})^2 - (a - \frac{3}{4})^2$.

Solve the equations:

6. $1\cdot25(y - 3) - 1\cdot75(5 - y) = 0\cdot25$.

7. $\dfrac{x - 1}{3} + \dfrac{y + 1}{2} = 1$, $\dfrac{2x + 1}{5} - \dfrac{3y + 1}{4} = 5$.

Factorise:

8. $x(y + z) - y - z$.

9. $4b^2 - 9(c - d)^2$.

10. Copy and complete, $4x^2 - x\ldots = (2x\ldots)^2$.

D.C.A.

M

TESTS 25–30 (Ch. I–XI)

Test 25

Simplify:

1. $1\frac{1}{3}x^3 \times 1\frac{1}{2}x^3$.

2. $(y + \frac{1}{2})^2 - (y - \frac{1}{2})^2$.

3. $\dfrac{a+3}{a+4} - \dfrac{a+1}{a+2}$.

4. $\dfrac{b^2 - 2b + 1}{b^2 + b - 2}$.

Factorise:

5. $5 - 45p^2$.

6. $y(y + 4z) - 3z(3y - 2z)$.

Solve the equations:

7. $3x^2 + 5x = 2$.

8. $y^2 - 10y = 7$ (to 2 places of decimals).

9. From $\dfrac{1}{t^2 - t}$ subtract $\dfrac{1}{t^3 - t}$.

10. Simplify $\left(\dfrac{a+b}{a-b} - 1\right)^2 \div \left(1 - \dfrac{a-b}{a+b}\right)^2$.

Test 26

Simplify:

1. $2(x - y + z) - 3(x + 2y - 3z) - 5(x - y + 2z)$.

2. $\dfrac{1}{2}a\left(a - \dfrac{1}{2a}\right) - \dfrac{1}{4}\left(a - \dfrac{1}{a}\right)^2$.

3. $\dfrac{c^2 - c + \frac{1}{4}}{c^2 - \frac{1}{4}}$.

4. $\dfrac{1}{x-2} - \dfrac{5}{x^2 + x - 6}$.

Factorise:

5. $3 - 6t - 9t^2$.

6. $x^2 + (a - b)x - ab$.

Solve the equations:

7. $\dfrac{1}{x+3} - \dfrac{1}{x-1} = 1$.

8. $\dfrac{1}{x} - y = 2$, $\quad \dfrac{1}{x} + y = 8$.

9. Divide $\dfrac{a}{b} + \dfrac{b}{a} - 2$ by $\dfrac{a}{2b} - \dfrac{1}{2}$.

10. Simplify $\dfrac{p + 2q}{p^2 - pq} + \dfrac{q + 2p}{q^2 - pq}$.

Test 27

Simplify:

1. $(-\frac{2}{3}a)^3 \div 4\frac{1}{2}ab.$

2. $\left(\dfrac{1}{x} - \dfrac{1}{y}\right) \div (x - y).$

3. $(z+1)^3 - z(z+1)(z+2).$

4. $(x^2 - 45x + 200) \div (x - 5).$

5. $\dfrac{1}{x-5} - \dfrac{x+6}{2x^2 - 9x - 5}.$

6. Factorise $ap + bp + cp + cq + bq + aq.$

Solve the equations:

7. $\dfrac{2}{y-1} + \dfrac{3}{y-2} = \dfrac{5}{y}.$

8. $z^2 + 3z = 5$ (to 2 places of decimals).

9. Divide $4x^2 + 4x + 1$ by $-2x - 1.$

10. Simplify $\left(1 - \dfrac{a}{2a+5}\right)\left(\dfrac{a}{a+5} + 1\right) - a^2\left(\dfrac{1}{a^2} - 1\right).$

Test 28

Simplify:

1. $1\frac{2}{3}x^3 - \dfrac{x^3}{6}.$

2. $\dfrac{1}{y^2 - y} - \dfrac{1}{y^2}.$

3. $2 \div \left(1 - \dfrac{a-b}{a+b}\right).$

4. $\dfrac{7}{x^2 + x - 12} - \dfrac{6}{x^2 + 2x - 8}.$

5. Factorise $a^3 - a^2b - ab^2 + b^3.$

Solve the equations:

6. $x + 2y + 3 = 4x + 4y - 1 = 3x + 3y + 2.$

7. $\dfrac{x+1}{x-2} - \dfrac{x-1}{x+2} = \dfrac{6}{x+1}.$

8. $3x^2 - 4x = 6$ (to 2 places of decimals).

9. Divide $(x^2 - x - 2)(4x^2 - 16x + 7)$ by $(2x^2 + x - 1).$

10. Simplify $\left\{\left(x + \dfrac{1}{a}\right)^2 - \left(a + \dfrac{1}{x}\right)^2\right\} \div (ax + 1)^2.$

Test 29

1. Divide $x^4 + x + 1$ by $x + 1$.

2. Subtract $(x - \frac{2}{3}y)(x + \frac{1}{2}y)$ from $x^2 + \frac{1}{6}y^2$.

Simplify:

3. $\dfrac{(3x - 6)^2}{(x - 2)^2}.$

4. $\dfrac{1}{a - b} + \dfrac{2b}{b^2 - a^2}.$

5. $\dfrac{1}{(y + 2)(y + 3)} - \dfrac{2}{(y + 2)(y + 3)(y + 4)}.$

Factorise:

6. $a^2b^2 - b^2c^4.$

7. $12x^2 - 7xy - 12y^2.$

Solve the equations:

8. $3x - 4 = \dfrac{4}{3x - 4}.$

9. $\dfrac{x + 3}{x - 1} + \dfrac{x - 3}{x + 2} = \dfrac{2x - 2}{x + 1}.$

10. Simplify $\dfrac{4b^3 - bc^2}{(b + c)^2 - b^2} \div \left(\dfrac{2b}{c} - 1 \right).$

Test 30

Simplify:

1. $\dfrac{a^3b^3}{a^3c^3} \div (b^3c^3).$

2. $(8a^6 - 4a^3) \div (-2a)^3.$

3. $\dfrac{2x^2 + 7x - 4}{2x^2 + 3x - 2}.$

4. $\dfrac{b + \frac{1}{2}c}{4b^2 - c^2}.$

Factorise:

5. $r^2 - rt + st - rs.$

6. $20a^2 + 9ab - 18b^2.$

Solve the equations:

7. $y = 2(x + y - 1) = -2(x + y + 3).$

8. $\dfrac{x}{x - 2} - \dfrac{x + 1}{x + 4} = 1.$

9. Simplify $\dfrac{1}{y(y - z)} + \dfrac{1}{y(y + z)} + \dfrac{1}{y^2 - z^2}.$

10. Simplify $\dfrac{px - q}{qx + p}$ if $x = \dfrac{p + q}{p - q}.$

TESTS 31–36 (Ch. I–XIII)

Test 31

1. Multiply $a - \dfrac{b}{2}$ by $a + \dfrac{3b}{2}$.　　**2.** Complete $\dfrac{3}{y-4} = \dfrac{\cdots}{y^2 - 3y - 4}$.

Simplify:

3. $\dfrac{5}{x+2} - \dfrac{2(x-8)}{x^2-4}$.　　　　**4.** $\left(\dfrac{r}{s} + \dfrac{s}{r} - 2\right) \div \left(1 - \dfrac{s}{r}\right)$.

Factorise:

5. $3(x+1)^2 - 20(x+1) - 63$.　　**6.** $1 + a(a + b + a^2 b)$.

Solve the equations:

7. $5x + \dfrac{4}{y} = 14$, $5x - \dfrac{6}{y} = 17$.

8. $x^2 + 11x = 20$, correct to two places of decimals.

9. $x^2 + y^2 = 34$, $x - y = 8$.

10. Find p if $x + 2$ is a factor of $x^4 + px - 6$.

Test 32

1. Divide $6x^3 - 5x^2 - 8x + 3$ by $2x - 3$.

2. Find the L.C.M. of $(2a - 2b)^2$, $(3a - 3b)^2$, $6a^3 - 6b^3$.

3. Simplify $\left(3 - \dfrac{24}{x+3}\right)\left(2 + \dfrac{16}{x-5}\right)$.

4. If $b = \dfrac{4 + 3a}{3 + 2a}$, express $\dfrac{b - a}{2 - b^2}$ in terms of a.

Factorise:

5. $4a^5 - 36ab^2$.　　　　　　　**6.** $x(p + q) - (pq + x^2)$.

Solve for x, y the equations:

7.　$x - y = 2b$,　　　　　**8.**　$2x + y = 1$,
　　$ax - by = a^2 + b^2$.　　　　　$x^2 - 2xy = 39$.

9. Find the value of $a^2 + \beta^2$ if a, β are the roots of $2x^2 - x - 8 = 0$.

10. If $c = a + b$, prove that $a^2 + b^2 + c^2 = 2(bc + ca - ab)$.

Test 33

1. Multiply $6a(a+b) + 5b(a-7b)$ by $6a(a-b) - 5b(a+7b)$.

Simplify:

2. $1 - x + x^2 - x^3 + \dfrac{x^4}{1+x}$.

3. $\dfrac{(a-b)^2 - 9c^2}{a^2 - (b+3c)^2}$.

Factorise:

4. $156x^2 + x - 1$.

5. $a^2b^2 + bc - b^3 - a^2c$.

Solve:

6. $\dfrac{5}{x} - \dfrac{2}{y} - 25 = \dfrac{4}{x} + \dfrac{9}{y} = -6$.

7. $4 + \dfrac{28}{x-5} - \dfrac{51}{(x-5)^2} = 0$.

8. If $x = \dfrac{2t}{1+t^2}$, $y = \dfrac{1-t^2}{1+t^2}$, simplify $x^2 + y^2$.

9. One root of $3x^2 - 8x + c = 0$ is 3 times the other root. Find c.

10. Make n the subject of the formula, $C = \dfrac{nE}{R + nr}$.

Test 34

1. Multiply $3x - 2 + \dfrac{1}{x}$ by $x + 1 - \dfrac{2}{x}$.

2. Find x if $(x-p)^2 = (x-q)^2$.

Simplify:

3. $\left(\dfrac{a}{b} + \dfrac{b}{a} - 2\right) \div \left(\dfrac{1}{a} - \dfrac{1}{b}\right)^2$.

4. $\dfrac{1}{(a-b)(a-c)} + \dfrac{1}{(b-c)(b-a)}$.

Factorise:

5. $8x^2 - x^5$.

6. $x^2 - y^2 - 2x + 1$.

Solve:

7. $\dfrac{x}{x-1} + 1 = \dfrac{x-2}{2x}$.

8. $x^2 + y^2 = -6x$,

$y - 2x = 3$.

9. Factorise $x^3 - 7x + 6$.

10. If α, β are the roots of $3x^2 + x - 5 = 0$ and if $\dfrac{\alpha}{\beta}$, $\dfrac{\beta}{\alpha}$ are the roots of $x^2 + qx + r = 0$, find q, r.

Test 35

1. Find the coefficients of x^2 and of x^4 in the expansion of
$$(x^3 - 3x^2 + x - 2)(2x^3 + x^2 - 3x + 1).$$

Simplify:

2. $\dfrac{b^2 + bc - 2c^2}{b^2 - bc - 6c^2} \times \dfrac{b - 3c}{b - 2c}.$ **3.** $\dfrac{x^3 + y^3}{x^2 + 2xy + y^2} - x - y.$

Factorise:

4. $(3a - 1)bc + ac^2 - 3b^2.$ **5.** $(x^2 - x - 8)^2 - 4(2x - 1)^2.$

Solve:

6. $\dfrac{x - 1}{x + 1} + \dfrac{x + 3}{x - 3} = \dfrac{2x + 4}{x - 2}.$ **7.** $x^2 + 2x = a^2 - 1.$

8. $2x - 3y = 1,\ x^2 + y^2 = 2x + 1.$

9. If $k = \sqrt{\{\frac{3}{8}l(l - x)\}}$, prove that $(l - \frac{1}{2}x)^2 = \dfrac{8k^2}{3} + \dfrac{1}{4}x^2$ and make l the subject of the formula.

10. Prove that $(2x - 1)^2$ is a factor of $4x^4 + 20x^3 + 13x^2 - 30x + 9$, and hence find the square root of this expression.

Test 36

1. If the coefficient of x^2 in the expansion of
$$(1 - 2x - x^2)(1 + px - 3x^2)$$
is zero, find the value of p.

2. If $a(x + y) = a^2 - xy$, express $x + y$ in terms of a, x only.

3. Simplify $\dfrac{x}{2x^2 - 3x + 1} + \dfrac{3x + 1}{2x^2 + x - 1} - \dfrac{4x - 2}{x^2 - 1}$ and find for what value of x the expression is zero.

4. Substitute $x = \frac{1}{2}(a - b)$ in $\dfrac{a}{(x - a)^2 - b^2} - \dfrac{b}{a^2 - (x + b)^2}$ and simplify the expression.

Factorise: **5.** $24x^3 + 18x^2 - 15x.$ **6.** $a + ab^3.$

Solve:

7. $\dfrac{1}{x + 1} + \dfrac{1}{x - 1} = \dfrac{4}{5}$, correct to two places of decimals.

8. $3x + 2y = 10,\ x^2 - 3xy = 28.$

9. Find the values of b, c if $x - 1$ and $x - 3$ are factors of $2x^3 - 7x^2 + bx + c$, and in this case find the remaining factor.

10. If a, β are the roots of $x^2 - 7x + p = 0$ and if $\dfrac{1 - a}{a}$, $\dfrac{1 - \beta}{\beta}$ are the roots of $3x^2 - qx + 1 = 0$, find p, q.

TESTS 37–42 (Ch. IX–XV)

Test 37

1. Factorise $(3r - s)^2 - (4r + t)^2$.

Solve:

2. $2x + \dfrac{1}{y} = 10, \quad 3x - \dfrac{2}{y} = 1.$ 3. $\dfrac{2x}{x - 1} - \dfrac{3}{x + 2} = 3.$

4. If $x = 2p - q$ and $y = p + 2q$, express in terms of p, q

$$\left(\frac{2}{x + y} - \frac{1}{x - y}\right) \div \left(\frac{3}{x - y} - \frac{2}{x + y}\right).$$

5. Write down the values of $8^{\frac{2}{3}}$ and $(\frac{2}{3})^{-1}$.

Simplify:

6. $12^{\frac{1}{2}} \times 75^{-\frac{1}{2}}$.   7. $(2\sqrt{5} - 3)(2\sqrt{5} + 3)$.   8. $\log 27 \div \log 3$.

9. If $a : (a + b - c) = 2 : 5$ and $b : (a + b + c) = 3 : 4$, find the values of the ratios $a : b$ and $b : c$.

10. If z varies directly as the cube of x and inversely as y, and if $z = 4$ when $x = 2$ and $y = 12$, find z in terms of x and y.

Test 38

1. Factorise $x^2 - (2y - 3z)x - 6yz$.

2. Solve $1 + 4x = 4x^2 + y^2 = 2 + 3y$.

3. Simplify $\left(\dfrac{1}{x} - \dfrac{b}{a}\right) \div \left(\dfrac{1}{x} + \dfrac{a}{b}\right)$ if $a(1 - x) = b(1 + x)$.

4. For what values of c is $x^2 - (c + 2)x + 3c + 6$ a perfect square?

5. Write down the values of $(\frac{1}{9})^{-\frac{1}{2}}$ and $16^{1\frac{1}{4}}$.

Simplify:

6. $20^{\frac{1}{2}} \times 5^{1\frac{1}{2}}$.   7. $(x + 2x^{\frac{1}{2}} + 1)(x - 2x^{\frac{1}{2}} + 1)$.

8. $\dfrac{\sqrt{12}}{(1 + \sqrt{2})(\sqrt{6} - \sqrt{3})}$.

9. $\log_{10} 1 \cdot 5 + \log_{10} 7 \cdot 5 + 3 \log_{10} 2 - 2 \log_{10} 3$.

10. If $\dfrac{a}{b} = \dfrac{c}{d}$, prove that $\dfrac{a + b}{b} = \dfrac{a + b - c - d}{b - d}$.

Test 39

1. If $x = a - \dfrac{1}{b}$ and $y = b - \dfrac{1}{a}$, express $\left(\dfrac{1}{x} - \dfrac{1}{y}\right) \div \left(\dfrac{1}{a} - \dfrac{1}{b}\right)$ in terms of a, b.

2. Solve $x^2 + xy + 4y^2 = 2x - 2y = 4$.

3. If a, β are the roots of $2x^2 - 7x - 3 = 0$, find the values of $a^2 + \beta^2$ and $(a+2)(\beta+2)$.

4. Write down the values of 5^0 and $(\tfrac{1}{4})^{-2}$.

Simplify:

5. $9^{2n} \div 3^n$.

6. $\dfrac{\sqrt{6}}{\sqrt{2}} + \dfrac{\sqrt{60}}{\sqrt{5}}$.

7. $(\tfrac{64}{125})^{\frac{2}{3}} \times (\tfrac{4}{25})^{-\frac{3}{2}}$.

8. $\log_{10} 4 + 2 \log_{10} 5$.

9. If $a : b = b : c$, prove that $(a^2 + b^2)(b^2 + c^2) = b^2(a+c)^2$.

10. If y is partly constant and partly varies as x^2, and if $y = 8$ when $x = 1$, and $y = 2$ when $x = 2$, find y when $x = 3$.

Test 40

1. Factorise $x^4 - 9x^2 + 12x - 4$.

2. Find the value of c if $x + 1$ is a factor of
$$cx^3 - (c-1)x^2 - (2c+1)x - c + 1,$$
and in this case find the remaining factors.

Solve:

3. $\dfrac{6}{x} + 5y = 24$, $\dfrac{9}{x} + 4y = 22$.

4. $x^2 - xy + y^2 = 7$, $2x - y = 5$.

5. If $x = 3 + \dfrac{7}{5+y}$, find y in terms of x, and prove that $(x-3)(y+7)$ equals $1 + 2x$.

Simplify:

6. $\sqrt{18} + \sqrt{32} - \sqrt{50}$.

7. $\tfrac{1}{3}$ of $9^{2n-1} \div 27^{n-1}$.

8. $\dfrac{\log (b^2 c) - \log (bc)}{\log (\sqrt{b})}$.

9. Multiply $2^x - 3^y$ by $2^y + 3^x$.

10. If x varies as the square of y and inversely as z, find the percentage change in x if y increases by 20 per cent. and if z decreases by 20 per cent.

Test 41

1. Factorise $(ac-bd)^2+(ad+bc)^2$.

2. Find the remainder if x^4-2x^3-x-3 is divided by $x+1$.

3. Solve $\dfrac{1}{x+1}+\dfrac{2}{x-1}=\dfrac{1}{x+3}$, correct to two places of decimals.

4. Substitute $\dfrac{ab-c^2}{a-b}$ for x in $\dfrac{(x+a)(x-b)}{(ax+c^2)(bx-c^2)}$ and simplify the result.

5. Find x correct to 3 places of decimals if $10^x=1\frac14$.

6. Express as powers of 8: 2, 4, $\frac12$, 0·125, $\sqrt2$.

Simplify:

7. $\dfrac{\sqrt3+1}{2+\sqrt3}$.

8. $(2x^{\frac12}-1-x^{-\frac12})^2$.

9. If $\dfrac{7a^2-4b^2}{a^2-2b^2}=\dfrac47$, find the ratio of a to b.

10. If t varies jointly as p and the square root of v^3, and if $t=224$ when $p=28$ and $v=16$, find t when $p=32$, $v=25$.

Test 42

1. Factorise $a(a^2-1)-b(b^2-1)$.

2. Solve $9y+x=x(x+y)$; $x-y=2$.

3. If $a=\dfrac{y-z}{x}$, $b=\dfrac{z-x}{y}$, $c=\dfrac{x-y}{z}$, simplify $a+b+c+abc$.

4. Find the value of b if one root of $bx^2-2bx+b-1=0$ is double the other.

5. Given $\log_{10}2=0\cdot301030$ and $\log_{10}3=0\cdot477121$, calculate the values of $\log_{10}24$ and $\log_{10}0\cdot015$ to 5 places of decimals.

6. Simplify $\log\left(\frac{75}{16}\right)-2\log\left(\frac59\right)+\log\left(\frac{32}{243}\right)$.

7. If $a=x^2$, $b=x\sqrt[3]{x}$, $c=x^{-\frac32}$, express $\sqrt[3]{(ab^3c^{-2})}$ as a power of x.

8. Simplify $\sqrt{(2\cdot5)}\times\left(\frac{4}{15}\right)^{-\frac12}\div(1\cdot5)^{\frac32}$.

9. If $x=3\sqrt2-2\sqrt3$ and $y=3\sqrt2+2\sqrt3$, simplify $\dfrac{x^2+y^2}{xy}$.

10. If $\dfrac ab=\dfrac cd=\dfrac ef$, prove that
$$(a^3+c^2e)(b+d+f)^3=(b^3+d^2f)(a+c+e)^3.$$

REVISION PAPERS, A. 51–65 (Ch. I–IX)

A. 51

1. If $a = -2$, $b = -5$, find the values of
(i) $(1 - a)^2$; (ii) $2ba^2$; (iii) $\dfrac{2b + a}{b - a}$.

2. Simplify (i) $(6x^4 - 4x^3y) \div (-2x^2)$; (ii) $\left(a + \dfrac{1}{a}\right)^2 - \left(a - \dfrac{1}{a}\right)^2$;
(iii) $(2z^3 - 3z^2 - 5z + 6) \div (z - 2)$.

3. Solve (i) $(2x + 1)(2x - 1) = (2x + 3)(2x - 5)$;
(ii) $3y - 4z = 13$, $\frac{1}{3}y + \frac{1}{4}z = 7$.

4. Factorise (i) $x^2 - 7x - 30$; (ii) $ab - ac + cd - bd$.

5. Find two consecutive odd numbers whose squares differ by 48.

A. 52

1. Simplify (i) $\dfrac{b}{ab + b}$; (ii) $\dfrac{3c - 3d}{2d - 2c}$;
(iii) $x(x + 1)(x - 2) - (x - 3)(x^2 + 2x - 1)$.

2. Solve (i) $\dfrac{t - 5}{7} = \dfrac{7 - t}{3}$; (ii) $\frac{1}{2}x + 2y = 5$, $\frac{1}{7}y = 2x + 8\frac{1}{2}$.

3. Factorise (i) $3b^2c - 6bcd + 12bc^2$;
(ii) $2y^3 - 18y$.

4. Find (i) the perimeter, (ii) the area of Fig. 155, if all the corners are right-angled, the units being inches. If the perimeter is $12p$ inches, find a in terms of b, p and then find the area in terms of b, p.

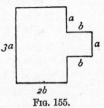
FIG. 155.

5. I am thinking of two numbers. If I halve the first, I get one less than the second; if I subtract 4 from the second, I get one-third of the first. Find the two numbers.

A. 53

1. Simplify (i) $a - \dfrac{a-b}{6} + \dfrac{2a+7b}{3}$.

    (ii) $(x-1)(x-2) + (3-x)(4-x) - 2(x-6)(1+x)$.

2. Solve (i) $\dfrac{2x+1}{5} - \dfrac{3x-1}{4} = \dfrac{1-x}{3}$; (ii) $y = \frac{1}{3}(x-5)$, $\dfrac{x}{y} = 5\frac{1}{2}$.

3. If $x = \dfrac{k+1}{2}$, express $x^2 - 2x + 1$ in terms of k.

4. Factorise (i) $2x^2 + 5x - 3$; (ii) $y^4 - y^8$.

5. A sum of money is divided equally among 50 children. If each boy had received 2 shillings more and each girl 6 pence less, there would have been 10 shillings left over. How many of the children were boys?

A. 54

1. (i) If $y = \dfrac{x^2+3x}{x+5}$, find the value of $x - y$ when $x = -7$.

    (ii) Subtract $\frac{1}{10}x^2 + \frac{3}{5}xy - \frac{3}{10}y^2$ from the sum of
$x^2 - \frac{2}{5}xy + 1\frac{1}{5}y^2$ and $\frac{3}{5}x^2 + xy - \frac{1}{2}y^2$.

2. (i) For what value of c does $x = -1$ satisfy $x^2 - 2cx = c + x$?

    (ii) Solve $y = \frac{1}{3}(4x-1)$, $x = \frac{1}{5}(4y-1)$.

3. Factorise (i) $2b - 2 + a - ab$; (ii) $30x^2 - 9x - 3$.

4. In Fig. 156, the straight line **EF** is the graph of $y = \dfrac{3x}{5} + 3$, and the unit for each axis is 1 inch.

    (i) What are the lengths of **OF** and **OE**?

    (ii) If **OM** $= 2$ in., what is **MP**?

    (iii) If **ON** $= -7$ in., what is **NQ**?

    (iv) If **MP** $= 6$ in., what is **OM**?

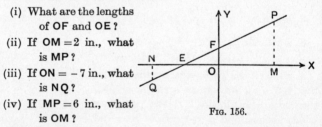

FIG. 156.

5. If 5 is added both to the numerator and the denominator of a fraction, the fraction reduces to $\frac{3}{4}$. If 4 is subtracted from both the numerator and the denominator, the fraction reduces to $\frac{3}{5}$. Find the fraction.

A. 55

1. (i) Add $\dfrac{1}{6xyz^2}$ to $\dfrac{1}{4x^2yz}$; (ii) Simplify $12a^3b^2 \div \left(\dfrac{2a}{3b}\right)^2$.

2. If $A = \frac{1}{2}h(a+b)$, express A in terms of h when $2b = 3a = 4\frac{1}{2}h$.

3. Solve (i) $\frac{1}{3}(x-4) - \frac{1}{4}(5-x) = \frac{1}{6}(7x+2)$.

      (ii) $5x + 11y + 20 = 7x + 4y - 29 = 0$.

4. (i) Factorise (a) $x^2 + 4x - 77$; (b) $3c^5 - 12cd^2$.

   (ii) If $y - 3$ is a factor of $y^2 + 2y + c$, find the value of c.

5. The price of eggs having risen by $\frac{1}{2}$d. each, it costs 4d. more to buy 20 eggs than it used to cost to buy 2 dozen eggs. Find the present price.

A. 56

1. (i) If $x = 2$, $y = -3$, $z = 5$, find the value of
$$(x+y-z)^2 - (x-y-z)^2;$$
(ii) If $S = 4\pi r^2$ and $V = \frac{4}{3}\pi r^3$, simplify $\dfrac{S^3}{V^2}$.

2. Simplify (i) $\dfrac{2a-3b}{4b} - \dfrac{a-b}{6b} + \dfrac{2b-a}{3b}$;

      (ii) $xy\left(\dfrac{2}{x^2} - \dfrac{3}{y^2}\right) - 2\left(\dfrac{x}{y} + \dfrac{y}{x}\right)$.

3. (i) The price of a carpet is £$(4x+1)$. If it is reduced by 20 per cent., it becomes £$(3x+3)$; find the value of x.

   (ii) Solve $5P = 2Q$, $\frac{1}{4}P - \frac{1}{6}Q + 1 = 0$.

4. Factorise (i) $1 - 6x - 16x^2$; (ii) $y^2 - \frac{1}{4}z^2$.

5. One car takes 7 hours over a journey which another car, travelling 5 miles per hour faster, does in 6 hours. Find the length of the journey.

A. 57

1. (i) What must be subtracted from $3p - p^2$ to leave $(1 - p)^2$?

   (ii) Simplify $\frac{1}{4}\{5c - (3\ \overline{2c + d} - 5\ \overline{c - d})\}$.

2. For what value of c is $x^3 + 2x^2 + cx - 6$ zero, when $x = 2$?

For which of the values $x = 1,\ -1,\ 3,\ -3$ is the expression zero for the same value of c ?

3. (i) Find u in terms of v if $\dfrac{v + 3}{u} = 2\dfrac{1}{4} + \dfrac{1}{u}$;

   (ii) Solve $x + \frac{1}{2}y = 14,\ \frac{1}{3}x - y + 7 = 0$.

4. (i) Factorise $(a)\ 35 + 2x - x^2$; $(b)\ y^2(c - d) - y(c^2 - d^2)$.

   (ii) Divide $x^3 - 2x + 1$ by $x - 2$.

5. A motorist averages 36 miles per hour on ordinary roads and 12 miles per hour on roads under repair. His average speed for a run of 50 miles is 24 miles per hour. What length of the road is under repair ?

A. 58

1. (i) Subtract $1 - (p - q)$ from $q - (1 - p)$.

   (ii) Simplify $(x + 2y)(3y - x) - (2x + y)(y - 3x)$.

2. Find the sum of the areas of the faces of the rectangular block in Fig. 157. Express it in terms of c if $a = 2\frac{1}{2}c$ and $b = 1\frac{1}{2}\,c$.

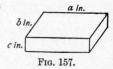

FIG. 157.

3. (i) Solve $\dfrac{2}{u} + \dfrac{1}{v} = 3,\ \dfrac{3}{u} - \dfrac{2}{v} = 4$.

   (ii) Factorise $(a)\ 6x^2 + 6x - 36$; $(b)\ r^3 - r(s - t)^2$.

4. Draw the graph of $y = x^2 - 4x - 5$ for values of x from -2 to $+6$. Use it for the following:

   (i) Find the least value of $x^2 - 4x - 5$.

   (ii) For what values of x is $y = -2$?

   (iii) Solve the equations $(x + 1)(x - 5) = 2,\ (x + 1)(x - 5) = -6$.

5. If the larger of two numbers is divided by the smaller, the quotient and remainder are each 3. If ten times the smaller is divided by the larger, the quotient and remainder are again each 3. Find the numbers.

A. 59

1. Simplify (i) $\dfrac{x^2 - 5x}{x} - \dfrac{3x - x^2}{-x}$;   (ii) $(n^3 - 8) \div (n - 2)$.

2. (i) Copy and complete, $y^2 - 7y \ldots = (y \ldots)^2$.

   (ii) Make **P** the subject of the formula, $\mathsf{A} = \mathsf{P} + \dfrac{\mathsf{PR}}{20}$.

3. Solve (i) $0 \cdot 25(t + 1) - 0 \cdot 4(t - 2) = 1 \cdot 02$;

   (ii) $\frac{1}{3}(x + 2) - \frac{1}{4}(y - 1) = 1$, $5x = 4y$.

4. Factorise (i) $ax^2 + b^2y - ab^2 - x^2y$;

   (ii) $(5x - 1)(x - 3) + (x - 5)(3 - x)$.

5. The cost of a book and the postage on it used to be 3 shillings. The price of the book is now 75 per cent. more, and the postal charge has been increased by 50 per cent., so that the present total cost is 5s. 2d. What was the original cost of the book and the postage on it?

A. 60

1. (i) Multiply $a - b$ by $b - a$ and subtract the result from $(a + b)^2$.

   (ii) Simplify $\dfrac{p^2 - q^2}{(p - 2q)(2p - q)}$ if $p = -2q$.

2. The expression $ax + b$, where a, b are constants, is equal to 5 when $x = -2$, and is equal to -2 when $x = 5$. Find the values of a and b. Find also the value of x for which the expression is equal to x.

3. (i) Solve $x(x + 1)(x + 7) - x(x + 3)^2 = 2(x - 3)^2$.

   (ii) Find a, b, c if $a + b = 6$, $b + c = 7$, $c + a = 8$.

4. Factorise (i) $x^2 - 2ax + 3bx - 6ab$;   (ii) $7y^2 + 9yz - 10z^2$.

5. A train, running between two towns, is 3 minutes late if it averages 45 miles an hour, and is 9 minutes late if it averages 40 miles an hour. Find the distance between the towns in miles, and the proper time for the journey in minutes.

A. 61 *

1. (i) Copy and complete $\dfrac{p}{q} = \dfrac{p^2}{\ldots} = \dfrac{\ldots}{q^2}$.

   (ii) Simplify $\frac{1}{2}(x-y)\left(\dfrac{1}{x}+\dfrac{1}{y}\right)$ if $x = 3y$.

2. Solve (i) $\dfrac{2t-1}{4\frac{1}{2}} - \dfrac{t-1}{1\frac{1}{2}} = 1$;

   (ii) $(x+2)(2y+2) = (2x-1)(y-1)$, $2x+y = 3$.

3. Factorise (i) $9x^2 - 15x - 14$; (ii) $a^2(b+c) - (b+c)^3$.

4. The angles of a triangle are $(2x+y)$, $(x+2y)$, $(5x-2y)$ degrees. If the triangle is isosceles, prove that it is equilateral and find the values of x and y.

5. A tank, capable of holding 1440 gallons, is supplied by two pipes **A** and **B**; **B** supplies 15 gallons a minute more than **A** does. The tank being empty, the pipe **A** is turned on for 4 minutes; after that, **B** is also turned on and the tank becomes full in another 12 minutes. How long would **A** take to fill the tank by itself?

A. 62 *

1. (i) Simplify $\{\frac{1}{2}x(x+y)\}^2 - \{\frac{1}{2}x(x-y)\}^2$.

   (ii) Express $\sqrt{\{(a+b+c)(b+c-a)(c+a-b)(a+b-c)\}}$ in terms of p if $a = 3p$, $b = 4p$, $c = 5p$.

2. Solve (i) $\frac{2}{3}(\frac{1}{4} - x) = \frac{1}{2}(\frac{1}{3} - x) + \frac{1}{4}(\frac{1}{5} - x)$;

   (ii) $\frac{1}{3}(x+1) - \frac{1}{2}(3y-1) = \frac{1}{5}(3-8y) - \frac{1}{4}(7-3x) = 1$.

3. Factorise (i) $12 - 33x - 9x^2$;

   (ii) $(a+b)^2 - 7c(a+b) + 12c^2$.

4. At the end of the War (1918), a man was 40 and his son was 12. In what year was the man just twice his son's age?

5. With the data of Fig. 158, find the value of x if

$$\angle\ \text{CBD} = 2\ \angle\ \text{CAD}.$$

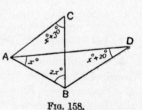

Fig. 158.

A. 63 *

1. (i) Subtract the sum of $\dfrac{x}{3}+\dfrac{y}{4}$ and $\dfrac{x}{6}-\dfrac{3y}{4}$ from $2(x-y)$.

  (ii) Simplify $\dfrac{6x^2yz}{(2xy)^3} \times \dfrac{(4yz)^2}{3yx^2} \div \left(\dfrac{3xz}{3xy}\right)^3$.

2. (i) If $2x=3y-4$ and $4y=3z+5$, find z in terms of x.

  (ii) Solve $\dfrac{r+s-5}{3}=\dfrac{2r-5}{21}=\dfrac{r-s-2}{15}$.

3. (i) If $x^2+ax+20$ can be expressed in the form $(x+b)(x+c)$ where b and c are positive integers, find all the possible values of a.

  (ii) Factorise $y^2-y-z+yz$.

4. Fig. 159 shows 3 circular arcs, centres **A, B, C**; $BC=10$ in., $CA=5$ in., $AB=9$ in. Calculate the length of **AP**

  (i) if $HK=\frac{1}{2}BC$; (ii) if **H** coincides with **K**.

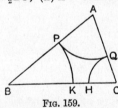

Fig. 159.

5. (i) What number exceeds 9 by r per cent.?

  (ii) The result of increasing **N** by r per cent. is the same as that of increasing $\frac{3}{4}$N by $3r$ per cent. Find the value of r.

A. 64 *

1. (i) Simplify $3(2a-\overline{n-1a}) \div a$.

  (ii) Subtract $3(2x^2-x-5)$ from $2x(x^2-3x-5)$ and arrange the result in *ascending* powers of x.

2. (i) Find **W** and x if $W(x-5)=9$ and $W(2x-1)=45$.

  (ii) If $x=2t^2-t-4$ and $y=t^2+2t+3$, find the values of x and y if $x=2y$.

3. Factorise (i) $6x^2-17xy-14y^2$; (ii) $z^2(z-1)-9z+9$.

4. As a rule, **P** bicycles twice as fast as **Q** walks. Each leaves **A** at 2 p.m., and they agree to meet at **B** (see Fig. 160). **P** follows the roads **AO, OB**; **Q** goes straight across country. Owing to the wind, their speeds are each one mile an hour less than usual. They arrive at **B** at the same time. What was the time of arrival?

Fig. 160.

5. If the nth day of January and the $(2n)$th day of February are both Sundays, find the value of n. [There is more than one answer.]

A. 65 *

1. Of which of the following expressions is $b - c$ a factor, and what is the other factor?

(i) $a(b-c)+a^2(b-c)$; (ii) $b(x+y)-c(x-y)$;
(iii) $x(b-c)+y(c-b)$; (iv) $a(b-c)-b-c$;
(v) $p(b-c)-b+c$; (vi) $a(a+b)-a(a+c)$.

2. (i) If $2x-5y=4$ and $3x-7y=5$, find the value of c for which $x+cy=-10$.

(ii) Find y and z if $yz+2y=18$ and $7y-2yz=8$.

3. (i) If $x=am^2$ and $y=2am$, express x in terms of a, y only.

(ii) Two numbers m and n are chosen so that their sum equals three times their difference. Find the value of $\dfrac{mn}{m^2+n^2}$.

4. In Fig. 161, $AC=AB=BD$, and $\angle\,BAD=\frac{3}{4}\,\angle\,BAC$. Find the values of x and y.

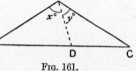

Fig. 161.

5. In a competition $(n+1)$ prizes are awarded if there are more than $(11n+5)$ competitors. (i) How many prizes are given if there are 75 competitors, 80 competitors? (ii) What can you say about the number of competitors if exactly 4 prizes are awarded?

REVISION PAPERS, A. 66–80. (Ch. I–XI)

A. 66

1. (i) Find the value of $9x^2 - 36x$ when $x = -1\frac{1}{3}$.

(ii) For what value of x has $9x^2 - 36x$ the same value as it has when $x = -3$?

2. Solve (i) $Q - 1 = \frac{1}{4}P$, $\frac{1}{5}P = \frac{2}{3}Q$; (ii) $(7 - x)(2x + 3) = x - 7$.

3. Simplify (i) $\dfrac{x^2 - 3x - 10}{xy + 2y}$; (ii) $\dfrac{1}{(x+2)^2} + \dfrac{1}{x+2} - \dfrac{1}{x+1}$.

4. If $x = 2$, $y = -5$ satisfy both of the equations,
$$ax + by + 1 = 0; \quad (b - 1)x + 5y + 3a = 0,$$
find the values of a, b.

5. A bus from P to Q at 15 m.p.h. takes 24 minutes less than the tram whose speed is 10 m.p.h.   How far is P from Q?

A. 67

1. (i) Multiply $x^2 + 3xy + 9y^2$ by $x - 3y$.

(ii) Simplify $\left(\dfrac{a}{x} - \dfrac{a^2}{x^2}\right) \div \dfrac{a^2}{x}$.

2. Solve (i) $(x - 1)(x - 3) - (x - 5)(x + 2) = 6$; (ii) $r^2 = 5r$.

3. Simplify (i) $\{(x - \frac{1}{2})^2 - 2\frac{1}{4}\} \div \left(x - 4 - \dfrac{5}{x}\right)$;

(ii) $\dfrac{a}{ab - b^2} - \dfrac{b}{a^2 - ab}$.

4. Find pairs of numbers, x and y, satisfying $2x - 11y = 4$ and such that one of the numbers is six times the other.

5. The lengths of the sides of a triangle are $x + \frac{1}{2}y$, $y + \frac{1}{3}x$, $5x - 4y + 3$, inches.   If the triangle is equilateral, prove that the triangle whose sides are of lengths xy, $\dfrac{x+3}{x}$, $\dfrac{y+4}{y}$, inches, is also equilateral.

A. 68

1. Express $n(n+1)(2n+1)$ in terms of p if $n = p - \frac{1}{2}$. Remove all brackets from the answer.

2. Solve (i) $\dfrac{3r}{4} - \dfrac{s}{3} = 2s - r = 6$; (ii) $t^2 + 2t = 15$.

3. Simplify (i) $\dfrac{6y^2 - y - 2}{3y^2 + y - 2} \times \left(2 - \dfrac{3y+1}{2y+1}\right)$;

(ii) $\dfrac{1}{a - 3b} - \dfrac{5b}{a^2 - ab - 6b^2}$.

4. (i) If $y = mx + c$ where m, c are constants and if $y = -3$ when $x = 2$, and $y = 5$ when $x = 4$, find y when $x = 5$.

(ii) If $x = \dfrac{4}{2-y}$ and $y = \dfrac{4}{2-z}$, find x in terms of z in as simple a form as possible; also find z in terms of x.

5. For a journey of 63 miles by rail, if the average speed of the train is 9 miles an hour less than the scheduled speed, the time taken is 14 minutes longer than the scheduled time. Find the scheduled time.

A. 69

1. (i) Multiply $2x^3 - x^2 - 3x$ by $x + 1 - \dfrac{1}{x}$.

(ii) Pick out the coefficients of x^2 and x^3 in
$$(3x^3 - x^2 - 2x + 4)(x^2 + 2x - 1).$$

2. Solve (i) $y = 3\cdot4 - 0\cdot6x$, $x = 3\cdot25 - 0\cdot7y$; (ii) $2p^2 - p = 3$.

3. Simplify (i) $\dfrac{a^2 + 3ab - 10b^2}{a^2 + 2ab - 15b^2} \div \dfrac{a^2 + 3ab + 2b^2}{a^2 - 4ab + 3b^2}$;

(ii) $\left(\dfrac{16}{x^2} - 1\right) \div \left(x + 3 - \dfrac{4}{x}\right)$.

4. The adjacent sides of a rectangle are $2(x-1)$ inches and $(x+3)$ inches; those of another rectangle of the same area are $3(x-2)$ inches and $(x+1)$ inches. Find their perimeters.

5. For a certain journey the charge for W lb. of luggage is P pence where P is given by the formula, $P = \frac{3}{2}(\frac{1}{6}W - 12)$. Find how much luggage can be taken for a shilling. How much can be taken free? Also express W in terms of P.

A. 70

1. (i) Simplify $(a-b+c)^2 - (a+b-c)^2$.

   (ii) Factorise $16(x^2-x-1)^2 - (x^2-9x-2)^2$.

2. Solve (i) $\dfrac{p+1}{q} = \dfrac{2}{3}, \ \dfrac{p-2}{q+3} = \dfrac{3}{7}$;

   (ii) $t^2 + 2t = 11$, correct to 2 places of decimals.

3. Simplify (i) $\dfrac{1-a-b+ab}{1-a+b-ab}$; (ii) $\dfrac{4}{x^2-2x-3} + \dfrac{2}{x^2+4x+3}$.

4. (i) If the roots of $x^2 + cx - 12 = 0$ are integers, find all the possible values of c.

   (ii) If α, β are the roots of $x^2 + x = 3$, find the values of $\dfrac{1}{\alpha} + \dfrac{1}{\beta}$ and $\dfrac{\alpha}{\beta} + \dfrac{\beta}{\alpha}$.

5. A man bought a certain number of articles of the same kind for £5. Three of them are broken; but he makes a profit of 8 shillings by selling the rest at 2 pence each above cost price. How many did he buy?

A. 71

1. Solve (i) $\dfrac{3}{x} - \dfrac{2}{x+5} = \dfrac{3}{3x-5}$; (ii) $2y^2 + 5y = 12$.

2. Simplify (i) $\left(x - \dfrac{1}{x}\right)\left(x + 1 - \dfrac{6}{x}\right) \div (3 - 2x - x^2)$;

   (ii) $\dfrac{a-b}{a^2-2ab-3b^2} - \dfrac{a+b}{a^2-4ab+3b^2}$.

3. (i) Factorise $b(b+1) - c(c+1)$.

   (ii) Find x and y if $\dfrac{x}{3} + \dfrac{y}{7} = 1$ and $(x-3y)(y-3x) = 0$.

4. Draw on the same diagram the graphs of $y = \dfrac{3x}{2} + 4$ and $y = 6 - \dfrac{x}{4}$, and solve graphically these simultaneous equations. Compare by solving algebraically.

5. The tickets for a concert cost 2s. 6d. and 1s.; tickets to the value of £24 were sold. If 25 per cent. more shilling tickets and 25 per cent. less half-crown tickets had been sold, the receipts would have been £25. How many tickets of each kind were sold?

A. 72

1. (i) Multiply $2 - 3x - x^2$ by $1 + 2x - 3x^2$.

(ii) Pick out the coefficients of x and x^3 in the expansion of $(4 - x - x^2 - 2x^3)^2$.

2. Solve (i) $a - 5 = \frac{1}{7}(b + 3)$, $b - 12 = \frac{1}{5}(4a - 2)$;

(ii) $x - \dfrac{15}{x} = 12$, to two places of decimals.

3. Simplify (i) $\left\{ 1 + \dfrac{1}{x} + \dfrac{1}{x(x+1)} \right\} \div \left(1 + x + \dfrac{1}{x+1} \right)$;

(ii) $\dfrac{a+b}{a-b} + \dfrac{a-b}{a+b} + \dfrac{4ab}{b^2 - a^2}$.

4. Draw the graph of $y = (3 - x)(x + 2)$ from $x = -3$ to $x = +4$. Solve graphically (i) $(3 - x)(x + 2) = 5$;   (ii) $(3 - x)(x + 2) = 2$; (iii) $(3 - x)(x + 2) + 3 = 0$.   What is the greatest value of $(3 - x)(x + 2)$?

5. A man rented a certain number of acres of land for £72. He worked 2 acres himself and by letting the rest at 8 shillings per acre more than he had to pay, he received for this portion an amount equal to the rent of the whole. How many acres did he rent altogether?

A. 73

1. Which of the following are perfect squares, and what are their square roots:

(i) $x^2 - 4x + 4$;   (ii) $x^2 + 8x + 64$;   (iii) $x^2 - 6x - 9$;

(iv) $9x^2 + 36x + 36$;   (v) $x^2 + x + \dfrac{1}{4}$;   (vi) $x^2 + \dfrac{1}{x^2} - 2$.

2. Solve (i) $x(x + 1) + (x + 2)(x + 3) = 2(x - 2)(x + 4)$;

(ii) $6t^2 + t = 2$.

3. Simplify (i) $\dfrac{a^2 - 3ab - 4b^2}{3ab - b^2} \div \dfrac{a^2 - 4ab}{a + 3b}$;   (ii) $\dfrac{x+1}{x^2 - x} - \dfrac{x+2}{x^2 - 1}$.

4. (i) What is b if $x - 5$ is a factor of $x^2 + bx - 30$?

(ii) What are b, c if $x + 4$ and $x - 7$ are both factors of $3x^2 + bx + c$?

5. For a run of 60 miles, a train can save 10 minutes if its ordinary speed is increased by 4 miles an hour. What is the ordinary speed?

A. 74

1. (i) Simplify $\dfrac{cx - dx}{dy - cy} \times \dfrac{y^3}{x^3}$.

(ii) For what value of x are the squares of $3x - 7$ and $3x + 8$ equal?

2. Solve (i) $\dfrac{z - 1}{z + 2} + \dfrac{2z + 3}{z - 1} = 3$;

(ii) $x^2 + 3x = 7$, correct to two places of decimals.

Find also the sum of the squares of the roots of the equation,
$$x^2 + 3x = 7.$$

3. Simplify (i) $\dfrac{1}{1 - x} - \dfrac{x}{(x - 1)^2} - 1$;

(ii) $\dfrac{ab - bc + cd - ad}{a^2 - c^2} - \dfrac{1 - a - d + ad}{a + c - a^2 - ac}$.

4. Draw the graph of $y = x^2 - 5x$ from $x = -1$ to $x = 6$. Solve graphically the equations (i) $x^2 - 5x = 3$; (ii) $x^2 - 5x = -3$; (iii) $x^2 - 5x + 5 = 0$; (iv) $2x^2 - 10x + 11 = 0$.

What can you say about c if $x^2 - 5x + c = 0$ has no roots?

5. When sugar falls in price 1d. per lb., I can buy for 8 shillings six more pounds than I formerly bought for 7s. 6d. What was the old price per lb.?

A. 75

1. Simplify (i) $\left(1 + \dfrac{x}{y}\right)\left(1 + \dfrac{y}{x}\right) \div \left(x - \dfrac{y^2}{x}\right)$;

(ii) $\dfrac{1}{(a + b)^2} - \dfrac{2}{a^2 - b^2} + \dfrac{3}{(a - b)^2}$.

2. Solve (i) $9x + 5y + 3 = \frac{1}{2}(2x - 5y - 4) = 5\frac{1}{2} - y$;

(ii) $x - \dfrac{10}{x} = 5$, correct to two places of decimals.

3. What can you say about the value of x, (i) if $(x + 4)(y - 7) = 0$; (ii) if $(2x + 1)(y^2 + 1) = 0$; (iii) if $(3x + 5)^2 + (y - 2)^2 = 0$?

4. (i) If the roots of $ax^2 + bx - 5 = 0$ are $2\frac{1}{2}$ and $-\frac{2}{3}$, find the values of a and b.

(ii) If α, β are the roots of $2x^2 + x = 5$, find the values of $(\alpha + 1)(\beta + 1)$ and $\alpha^2 + \beta^2$.

5. If $4n$ minutes past ten is the same time as n^2 minutes to eleven, find the value of n.

A. 76 *

1. Factorise (i) $(ax + by)^2 - (ay + bx)^2$;

(ii) $a^2 + 3ab + 2b^2 + ac + bc$.

2. Solve (i) $2x + 3y = 1 - \frac{1}{2}(x + 7y) = \frac{1}{3}x - 2y$;

(ii) $\dfrac{1}{x+1} - \dfrac{1}{x+2} = \dfrac{1}{3}$, correct to two places of decimals.

3. Simplify (i) $\dfrac{x-y}{x-z} \times \dfrac{y-z}{y-x} \times \left(1 - \dfrac{z^2}{x^2}\right)$;

(ii) $\dfrac{1}{a^2 - b^2} - \dfrac{1}{a^2 + 2ab - 3b^2} - \dfrac{b}{(a^2 - b^2)(a + 2b)}$.

4. For what integral values of x does $\dfrac{x+3}{2x+1}$ lie between $\frac{2}{3}$ and $\frac{3}{4}$?

5. The sides of a box are n, $n-1$, $2n$, inches long and its diagonal is $2n + 1$ inches long. Find the value of n.

A. 77 *

1. Simplify (i) $\left(\dfrac{a}{b} - \dfrac{a-b}{a+b}\right) \div \left(\dfrac{b}{a} + \dfrac{b+a}{b-a}\right)$;

(ii) $\dfrac{4xy}{x^4 - y^4} - \dfrac{1}{x(x-y)} - \dfrac{1}{y(x+y)}$.

2. (i) For what values of v is $v^2(2v + 2\frac{1}{3})$ equal to v?

(ii) Solve $\dfrac{x}{x-1} = \dfrac{x+3}{5}$, correct to 2 places of decimals.

3. Find the sums of the squares of the roots of the following equations (i) $x^2 + 4x = 32$; (ii) $3x^2 - 7x + 3 = 0$; (iii) $\dfrac{1}{x} + \dfrac{1}{x+1} = 1$.

4. If a, b, c, d are consecutive integers, prove that $a^2 + b^2 + c^2 + d^2 - 5$ is the square of $\frac{1}{2}(a + b + c + d)$.

5. After the price of bread has been lowered r per cent., a family eats each year r per cent. more bread. The yearly bread-bill is thereby reduced from £16 to £15, 15s. Find the value of r.

A. 78 *

1. Factorise (i) $x^3 + y - x^2y - x$; (ii) $a(b^2 - 2bc + c^2) - d(b^2 - c^2)$

2. Solve (i) $\frac{1}{5}(x - 2) - \frac{1}{4}(y - 3) = 2\frac{3}{4}$, $\frac{1}{4}(3 - x) - \frac{1}{5}(y + 2) = -\frac{3}{5}$;

(ii) $3x^2 + 4x = 8$, correct to 2 places of decimals.

3. Simplify (i) $\left(\frac{a}{b} + \frac{b}{a} + 2\right)\left(\frac{a}{b} + \frac{b}{a} - 2\right) \div \left(\frac{a^3}{b} - \frac{b^3}{a}\right)$;

(ii) $\dfrac{x^2 - (c + 1)x + c}{x^2 - (d + 1)x + d} - \dfrac{x + c}{x + d}$.

4. For what values of b, c do the equations, $2x^2 + 5bx + 3c = 0$, $3x^2 + (4c - 1)x + 9b = 0$, have the same roots for x?

5. If $(x + 1)(2x - 3)$ and $(x - 1)(3x - 5)$ are either consecutive even numbers or consecutive odd numbers, find all possible pairs of numbers they can be.

A. 79 *

1. Simplify (i) $\left(\dfrac{1}{a^2} - \dfrac{1}{b^2}\right) \div \left(\dfrac{a}{b} - \dfrac{2b}{a} + 1\right)$;

(ii) $\dfrac{x + z}{(a - x)(x - y)} + \dfrac{y + z}{(a - y)(y - x)}$.

2. Solve (i) $x^3 - x = 6(x + 1)$; (ii) $x - 1 = \dfrac{x^2 + 2}{x - 1} + \dfrac{x + 2}{x - 6}$.

3. If $2x - y + z = 0$, show how to express $xy + yz$ in the form $ax^2 + by^2 + cz^2$, and find the numerical values of a, b, c.

4. Find x and R if $\mathsf{R}x = 12$ and $\mathsf{R}\sqrt{(1 - x^2)} = 5$.

5. A man pays 4s. in the £ income tax on the part of his income above £160. Next year with the same income he pays 4s. 6d. in the £ on the part above £120. His tax is £20 more for the second year than for the first. Find his income.

A. 80 *

1. Simplify:

   (i) $\left\{\dfrac{y}{(x-y)^2} - \dfrac{1}{x-y}\right\}\left(\dfrac{1}{x} - \dfrac{1}{y}\right)$;

   (ii) $\dfrac{3}{x^2+x-2} - \dfrac{2}{x^2+2x-3} + \dfrac{1}{x^2+5x+6}$.

2. Solve:

   (i) $(x-2)(x-1)(x+2) = 12(x-1)$;

   (ii) $\dfrac{1}{x+1\frac{1}{2}} + \dfrac{1}{x+1\frac{1}{3}} = 1$, correct to 2 places of decimals.

3. (i) What is the value of c if the roots of $x^2 - 3x + c = 0$ are equal?

   (ii) If a, β are the roots of $ax^2 + bx + c = 0$, find in terms of a, β the roots of $a(2y-3)^2 + b(2y-3) + c = 0$.

4. What digit must x represent if the product of the two numbers "$x1$" and "$4x$" is the number "$3xxx$"?

5. From the data of a problem in which y is the number of articles bought and £x is their total cost, a boy obtains the equation, $\dfrac{1 \cdot 5 + 0 \cdot 3(y-x)}{y+x} + 0 \cdot 3 = \dfrac{1 \cdot 5}{x}$. Is it possible for him to find the *numerical* value of x without obtaining a second equation?

REVISION PAPERS, A. 81–95 (Ch. I–XIII)

A. 81

1. (i) Simplify $\left\{ \dfrac{c-ac}{e-ae} - \dfrac{d-bd}{e-be} \right\} \div \left(\dfrac{c}{d} - \dfrac{d}{c} \right)$.

   (ii) Find the L.C.M. of $x^2 - 2x - 8$, $x^2 + 5x + 6$, $x^2 - 8x + 16$.

2. Solve (i) $\dfrac{x+1}{\frac{1}{2}} - \dfrac{x-1}{\frac{1}{3}} = \dfrac{x-3}{\frac{1}{4}}$; (ii) $x - 2y = 1$, $xy = 1$.

3. In Fig. 162, calculate $\angle$ **PQR**.

4. Prove that the equation $\dfrac{x^2 + 8x + 11}{(x+2)^2} = c$ is satisfied by only one value of x if $c = 5$ and if $c = 1$. What are the roots if $c = -4$?

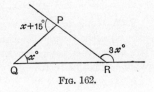

Fig. 162.

5. A merchant spends £90 in buying coal of one grade and £52, 10s. in buying a poorer grade 5s. per ton cheaper. In all he buys 75 tons. Find the cost per ton of each grade.

A. 82

1. (i) Simplify $\dfrac{y^6(x+z)^3}{x^3y^3 + y^3z^3}$;

   (ii) Divide $x^4 - 7x^2 + 1$ by $x^2 - 3x + 1$.

2. Factorise (i) $px - py + qy - qx$; (ii) $(x^2 - 6x + 3)^2 - (x-9)^2$.

3. (i) If $x = 1\frac{1}{2}$ is one root of $2x^2 + x + c = 0$, what is the other root and what is the value of c?

   (ii) Solve $2xy - 7x = 7$, $3xy - 10x = 14$.

4. (i) Make b the subject of the formula, $c = \dfrac{ax - 2by}{ax + 2by}$.

   (ii) If $(n+1)f = u$ and $\left(1 + \dfrac{1}{n}\right)f = v$, find f in terms of u, v only.

5. The hot-water tap takes 4 minutes longer than the cold-water tap to fill a bath. Both taps together take $3\frac{3}{4}$ minutes. How long does the hot-water tap take by itself?

A. 83

1. (i) One factor of $24x^3 - 50x^2y - 3xy^2 + 36y^3$ is $2x - 3y$, find the others.

   (ii) Factorise $1 - (a - b)^2$.

2. Simplify (i) $(y + z)(y - z) + (z + x)(z - x) - (y + x)(y - x)$;

   (ii) $\left(a - 3 - \dfrac{10}{a}\right)\left(a + 1 - \dfrac{12}{a}\right) \div \left(a - 1 - \dfrac{20}{a}\right).$

3. (i) Find the value of b if $x - 5$ is a factor of $x^2 + bx - 30$.

   (ii) Solve $2x^2 + y^2 = 3$, $x + y = 2$.

4. A stone projected vertically upwards is s feet above the ground after t seconds, where $s = 104t - 16t^2$. How long is it in the air? If it takes the same time to go up as to come down, what is the greatest height it reaches?

5. A motor cyclist went in pursuit of a car which had 20 minutes start and caught it when he had gone 80 miles. If the average speed of the cyclist was 8 miles an hour greater than that of the car, find the speed of each.

A. 84

1. (i) Find the L.C.M. of $x^2 - y^2$, $x^2 + 2xy + y^2$, $x^2 - xy$.

   (ii) Divide $a^4 + 4b^4$ by $a^2 - 2ab + 2b^2$; hence write down the factors of $x^4 + 4$.

2. Factorise (i) $x^4 - 16(y - z)^4$; (ii) $2x^4 + x^3 - 9x^2 - 4x + 4$.

3. (i) Solve $36x^2 - 11x = 12$.

   (ii) If $x + y = a$ and $x - y = b$, express $x^2 + y^2$ and $x^4 - y^4$ in terms of a, b.

4. The result of increasing b by x per cent. is the same as that of decreasing c by x per cent. Find x in terms of b, c.

5. A woman buys equal quantities of tea at 2s. 6d. per lb. and 2s. per lb. If she had divided the same amount of money equally between the two kinds, she would have obtained altogether half a pound more. How much money does she spend?

A. 85

1. (i) Factorise $4a^2 - b^2 - 4b - 4$.

   (ii) Simplify $\left\{\dfrac{1}{3} - \dfrac{4}{x} + \dfrac{4}{x+1}\right\} \div \left\{\dfrac{1}{4} + \dfrac{2}{x} - \dfrac{5}{4(x-1)}\right\}$.

2. Solve (i) $2x^2 - x = 10$; (ii) $x^2 - 2y^2 = 3x + 4y = 1$.

3. If x shillings per cwt. is the same rate of cost as f farthings per lb., express x in terms of f.

4. 100 cu. ft. of a mixed gas weigh 8 lb. The two gases which are mixed weigh respectively 0·077 lb. per cu. ft. and 0·087 lb. per cu. ft. How many cu. ft. of each gas go to form the mixture?

5. A motorist completes a journey of 200 miles in two stages with a rest of half an hour before the second stage. His average speed during the first stage of 150 miles is 36 miles an hour, while during the second stage his average speed is 5 miles an hour less than the average speed for the whole journey. Find his average speed for the whole journey.

A. 86

1. (i) Find the square root of $1 - \dfrac{1}{x} + \dfrac{1}{4x^2}$.

   (ii) Simplify $\left(\dfrac{1}{3a-3b} + \dfrac{1}{4b-4a}\right)\left(\dfrac{a}{b^2} - \dfrac{b}{a^2}\right) - \dfrac{1}{3}\left(\dfrac{1}{2a} - \dfrac{1}{2b}\right)^2$.

2. Factorise (i) $1 + 2yz^2 - 15y^2z^4$; (ii) $(a^2 - b^2 - c^2)^2 - 4b^2c^2$.

3. Solve (i) $12(x^2 - 1) = 7x$;

   (ii) $(x+2)(x-5) = (y+2)(y-5)$, $x - y = 6$.

4. Draw the graph of $y = \tfrac{1}{2}(x-3)(x+1)$ from $x = -3$ to $x = 5$. Use it to solve the equations:

   (i) $(x-3)(x+1) = 2$; (ii) $(x-3)(x+1) = -x$.

   What can you say about the value of c if $(x-3)(x+1) = c$ has no roots?

5. The resistance, R lb. per ton, to the motion of a train travelling at v miles an hour is given by the formula, $R = a + bv^2$ where a, b are constants. When $v = 20$, $R = 9·6$, and when $v = 40$, $R = 20·4$. Find a, b. Find, correct to 2 significant figures, the value of R when $v = 35$.

A. 87

1. Factorise (i) $6x^2 + xy - 15y^2$; (ii) $a(x-a)^2 + b(a^2 - x^2)$.

2. (i) Write down the square of $3ab - bc$.

(ii) Simplify $\left\{ \dfrac{x}{x-y} + \dfrac{x}{x+y} \right\} \div \left\{ \dfrac{y}{x-y} + \dfrac{y^2}{(x-y)^2} \right\}$.

3. Solve (i) $6t^2 + t = 15$; (ii) $2x^2 + 5xy = 2x - 3y = -12$.

4. $\mathbf{W}$ lb. of gun-cotton will demolish a wall h ft. high, t ft. thick, per foot length, if $\mathbf{W} = cht^2$, where c is a constant. If 45 lb. of gun-cotton is needed per foot length for a wall 10 ft. high, 3 ft. thick, how much is needed for a similar wall 12 ft. high, 5 ft. thick, 80 ft. long?

5. If the average speed of a motorist is 4 miles per hour below his usual speed, he takes three-quarters of an hour longer than usual for a journey. If his average speed is 4 miles per hour above his usual speed, he takes half an hour less than usual for the journey. Find his usual average speed and usual time for the journey.

A. 88

1. (i) Factorise $cx - dx + dx^2 - cx^2$.

(ii) Find the value of a if $x^2 + 3$ is a factor of

$$2x^4 + 3x^3 + 4x^2 + ax - 6,$$

and in this case find the remaining factors.

2. If $\dfrac{1}{x} = \dfrac{1}{p} - \dfrac{1}{a}$, $\dfrac{1}{y} = \dfrac{1}{q} + \dfrac{1}{a}$, express $\dfrac{xy}{x+y}$ in a form not containing x or y.

3. Solve (i) $3x^2 + 8x - 21 = 0$, correct to two places of decimals; (ii) $7xy = x + 2y$, $3x - 4y = 1$.

4. Draw the graph of $y = x^3$ from $x = -2$ to $x = +2$. Solve graphically the equations (i) $x^3 = 3x$; (ii) $x^3 - 3x + 1 = 0$.

5. A man has to travel 50 miles in 4 hours. He does it by walking the first 7 miles at x m.p.h., bicycling the next 7 miles at $4x$ m.p.h. and motoring the remainder at $(6x+3)$ m.p.h. Find x.

A. 89

1. Simplify (i) $\dfrac{x^2 - y^2 - z^2 + 2yz}{x^2 + y^2 - z^2 - 2xy}$; (ii) $\left(\dfrac{3a+3b}{2a+b} - \dfrac{a+2b}{a+b}\right) \div \dfrac{a^3-b^3}{a^3+b^3}$.

2. $\frac{1}{2}(x+4)$ is greater than $\frac{1}{3}(10-x)$ by 50 per cent. of it; find x.

3. (i) Solve for x and y, $x+y = a+1 = ax-y$.

   (ii) Solve $7\cdot5(x-1) = \dfrac{8}{x+2} - 1$.

4. When petrol costs 3s. 6d. a gallon and oil 4s. a quart, a cyclist finds that the cost of petrol and oil is £4, 10s. per 1000 miles. When the prices are reduced to 3s. and 3s. 6d. respectively, the cost is £3, 17s. 6d. per 1000 miles. How many miles does he run on 1 gallon of petrol?

5. A man converted some English money into francs. If he had done so two days later, he would have obtained 4 francs less for each £1 because the value of a franc in English money had risen $\frac{1}{8}$d. How many francs, correct to 1 place of decimals, did he actually obtain for £1?

A. 90

1. Factorise (i) $a^6 + 8a^3b^3$; (ii) $2x^3 + x^2 - 13x + 6$.

2. (i) Pick out the coefficients of x and x^3 in the expansion of
   $(4 - 2x + x^2 - 3x^3)(1 + 5x - x^2 - 2x^3)$.

   (ii) Simplify $\left(1 + \dfrac{a}{b}\right) \div \left(1 - \dfrac{a^2}{b^2}\right) + \left(1 - \dfrac{b}{a}\right) \div \left(1 - \dfrac{2b}{a} + \dfrac{b^2}{a^2}\right)$.

3. Solve (i) $2x + 3y = 8$, $2x^2 = y$; (ii) $x - x^2 = 25x - 25$.

4. The base of a box is a square of side x feet and the length of cord (exclusive of knots) needed for binding it once round each way is 40 feet. Show that the volume of the box is $2x^2(5-x)$ cu. feet. Represent this function by a graph, from $x=0$ to $x=5$. For what value of x is the volume greatest?

   Solve graphically (i) $2x^2(5-x) = 25$; (ii) $5x^2 - x^3 = 15$.

5. In a race for boys between 13 and 15, each was given a start of y yards calculated from $y = a - bx^2$, where a, b are constants and x is the number of completed months by which the competitor's age exceeded 13 years. Boys of age 15 had no start; boys of age 14 years 2 months had 95 yards start. What was the age of a boy who received 44 yards start.

A. 91 *

1. (i) Divide $1 - 8y^3$ by $1 - 2y$.
   (ii) Factorise (a) $cx + dx - x^2 - cd$;
                (b) $4x^4 - 12x^3 - 7x^2 + 18x + 9$.

2. (i) What is c if $x + 3$ is a factor of $x^2 - cx - (c^2 - 1)$?
   (ii) Solve for x, $(x + a)^2 = 2x^2$.

3. If the diameter of a sphere is d inches, the volume in cu. inches exceeds $\frac{1}{2}d^3$ by about 5 per cent. Find an approximate expression for the volume of a sphere of radius r inches.

4. At an entertainment, the tickets cost 1s. 3d. and 6d.; the programmes were 2d. each. Three-quarters of the 1s. 3d. ticketholders and two-thirds of the others bought programmes. The receipts from the tickets were £6, 9s. and from the programmes 19s. 6d. How many bought 1s. 3d. tickets?

5. The time for a journey is reduced by 25 minutes by increasing the average speed by 5 miles an hour; a further increase of 5 miles an hour causes a further reduction of 20 minutes. Find the length of the journey and the final speed.

A. 92 *

1. Factorise (i) $x^4 - 8x^2 + 16$; (ii) $a^6 - 7a^3 - 8$.

2. Find a, b if the roots of $ax = \dfrac{35}{x + b}$ are double the roots of

$$4x = \frac{35}{x + 1}.$$

3. Solve (i) $(t^2 + 10t)^2 = 576$;

   (ii) $\dfrac{2x + 2}{x - 1} - \dfrac{x - 1}{x + 1} = \dfrac{x}{x - 2}$, correct to 2 places of decimals.

4. The base of an open cistern is a square of side x feet; its volume is 300 cu. ft.; show that the total area of the base and sides, y sq. ft., is given by $y = x^2 + \dfrac{1200}{x}$. Represent this function graphically for values of x from 6 to 12. Find from the graph the value of x for which this total area is least.

   Solve graphically:

       (i) $x^2 + \dfrac{1200}{x} = 230$; (ii) $x^3 - 225x + 1200 = 0$.

5. A number formed by two digits exceeds the number formed by reversing the digits by 18, and three times the product of the digits exceeds five times their sum by 5. Find the number.

A. 93 *

1. (i) Expand in ascending powers of x, as far as x^3,
$$(1 - 2x + 3x^2 - 4x^3 + 5x^4)^2.$$

(ii) Simplify $\left(\dfrac{2}{y+z} - \dfrac{1}{y+2z}\right) \div \left(\dfrac{2}{y+3z} - \dfrac{1}{y+2z}\right).$

2. Solve (i) $\dfrac{x-2}{x-3} + \dfrac{x-5}{x-6} = \dfrac{x-3}{x-4} + \dfrac{x-4}{x-5}$;

(ii) $x - y = 5, \quad x^2 + xy + y^2 = 7.$

3. (i) If a, b, c, d are consecutive integers, prove that $abcd + 1$ is the square of $bc - 1$.

(ii) If $2s = a + b + c$, prove that $s(s-a) + (s-b)(s-c) = bc.$

4. If I deduct $(5k)$ per cent. from N the result is the same as if I increase M by $(5k)$ per cent. Find k in terms of M and N.

5. A and B bicycle towards each other from towns 51 miles apart. A starts at noon and rides at x miles per hour; B starts at 2 p.m. and rides at y miles per hour. Write down an expression for the distance between them t hours after A has started, assuming that t is greater than 2. They meet at 4 p.m. If they had both started at noon, they would have met at 2.50 p.m. Find the values of x and y.

A. 94 *

1. (i) Factorise $2ab - a^2 - b^2$.

(ii) Simplify $\left(\dfrac{x+1}{y} - \dfrac{y+1}{x}\right) \div \left(\dfrac{1}{y^3} - \dfrac{1}{x^3}\right).$

2. If $\dfrac{1}{u} + \dfrac{1}{v} = \dfrac{1}{a}$ and $u + v = k$, express in terms of a, k:

(i) uv; (ii) $u^2 + v^2$; (iii) $(u-v)^2$.

3. (i) *Without* solving the equation, $7x^2 - 45x - 11 = 0$, prove that one root is greater than 6.

(ii) Solve $x = y^2 - 6$; $y = \tfrac{1}{2}x - 1$.

4. The hypotenuse of a right-angled triangle is c inches, and the lengths of the other two sides are a, b inches. If $a + c = \dfrac{3b}{2}$, prove that $a = \dfrac{5c}{13}$.

5. Grade **B** rose-bushes are cheaper than Grade **A** by 3d. each; "standard" trees are dearer than Grade **A** by one shilling each. A man who has a certain sum of money to spend finds that he can obtain 24 more bushes by buying Grade **B** instead of Grade **A**. If, however, he buys "standard" trees instead of Grade **A** he will get 48 less. How much has he to spend and what is the price of Grade **A** rose-bushes?

A. 95 *

1. (i) Factorise $(3a - 6b)(3c - 2d) + (4b - 2a)(d - c)$.

    (ii) Simplify $\dfrac{3x - 7}{x^2 - 5x + 6} - \dfrac{5}{x^2 + x - 6} - \dfrac{x + 9}{x^2 - 9}$.

2. (i) Prove that $(x - 1)^2$ is a factor of $x^4 - 4x + 3$.

    (ii) If $\dfrac{1}{u} + \dfrac{1}{v} = \dfrac{1}{u + 1} + \dfrac{1}{v - 1}$, find u in terms of v.

3. Solve (i) $\dfrac{3x + 6}{x - 1} = \dfrac{2x + 4}{x} + \dfrac{x + 2}{x + 1}$;

    (ii) $x^2 - y^2 = 16$, $x + y = 8$.

4. (i) b cwt. and $2(b + 1)$ qr. amount to 13 tons; find the value of b.

    (ii) **A** runs x yards in p seconds and beats **B** over this distance by y yards. If **A**, **B** run at uniform rates, by how many seconds will **A** beat **B** over a course of z yards?

5. **OA**, **OB** are two perpendicular radii of a circle. Two other circles are drawn to touch this circle externally at **A**, **B** and also to touch one another externally. If the radii of these two circles are **4** inches and **7** inches respectively, find the radius of the first circle, correct to $\frac{1}{10}$ inch.

REVISION PAPERS, A. 96–110 (Ch. I–XVI)

A. 96

1. Simplify (i) $\left(1 - \dfrac{2ab}{a^2 + b^2}\right)\left(\dfrac{a}{b} - \dfrac{2a - b}{a + 2b}\right)\left(\dfrac{2ab}{a - b} - b\right)\left(\dfrac{a}{b} - \dfrac{2a}{a + b}\right);$

(ii) $(2x + 3x^{\frac{1}{2}}y^{-1} + y^{-2}) \div (x^{\frac{1}{2}} + y^{-1}).$

2. (i) Make n the subject of the formula, $\mathsf{P} = \dfrac{\mathsf{Q} + (n + 1)\mathsf{R}}{1 - n}.$

(ii) Find r in terms of h, t if $r^2 - 2rh = t^2.$

3. Evaluate (i) $27^{1\frac{1}{3}}$; (ii) $32^{0\cdot8}$; (iii) $8^{-\frac{2}{3}}$; (iv) $(0\cdot8)^{-1}.$

4. Simplify (i) $6\sqrt{\frac{1}{2}}$; (ii) $\dfrac{\sqrt{96}}{\sqrt{18}}$; (iii) $\dfrac{3 + \sqrt{3}}{3 - \sqrt{3}}.$

5. If $y \propto x^3$ and if $y = 4\cdot8$ when $x = 2$, find y in terms of x, and find to the nearest unit the percentage increase in y if x is increased by 20 per cent.

A. 97

1. Solve (i) $(x + 1)(x - 2) - \frac{1}{2}(x - 1)(x + 2) = \frac{1}{2}(x + 3)(x - 1);$

(ii) $2x^2 - 12x = 7$, to 2 places of decimals.

2. Simplify (i) $3 + \dfrac{x^2 + x}{x^2 - 3x + 2} - \dfrac{6}{x - 2};$

(ii) $\sqrt{12} \times \sqrt{27}$; (iii) $\sqrt{2} - \sqrt{(4\frac{1}{2})}.$

3. Simplify (i) $8^{-\frac{2}{3}} + 4^{-1} - 6^{-1}$; (ii) $3x^{\frac{1}{3}}y^{\frac{2}{3}} \times (3x^{-\frac{1}{3}}y)^{-2}.$

4. The cost of manufacturing a car is partly constant and partly varies inversely as the number of cars produced per day. When the daily output is 40 cars, the cost of each is £170; for 50 cars daily, the cost of each is £160. Find the cost of each when the daily output is 80 cars.

5. Find (i) the number of terms, (ii) the sum, of the A.P.,

$$23,\ 29,\ 35,\ ...,\ 125.$$

Prove that $10^n + 1$ belongs to this A.P. if n is any positive integer.

A. 98

1. Simplify (i) $\dfrac{c}{c+d} - \dfrac{c+d}{c+2d}$; (ii) $\dfrac{x^2-4x+3}{x^2-5x+6} \div \dfrac{x^3-1}{\frac{1}{2}x-1}$;

(iii) $25^{2n} \div 5^n$; (iv) $(16a^{-4}b^2)^{-\frac{1}{2}}$.

2. Simplify (i) $\log 14 + 2\log 2 - \log 8$; (ii) $\log 125 \div \log 5$;

(iii) $(2\frac{1}{4})^{-\frac{1}{2}}$; (iv) $(-1)^{-3}$.

3. (i) Multiply $a^{\frac{1}{2}} + \sqrt{3} + 2a^{-\frac{1}{2}}$ by $a^{\frac{1}{2}} - \sqrt{3} + 2a^{-\frac{1}{2}}$.

(ii) Simplify $\dfrac{\sqrt{6} - \sqrt{2}}{6 - 2\sqrt{3}}$.

4. If $\dfrac{a}{b} = \dfrac{b}{c}$, prove that $\dfrac{b^2-c^2}{a^2-c^2} = \dfrac{b^2}{a^2+b^2}$.

5. Sum the series (i) $3 + 6 + 9 + 12 + \ldots$, 30 terms;

(ii) $3 + 6 + 12 + 24 + \ldots$, 30 terms.

Use logarithms to evaluate the sum of (ii), correct to 2 figures.

A. 99

1. Factorise (i) $ab - a - b + 1$; (ii) $c^2 + c^5$;

(iii) $6y^2 - 23yz - 18z^2$; (iv) $x^3 - 2x^2 - 5x + 6$.

2. Find x if (i) $3^x = 81$; (ii) $81^x = 3$; (iii) $3^x = \frac{1}{9}$;

(iv) $9^{-x} = 3$; (v) $27^x = \sqrt{3}$; (vi) $9^x = \frac{1}{3}\sqrt{3}$.

3. (i) Evaluate $x^2 - \dfrac{1}{x^2}$ if $x = 3 - \sqrt{7}$.

(ii) Simplify $\log_{10} 2 \div \log_{10} 0\cdot 5$ and $\log_{10} 2 - \log_{10} 0\cdot 2$.

4. The horse-power rating of a car varies jointly as the number of cylinders and the square of their diameter. A 4-cylinder car with cylinders of diameter 3 in. is rated as $14\cdot 4$ horse-power. Find the horse-power of a 6-cylinder car with cylinders of diameter $2\cdot 5$ in. Find also a general formula.

5. The 1st, 4th, and 8th terms of an A.P. are in G.P., and the 1st term is 9. Find the 2nd term of the A.P. and the sum of $2n$ terms of the A.P.

A. 100

1. Solve (i) $\dfrac{1}{2(x-1)} + \dfrac{3}{x^2-1} = \dfrac{1}{4}$; (ii) $x+y=2,\ x^2+4y=2y^2$.

2. Express as powers of y:

(i) $\dfrac{1}{\sqrt[3]{y}}$; (ii) $\sqrt[3]{y^2} \times \sqrt{y^3}$; (iii) $\dfrac{\sqrt{y} \times \sqrt{y}}{y^2}$; (iv) $\dfrac{y^{2n}}{y^{n+2}}$.

3. Simplify (i) $\sqrt{54} \times \sqrt{75}$; (ii) $\sqrt{32} - \sqrt{18} + \sqrt{8}$;

(iii) $\dfrac{6}{\sqrt{5} - \sqrt{2}}$; (iv) $(\sqrt{\tfrac{1}{2}})^3$.

4. Find without using tables the values of x if

(i) $\log_{10} x = 1 + \log_{10} 3$; (ii) $\log_{10} x = 3 - \log_{10} 8$;

(iii) $\log_{10} \sqrt{x} = 1\cdot 5$; (iv) $\log_{10} x = 3\log_{10} 2 - 2\log_{10} 3$.

5. (i) Evaluate $(401 + 403 + 405 + \dots + 499) \div (1 + 3 + 5 + \dots + 99)$.

(ii) The geometric mean of p and q is 6 and the arithmetic mean of $\dfrac{1}{p}$ and $\dfrac{1}{q}$ is $\dfrac{5}{18}$. Find the values of p and q.

Find also the nth term of the G.P., p, 6, q, ... (two answers).

A. 101

1. (i) Prove that $x^2 + x - 1$ is a factor of $x^5 + 5x^2 - 2$.

(ii) Make W the subject of the formula, $t = \dfrac{2a\mathsf{W}}{\mathsf{W}+w}\left(1 + \dfrac{\mathsf{V}}{v}\right)$.

2. Simplify (i) $\sqrt{75} + \sqrt{48} - 2\sqrt{27}$; (ii) $(a^{-\frac{1}{2}}b^{\frac{2}{3}})^{-2}$;

(iii) $\dfrac{1}{\sqrt{3}-\sqrt{2}} + \dfrac{2}{\sqrt{3}+\sqrt{2}}$; (iv) $\log\dfrac{1}{9} \div \log\dfrac{1}{27}$.

3. (i) If $2\cdot 37v^{1\cdot 6} = 14\cdot 8$, find v, correct to 3 figures.

(ii) How many terms of the G.P., 2, 3, $4\frac{1}{2}$, ... must be taken to obtain a sum exceeding 10,000?

4. If a, β are the roots of $\dfrac{1}{x+1} + \dfrac{1}{x+2} = \dfrac{1}{3}$, find the values of $a^2 + \beta^2$ and $\dfrac{1}{a+1} + \dfrac{1}{\beta+1}$.

5. If $\dfrac{a}{b} = \dfrac{c}{d}$, prove that $(ab - cd)^2 = (a^2 - c^2)(b^2 - d^2)$.

A. 102

1. Simplify (i) $\dfrac{x-4}{(x-2)(x+3)} - \dfrac{14}{(5+x)(3+x)(2-x)}$;

(ii) $\dfrac{a^2 - ab}{a^2 - 2a - 3} \div \dfrac{a^2 + ab - 2b^2}{a^2 + 2ab - 3a - 6b}$.

2. Simplify (i) $(1\cdot5)^{2n} \times 12^n$; (ii) $\dfrac{\sqrt{5}}{(3 - \sqrt{2})(\sqrt{10} + \sqrt{5})}$;

(iii) $\log_{10} 750 - 2 \log_{10} 3 + \log_{10} 1\cdot2$.

3. R is partly constant and partly varies as the square root of v. If $R = 10$ when $v = 64$ and if $R = 11\cdot2$ when $v = 81$, find the general formula for R in terms of v.

4. Draw the graph of $y = x^3 - 3x + 3$ for values of x from -3 to $+2$. Hence (i) find the least value of y for positive values of x; (ii) solve $x^3 - 3x + 3 = 0$; (iii) solve $x^3 - 3x = 1$.

5. (i) The common difference of an A.P. is 4 and the sum of the first 10 terms is 230; find the first term.

(ii) The rth term of a series is $2(3^r) - \frac{1}{3}r$. Find the sum of the first n terms.

A. 103

1. (i) Solve $x - 2y = 3$, $x^2 - 3y^2 = 22$.

(ii) If $x = \dfrac{a-1}{a+1}$ and $y = \dfrac{2a-1}{2a+1}$, find y in terms of x only.

2. Simplify (i) $\sqrt{6} \times \sqrt{10} \times \sqrt{20}$; (ii) $(\frac{3}{4})^{-\frac{1}{2}} \times (\frac{8}{27})^{-\frac{2}{3}}$;

(iii) $\dfrac{1}{(\sqrt{10} - 2\sqrt{2})^2}$; (iv) $(x^{-1} - 1) \div (x^{-\frac{1}{2}} - 1)$.

3. The maximum velocity attainable by a car varies directly as its horse-power and inversely as the resistance. The resistance varies directly as the square of the velocity. Find how the velocity varies with the horse-power. Find also, correct to 2 figures, the percentage increase in the velocity if the horse-power is increased by 40 per cent.

4. (i) Find n, correct to 3 figures, if $7^{n+1} = 10^n$.

(ii) Find y in terms of x if $\log_{10} y = 0\cdot75 \log_{10} x + 0\cdot82$.

5. (i) If $10p = 15q = 6r$, find the value of $\dfrac{3p - r}{q + 2r}$.

(ii) If $6x^2 = xy + 15y^2$, find the possible values of $\dfrac{x+y}{x-y}$.

A. 104

1. If $x = 3$ is a root of $x^3 + x^2 + ax + 12 = 0$, find the value of a, and in this case find the other roots, correct to two places of decimals.

2. Simplify (i) $\dfrac{\sqrt{45}}{\sqrt{5}}$; (ii) $\dfrac{\sqrt{5}}{\sqrt{20}}$; (iii) $\dfrac{\sqrt{56}}{\sqrt{8} - \sqrt{7}}$; (iv) $4^{\frac{2}{3}} \times 2^{-\frac{1}{3}}$.

3. (i) If a, β are the roots of $2x^2 + bx - 7 = 0$, and if $\dfrac{1}{a}$, $\dfrac{1}{\beta}$ are the roots of $cx^2 - 3x - 4 = 0$, find the values of b, c.

(ii) Solve $5x - 2y = 2$, $x^2 + 36 = xy + 2y^2$.

4. The annual cost of running a car is partly constant and partly varies as the mileage. If the cost is £40 in a year when the mileage is 3000, and £47, 10s. when the mileage is 4500, find the cost when the mileage for the year is 7000.

5. Sum to n terms the series,

$$\text{(i) } \tfrac{5}{6} - \tfrac{5}{9} + \tfrac{10}{27} - \ldots; \quad \text{(ii) } \tfrac{5}{6} + \tfrac{7}{12} + \tfrac{1}{3} + \ldots,$$

if one of these is an A.P. and the other a G.P.

A. 105

1. If $x = cy^{1 \cdot 25} z^{-0 \cdot 5}$, evaluate c, correct to 3 figures, if $x = 11 \cdot 14$, $y = 18 \cdot 73$, $z = 6 \cdot 215$.

2. Simplify (i) $28^{\frac{1}{2}} \times 7^{1\frac{1}{2}}$; (ii) $(2 \cdot 25)^{-1 \cdot 5}$;

(iii) $3 \log 1 \cdot 2 + 2 \log \dfrac{\sqrt{10}}{3} - \log 0 \cdot 96$.

3. (i) What number must be added to each of the numbers 2, 4, 6, 9 to obtain four numbers such that the first two are proportional to the second two?

(ii) If $\dfrac{a}{b} = \dfrac{c^2}{d^2}$, prove that $\dfrac{2a^2 - 3c^4}{2b^2 - 3d^4} = \dfrac{pac^2 - c^4}{pbd^2 - d^4}$.

4. (i) Prove that $\sqrt{2} + \sqrt{3}$ is a root of $x^4 + 1 = 10x^2$.

(ii) If the sum of the roots of $x^2 - (c+1)x + 2(c-1) = 0$ is three-quarters of their product, find the value of c. Find also the roots.

5. A series of similar articles is made in different sizes. Their weights form a series in A.P., and their values a series in G.P. Size 1 weighs 3 lb. and is worth 2s. 8d.; size 4 weighs $7\frac{1}{2}$ lb. and is worth 9s. Find the weight and value of size 7.

A. 106 *

1. Solve (i) $\frac{1}{2}x^2 + x = 3$, correct to 2 places of decimals;

   (ii) $3x + 4y = 18$, $(x + y)(x + 2y) = 40$.

2. Simplify (i) $(125^{\frac{2}{3}} + 25^{\frac{3}{2}}) \times 625^{-\frac{3}{4}}$; (ii) $2^{n+3} - 6 \times 2^n$;

   (iii) $ab^{-2} + ba^{-2}$ if $a = 2\sqrt{2} - \sqrt{7}$ and $b = 2\sqrt{2} + \sqrt{7}$.

3. (i) If $x^4 + 2x^3 - 3x^2 - 8x - 4$ can be expressed in the form $(x^2 + ax + 2)(x^2 + bx - 2)$, find the values of a and b, and show that the assumption is correct.

   (ii) If $\dfrac{p+x}{p-x} = \dfrac{y-q}{y+q}$, express y in terms of p, q, x.

4. The cost of a spoon of a certain design varies partly as the square of the length and partly as the cube of the length. The costs of two such spoons of lengths l inches, $2l$ inches are p shillings, q shillings respectively. Find the cost of a spoon of this design of length $1\frac{1}{2}l$ inches.

5. (i) Find the value of n if the sums of the first n terms of the two A.P.'s, 2, 5, 8, ... and 47, 45, 43, ... are equal.

   (ii) The first term of a G.P. is x, its last term is x^2, and its sum is x^3; find the common ratio in terms of x.

A. 107 *

1. (i) Factorise $2x^3 - 3x^2 - 3x + 2$ and $a^2 - a(b + 1) + 2(b - 1)$.

   (ii) Find the values of b, c if $x + 2$ and $x - 3$ are factors of $x^4 + 2x^3 + bx^2 + cx + 24$, and in this case find the remaining factors.

2. (i) Find x, to 3 places of decimals, if $6^{2x-1} = 8^x$.

   (ii) If $a = \dfrac{1}{2}(\sqrt{13} - 1)$, evaluate $\dfrac{5-a}{2-a} - a$.

3. Simplify (i) $\dfrac{3^{n+3} - 3 \times 3^n}{4 \times 3^{n+2}}$; (ii) $(1.44)^{-\frac{1}{2}}$;

   (iii) $\log_{10} 1.2 + 2\log_{10} 0.75 - \log_{10} 6.75$.

4. (i) If $\dfrac{a}{b} = \dfrac{c}{d} = \dfrac{e}{f}$, prove that $\dfrac{a^n}{b^{n-1}} + \dfrac{c^n}{d^{n-1}} - \dfrac{e^n}{f^{n-1}} = \dfrac{(a+c-e)^n}{(b+d-f)^{n-1}}$.

   (ii) The weight that can be supported by a cylindrical strut varies as the fourth power of the diameter and inversely

as the square of the length. If one strut is twice as
long as another, and if they can carry equal weights,
find the ratio of their diameters.

5. The sum of the first 5 terms of an A.P. is -2, and the sum
of the first 9 terms is 0. Find the sum of the first n terms.

A. 108 *

1. (i) Make **G** the subject of the formula, $d = 1 \cdot 25 G^{\frac{3}{4}} H^{-\frac{1}{4}}$,
   expressing the numerical coefficient correct to 3 figures.

  (ii) If $xy - ab = a(x + y)$, express $x + y$ in terms of x, a, b, only.

2. Simplify (i) $4^{n+3} \times 8^{2-n} \div 16^{3-n}$; (ii) $(\frac{9}{10})^{-\frac{1}{2}} \times (3\frac{3}{8})^{\frac{1}{3}}$;

  (iii) $\dfrac{a}{b} + \dfrac{b}{a}$ if $a = 3\sqrt{2} - 2\sqrt{3}$ and $b = 3\sqrt{2} + 2\sqrt{3}$.

3. (i) If $\dfrac{a+b}{b+c} = \dfrac{c+d}{d+a}$ and if a is not equal to c, prove that
   $a + b + c + d = 0$.

  (ii) Factorise $x^2 - xy - 6y^2 - 3x + 19y - 10$.

4. The time for a railway journey varies directly as the distance
and inversely as the velocity. The velocity varies directly as
the square root of the amount of coal used per mile and inversely
as the number of coaches in the train. For a journey of 25 miles
in half an hour with 18 coaches, 10 cwt. of coal is used. How
much coal is used in a journey of 15 miles in 20 minutes with
24 coaches ?

5. (i) The 3rd term of an A.P. is 8, and the 10th term is 36.
   Find the sum of n terms.

  (ii) What is the least number of terms of the G.P., 4, 6, 9, ...,
   starting from the beginning, whose sum is greater
   than 10,000 ?

A. 109 *

1. Find the possible values of c if $x + 2$ is a factor of
$$x^3 + 4cx^2 + (c+1)^2 x - 6,$$
and for these values of c, find, correct to 2 places of decimals, the
roots of $x^3 + 4cx^2 + (c+1)^2 x - 6 = 0$.

2. (i) If a, β are the roots of $3x^2 + x - 7 = 0$, prove that
$$(3a+1)^2 + (3\beta+1)^2 + 9(a+\beta) = 40.$$

(ii) Find the value of c if $3x^2 + x = c$ has equal roots.

3. Simplify (i) $\dfrac{12 \times 18^n}{6^{2n+1} \times (0 \cdot 5)^n}$;   (ii) $\sqrt{\left(\dfrac{x^3}{\sqrt{y}}\right)} \div (x^{\frac{1}{3}} y^{-\frac{1}{6}})^{\frac{3}{2}}$;

(iii) $\dfrac{(\sqrt{2}+\sqrt{3}+\sqrt{5})(\sqrt{2}-\sqrt{3}+\sqrt{5})}{(\sqrt{2}+\sqrt{3}-\sqrt{5})(\sqrt{3}-\sqrt{2}+\sqrt{5})}$;   (iv) $\dfrac{(\log 8)(\log 9)}{\log 27}$.

4. Draw the graph of $y = \dfrac{24(2-x)}{x^2 - 2x + 4}$ for values of x from -2 to $+6$, and use it to solve the equations,

(i) $12(2-x) = 5(x^2 - 2x + 4)$;   (ii) $20(2-x) + 3(x^2 - 2x + 4) = 0$.
Also solve graphically $24(2-x) = x(x^2 - 2x + 4)$.

5. (i) Sum $1 + \left(3 + \dfrac{1}{3}\right) + \left(3^2 + \dfrac{1}{3^2}\right) + \left(3^3 + \dfrac{1}{3^3}\right) + \dots + \left(3^n + \dfrac{1}{3^n}\right)$.

(ii) Sum to $(2n+1)$ terms, where n is integral, the series $1 - 4 + 7 - 10 + 13 - \dots$.

A. 110 *

1. (i) If $ab + bc + ca = 0$, prove that $a^2(b+c) = b^2(a+c)$.

(ii) Factorise $4y^2 - (y^2 - z^2 + 1)^2$.

2. Simplify: (i) $9^{2n+1} \times 6^{2n-3} \div (3^{5n-2} \times 18 \times 4^{n-2})$;

(ii) $(a^3 b^{-1})^{-2} \times (a^{-3} b^3)^{-1}$;   (iii) $\log(\log x^p) - \log(\log x^q)$.

3. (i) If $\dfrac{a}{b} = \dfrac{c}{d}$, prove that $\dfrac{ac - c^2}{b - d} = \dfrac{d(a^2 + c^2)}{b^2 + d^2}$.

(ii) If $\dfrac{a}{b} = \dfrac{b}{c} = \dfrac{c}{d}$, prove that $\dfrac{a}{d} = \dfrac{b(b^2 - c^2)}{c(c^2 - d^2)}$.

4. P varies inversely as the square of r; v^2 is partly constant and partly varies inversely as r; also r and v are positive. If P $= 2$ and $v = 2\frac{1}{2}$ when $r = 3$, and if P $= 8$ when $v = 3$, express v in terms of r, and express P in terms of v.

5. (i) Find the sum of all the positive integers less than 600 which are not divisible either by 2 or by 3.

(ii) Use logarithms to evaluate, correct to 3 figures, the sum to 10 terms of the G.P., $3 + 2^{\frac{1}{4}} \cdot 3^{\frac{3}{4}} + 2^{\frac{1}{2}} \cdot 3^{\frac{1}{2}} + \dots$.

LOGARITHM TABLES

	0	1	2	3	4	5	6	7	8	9	1	2	3	4	5	6	7	8
10	·0000	0043	0086	0128	0170	0212	0253	0294	0334	0374	4	8	12	17	21	25	29	33
11	·0414	0453	0492	0531	0569	0607	0645	0682	0719	0755	4	8	11	15	19	23	26	30
12	·0792	0828	0864	0899	0934	0969	1004	1038	1072	1106	3	7	10	14	17	21	24	28
13	·1139	1173	1206	1239	1271	1303	1335	1367	1399	1430	3	6	10	13	16	19	23	26
14	·1461	1492	1523	1553	1584	1614	1644	1673	1703	1732	3	6	9	12	15	18	21	24
15	·1761	1790	1818	1847	1875	1903	1931	1959	1987	2014	3	6	8	11	14	17	20	22
16	·2041	2068	2095	2122	2148	2175	2201	2227	2253	2279	3	5	8	11	13	16	18	21
17	·2304	2330	2355	2380	2405	2430	2455	2480	2504	2529	2	5	7	10	12	15	17	20
18	·2553	2577	2601	2625	2648	2672	2695	2718	2742	2765	2	5	7	9	12	14	16	19
19	·2788	2810	2833	2856	2878	2900	2923	2945	2967	2989	2	4	7	9	11	13	16	18
20	·3010	3032	3054	3075	3096	3118	3139	3160	3181	3201	2	4	6	8	11	13	15	17
21	·3222	3243	3263	3284	3304	3324	3345	3365	3385	3404	2	4	6	8	10	12	14	16
22	·3424	3444	3464	3483	3502	3522	3541	3560	3579	3598	2	4	6	8	10	12	14	15
23	·3617	3636	3655	3674	3692	3711	3729	3747	3766	3784	2	4	6	7	9	11	13	15
24	·3802	3820	3838	3856	3874	3892	3909	3927	3945	3962	2	4	5	7	9	11	12	14
25	·3979	3997	4014	4031	4048	4065	4082	4099	4116	4133	2	3	5	7	9	10	12	14
26	·4150	4166	4183	4200	4216	4232	4249	4265	4281	4298	2	3	5	7	8	10	11	13
27	·4314	4330	4346	4362	4378	4393	4409	4425	4440	4456	2	3	5	6	8	9	11	13
28	·4472	4487	4502	4518	4533	4548	4564	4579	4594	4609	2	3	5	6	8	9	11	12
29	·4624	4639	4654	4669	4683	4698	4713	4728	4742	4757	1	3	4	6	7	9	10	12
30	·4771	4786	4800	4814	4829	4843	4857	4871	4886	4900	1	3	4	6	7	9	10	11
31	·4914	4928	4942	4955	4969	4983	4997	5011	5024	5038	1	3	4	6	7	8	10	11
32	·5051	5065	5079	5092	5105	5119	5132	5145	5159	5172	1	3	4	5	7	8	9	11
33	·5185	5198	5211	5224	5237	5250	5263	5276	5289	5302	1	3	4	5	6	8	9	10
34	·5315	5328	5340	5353	5366	5378	5391	5403	5416	5428	1	3	4	5	6	8	9	10
35	·5441	5453	5465	5478	5490	5502	5514	5527	5539	5551	1	2	4	5	6	7	9	10
36	·5563	5575	5587	5599	5611	5623	5635	5647	5658	5670	1	2	4	5	6	7	8	10
37	·5682	5694	5705	5717	5729	5740	5752	5763	5775	5786	1	2	3	5	6	7	8	9
38	·5798	5809	5821	5832	5843	5855	5866	5877	5888	5899	1	2	3	5	6	7	8	9
39	·5911	5922	5933	5944	5955	5966	5977	5988	5999	6010	1	2	3	4	5	7	8	9
40	·6021	6031	6042	6053	6064	6075	6085	6096	6107	6117	1	2	3	4	5	6	8	9
41	·6128	6138	6149	6160	6170	6180	6191	6201	6212	6222	1	2	3	4	5	6	7	8
42	·6232	6243	6253	6263	6274	6284	6294	6304	6314	6325	1	2	3	4	5	6	7	8
43	·6335	6345	6355	6365	6375	6385	6395	6405	6415	6425	1	2	3	4	5	6	7	8
44	·6435	6444	6454	6464	6474	6484	6493	6503	6513	6522	1	2	3	4	5	6	7	8
45	·6532	6542	6551	6561	6571	6580	6590	6599	6609	6618	1	2	3	4	5	6	7	8
46	·6628	6637	6646	6656	6665	6675	6684	6693	6702	6712	1	2	3	4	5	6	7	7
47	·6721	6730	6739	6749	6758	6767	6776	6785	6794	6803	1	2	3	4	5	5	6	7
48	·6812	6821	6830	6839	6848	6857	6866	6875	6884	6893	1	2	3	4	5	5	6	7
49	·6902	6911	6920	6928	6937	6946	6955	6964	6972	6981	1	2	3	4	4	5	6	7
50	·6990	6998	7007	7016	7024	7033	7042	7050	7059	7067	1	2	3	3	4	5	6	7
51	·7076	7084	7093	7101	7110	7118	7126	7135	7143	7152	1	2	3	3	4	5	6	7
52	·7160	7168	7177	7185	7193	7202	7210	7218	7226	7235	1	2	2	3	4	5	6	7
53	·7243	7251	7259	7267	7275	7284	7292	7300	7308	7316	1	2	2	3	4	5	6	6
54	·7324	7332	7340	7348	7356	7364	7372	7380	7388	7396	1	2	2	3	4	5	6	6

	0	1	2	3	4	5	6	7	8	9	1	2	3	4	5	6	7	8	9
55	·7404	7412	7419	7427	7435	7443	7451	7459	7466	7474	1	2	2	3	4	5	5	6	7
56	·7482	7490	7497	7505	7513	7520	7528	7536	7543	7551	1	2	2	3	4	5	5	6	7
57	·7559	7566	7574	7582	7589	7597	7604	7612	7619	7627	1	2	2	3	4	5	5	6	7
58	·7634	7642	7649	7657	7664	7672	7679	7686	7694	7701	1	1	2	3	4	4	5	6	7
59	·7709	7716	7723	7731	7738	7745	7752	7760	7767	7774	1	1	2	3	4	4	5	6	7
60	·7782	7789	7796	7803	7810	7818	7825	7832	7839	7846	1	1	2	3	4	4	5	6	6
61	·7853	7860	7868	7875	7882	7889	7896	7903	7910	7917	1	1	2	3	4	4	5	6	6
62	·7924	7931	7938	7945	7952	7959	7966	7973	7980	7987	1	1	2	3	3	4	5	6	6
63	·7993	8000	8007	8014	8021	8028	8035	8041	8048	8055	1	1	2	3	3	4	5	5	6
64	·8062	8069	8075	8082	8089	8096	8102	8109	8116	8122	1	1	2	3	3	4	5	5	6
65	·8129	8136	8142	8149	8156	8162	8169	8176	8182	8189	1	1	2	3	3	4	5	5	6
66	·8195	8202	8209	8215	8222	8228	8235	8241	8248	8254	1	1	2	3	3	4	5	5	6
67	·8261	8267	8274	8280	8287	8293	8299	8306	8312	8319	1	1	2	3	3	4	5	5	6
68	·8325	8331	8338	8344	8351	8357	8363	8370	8376	8382	1	1	2	3	3	4	4	5	6
69	·8388	8395	8401	8407	8414	8420	8426	8432	8439	8445	1	1	2	2	3	4	4	5	6
70	·8451	8457	8463	8470	8476	8482	8488	8494	8500	8506	1	1	2	2	3	4	4	5	6
71	·8513	8519	8525	8531	8537	8543	8549	8555	8561	8567	1	1	2	2	3	4	4	5	5
72	·8573	8579	8585	8591	8597	8603	8609	8615	8621	8627	1	1	2	2	3	4	4	5	5
73	·8633	8639	8645	8651	8657	8663	8669	8675	8681	8686	1	1	2	2	3	4	4	5	5
74	·8692	8698	8704	8710	8716	8722	8727	8733	8739	8745	1	1	2	2	3	4	4	5	5
75	·8751	8756	8762	8768	8774	8779	8785	8791	8797	8802	1	1	2	2	3	3	4	5	5
76	·8808	8814	8820	8825	8831	8837	8842	8848	8854	8859	1	1	2	2	3	3	4	5	5
77	·8865	8871	8876	8882	8887	8893	8899	8904	8910	8915	1	1	2	2	3	3	4	4	5
78	·8921	8927	8932	8938	8943	8949	8954	8960	8965	8971	1	1	2	2	3	3	4	4	5
79	·8976	8982	8987	8993	8998	9004	9009	9015	9020	9025	1	1	2	2	3	3	4	4	5
80	·9031	9036	9042	9047	9053	9058	9063	9069	9074	9079	1	1	2	2	3	3	4	4	5
81	·9085	9090	9096	9101	9106	9112	9117	9122	9128	9133	1	1	2	2	3	3	4	4	5
82	·9138	9143	9149	9154	9159	9165	9170	9175	9180	9186	1	1	2	2	3	3	4	4	5
83	·9191	9196	9201	9206	9212	9217	9222	9227	9232	9238	1	1	2	2	3	3	4	4	5
84	·9243	9248	9253	9258	9263	9269	9274	9279	9284	9289	1	1	2	2	3	3	4	4	5
85	·9294	9299	9304	9309	9315	9320	9325	9330	9335	9340	1	1	2	2	3	3	4	4	5
86	·9345	9350	9355	9360	9365	9370	9375	9380	9385	9390	1	1	2	2	3	3	4	4	5
87	·9395	9400	9405	9410	9415	9420	9425	9430	9435	9440	0	1	1	2	2	3	3	4	4
88	·9445	9450	9455	9460	9465	9469	9474	9479	9484	9489	0	1	1	2	2	3	3	4	4
89	·9494	9499	9504	9509	9513	9518	9523	9528	9533	9538	0	1	1	2	2	3	3	4	4
90	·9542	9547	9552	9557	9562	9566	9571	9576	9581	9586	0	1	1	2	2	3	3	4	4
91	·9590	9595	9600	9605	9609	9614	9619	9624	9628	9633	0	1	1	2	2	3	3	4	4
92	·9638	9643	9647	9652	9657	9661	9666	9671	9675	9680	0	1	1	2	2	3	3	4	4
93	·9685	9689	9694	9699	9703	9708	9713	9717	9722	9727	0	1	1	2	2	3	3	4	4
94	·9731	9736	9741	9745	9750	9754	9759	9763	9768	9773	0	1	1	2	2	3	3	4	4
95	·9777	9782	9786	9791	9795	9800	9805	9809	9814	9818	0	1	1	2	2	3	3	4	4
96	·9823	9827	9832	9836	9841	9845	9850	9854	9859	9863	0	1	1	2	2	3	3	4	4
97	·9868	9872	9877	9881	9886	9890	9894	9899	9903	9908	0	1	1	2	2	3	3	4	4
98	·9912	9917	9921	9926	9930	9934	9939	9943	9948	9952	0	1	1	2	2	3	3	4	4
99	·9956	9961	9965	9969	9974	9978	9983	9987	9991	9996	0	1	1	2	2	3	3	3	4

	0	1	2	3	4	5	6	7	8	9	1	2	3	4	5	6	7	8
·00	1000	1002	1005	1007	1009	1012	1014	1016	1019	1021	0	0	1	1	1	1	2	2
·01	1023	1026	1028	1030	1033	1035	1038	1040	1042	1045	0	0	1	1	1	1	2	2
·02	1047	1050	1052	1054	1057	1059	1062	1064	1067	1069	0	0	1	1	1	1	2	2
·03	1072	1074	1076	1079	1081	1084	1086	1089	1091	1094	0	0	1	1	1	1	2	2
·04	1096	1099	1102	1104	1107	1109	1112	1114	1117	1119	0	1	1	1	1	2	2	2
·05	1122	1125	1127	1130	1132	1135	1138	1140	1143	1146	0	1	1	1	1	2	2	2
·06	1148	1151	1153	1156	1159	1161	1164	1167	1169	1172	0	1	1	1	1	2	2	2
·07	1175	1178	1180	1183	1186	1189	1191	1194	1197	1199	0	1	1	1	1	2	2	2
·08	1202	1205	1208	1211	1213	1216	1219	1222	1225	1227	0	1	1	1	1	2	2	2
·09	1230	1233	1236	1239	1242	1245	1247	1250	1253	1256	0	1	1	1	1	2	2	2
·10	1259	1262	1265	1268	1271	1274	1276	1279	1282	1285	0	1	1	1	1	2	2	2
·11	1288	1291	1294	1297	1300	1303	1306	1309	1312	1315	0	1	1	1	2	2	2	2
·12	1318	1321	1324	1327	1330	1334	1337	1340	1343	1346	0	1	1	1	2	2	2	3
·13	1349	1352	1355	1358	1361	1365	1368	1371	1374	1377	0	1	1	1	2	2	2	3
·14	1380	1384	1387	1390	1393	1396	1400	1403	1406	1409	0	1	1	1	2	2	2	3
·15	1413	1416	1419	1422	1426	1429	1432	1435	1439	1442	0	1	1	1	2	2	2	3
·16	1445	1449	1452	1455	1459	1462	1466	1469	1472	1476	0	1	1	1	2	2	2	3
·17	1479	1483	1486	1489	1493	1496	1500	1503	1507	1510	0	1	1	1	2	2	2	3
·18	1514	1517	1521	1524	1528	1531	1535	1538	1542	1545	0	1	1	1	2	2	3	3
·19	1549	1552	1556	1560	1563	1567	1570	1574	1578	1581	0	1	1	1	2	2	3	3
·20	1585	1589	1592	1596	1600	1603	1607	1611	1614	1618	0	1	1	1	2	2	3	3
·21	1622	1626	1629	1633	1637	1641	1644	1648	1652	1656	0	1	1	2	2	2	3	3
·22	1660	1663	1667	1671	1675	1679	1683	1687	1690	1694	0	1	1	2	2	2	3	3
·23	1698	1702	1706	1710	1714	1718	1722	1726	1730	1734	0	1	1	2	2	2	3	3
·24	1738	1742	1746	1750	1754	1758	1762	1766	1770	1774	0	1	1	2	2	2	3	3
·25	1778	1782	1786	1791	1795	1799	1803	1807	1811	1816	0	1	1	2	2	2	3	3
·26	1820	1824	1828	1832	1837	1841	1845	1849	1854	1858	0	1	1	2	2	3	3	3
·27	1862	1866	1871	1875	1879	1884	1888	1892	1897	1901	0	1	1	2	2	3	3	3
·28	1905	1910	1914	1919	1923	1928	1932	1936	1941	1945	0	1	1	2	2	3	3	4
·29	1950	1954	1959	1963	1968	1972	1977	1982	1986	1991	0	1	1	2	2	3	3	4
·30	1995	2000	2004	2009	2014	2018	2023	2028	2032	2037	0	1	1	2	2	3	3	4
·31	2042	2046	2051	2056	2061	2065	2070	2075	2080	2084	0	1	1	2	2	3	3	4
·32	2089	2094	2099	2104	2109	2113	2118	2123	2128	2133	0	1	1	2	2	3	3	4
·33	2138	2143	2148	2153	2158	2163	2168	2173	2178	2183	0	1	1	2	2	3	3	4
·34	2188	2193	2198	2203	2208	2213	2218	2223	2228	2234	1	1	2	2	3	3	4	4
·35	2239	2244	2249	2254	2259	2265	2270	2275	2280	2286	1	1	2	2	3	3	4	4
·36	2291	2296	2301	2307	2312	2317	2323	2328	2333	2339	1	1	2	2	3	3	4	4
·37	2344	2350	2355	2360	2366	2371	2377	2382	2388	2393	1	1	2	2	3	3	4	4
·38	2399	2404	2410	2415	2421	2427	2432	2438	2443	2449	1	1	2	2	3	3	4	4
·39	2455	2460	2466	2472	2477	2483	2489	2495	2500	2506	1	1	2	2	3	3	4	5
·40	2512	2518	2523	2529	2535	2541	2547	2553	2559	2564	1	1	2	2	3	4	4	5
·41	2570	2576	2582	2588	2594	2600	2606	2612	2618	2624	1	1	2	2	3	4	4	5
·42	2630	2636	2642	2649	2655	2661	2667	2673	2679	2685	1	1	2	2	3	4	4	5
·43	2692	2698	2704	2710	2716	2723	2729	2735	2742	2748	1	1	2	3	3	4	4	5
·44	2754	2761	2767	2773	2780	2786	2793	2799	2805	2812	1	1	2	3	3	4	4	5
·45	2818	2825	2831	2838	2844	2851	2858	2864	2871	2877	1	1	2	3	3	4	5	5
·46	2884	2891	2897	2904	2911	2917	2924	2931	2938	2944	1	1	2	3	3	4	5	5
·47	2951	2958	2965	2972	2979	2985	2992	2999	3006	3013	1	1	2	3	3	4	5	5
·48	3020	3027	3034	3041	3048	3055	3062	3069	3076	3083	1	1	2	3	4	4	5	6
·49	3090	3097	3105	3112	3119	3126	3133	3141	3148	3155	1	1	2	3	4	4	5	6

	0	1	2	3	4	5	6	7	8	9	1	2	3	4	5	6	7	8	9
.50	3162	3170	3177	3184	3192	3199	3206	3214	3221	3228	1	1	2	3	4	4	5	6	7
.51	3236	3243	3251	3258	3266	3273	3281	3289	3296	3304	1	2	2	3	4	5	5	6	7
.52	3311	3319	3327	3334	3342	3350	3357	3365	3373	3381	1	2	2	3	4	5	5	6	7
.53	3388	3396	3404	3412	3420	3428	3436	3443	3451	3459	1	2	2	3	4	5	6	6	7
.54	3467	3475	3483	3491	3499	3508	3516	3524	3532	3540	1	2	2	3	4	5	6	6	7
.55	3548	3556	3565	3573	3581	3589	3597	3606	3614	3622	1	2	2	3	4	5	6	7	7
.56	3631	3639	3648	3656	3664	3673	3681	3690	3698	3707	1	2	3	3	4	5	6	7	8
.57	3715	3724	3733	3741	3750	3758	3767	3776	3784	3793	1	2	3	3	4	5	6	7	8
.58	3802	3811	3819	3828	3837	3846	3855	3864	3873	3882	1	2	3	4	4	5	6	7	8
.59	3890	3899	3908	3917	3926	3936	3945	3954	3963	3972	1	2	3	4	5	5	6	7	8
.60	3981	3990	3999	4009	4018	4027	4036	4046	4055	4064	1	2	3	4	5	6	6	7	8
.61	4074	4083	4093	4102	4111	4121	4130	4140	4150	4159	1	2	3	4	5	6	7	8	9
.62	4169	4178	4188	4198	4207	4217	4227	4236	4246	4256	1	2	3	4	5	6	7	8	9
.63	4266	4276	4285	4295	4305	4315	4325	4335	4345	4355	1	2	3	4	5	6	7	8	9
.64	4365	4375	4385	4395	4406	4416	4426	4436	4446	4457	1	2	3	4	5	6	7	8	9
.65	4467	4477	4487	4498	4508	4519	4529	4539	4550	4560	1	2	3	4	5	6	7	8	9
.66	4571	4581	4592	4603	4613	4624	4634	4645	4656	4667	1	2	3	4	5	6	7	9	10
.67	4677	4688	4699	4710	4721	4732	4742	4753	4764	4775	1	2	3	4	5	7	8	9	10
.68	4786	4797	4808	4819	4831	4842	4853	4864	4875	4887	1	2	3	4	6	7	8	9	10
.69	4898	4909	4920	4932	4943	4955	4966	4977	4989	5000	1	2	3	5	6	7	8	9	10
.70	5012	5023	5035	5047	5058	5070	5082	5093	5105	5117	1	2	4	5	6	7	8	9	11
.71	5129	5140	5152	5164	5176	5188	5200	5212	5224	5236	1	2	4	5	6	7	8	10	11
.72	5248	5260	5272	5284	5297	5309	5321	5333	5346	5358	1	2	4	5	6	7	9	10	11
.73	5370	5383	5395	5408	5420	5433	5445	5458	5470	5483	1	3	4	5	6	8	9	10	11
.74	5495	5508	5521	5534	5546	5559	5572	5585	5598	5610	1	3	4	5	6	8	9	10	12
.75	5623	5636	5649	5662	5675	5689	5702	5715	5728	5741	1	3	4	5	7	8	9	10	12
.76	5754	5768	5781	5794	5808	5821	5834	5848	5861	5875	1	3	4	5	7	8	9	11	12
.77	5888	5902	5916	5929	5943	5957	5970	5984	5998	6012	1	3	4	5	7	8	10	11	12
.78	6026	6039	6053	6067	6081	6095	6109	6124	6138	6152	1	3	4	6	7	8	10	11	13
.79	6166	6180	6194	6209	6223	6237	6252	6266	6281	6295	1	3	4	6	7	9	10	11	13
.80	6310	6324	6339	6353	6368	6383	6397	6412	6427	6442	1	3	4	6	7	9	10	12	13
.81	6457	6471	6486	6501	6516	6531	6546	6561	6577	6592	2	3	5	6	8	9	11	12	14
.82	6607	6622	6637	6653	6668	6683	6699	6714	6730	6745	2	3	5	6	8	9	11	12	14
.83	6761	6776	6792	6808	6823	6839	6855	6871	6887	6902	2	3	5	6	8	9	11	13	14
.84	6918	6934	6950	6966	6982	6998	7015	7031	7047	7063	2	3	5	6	8	10	11	13	15
.85	7079	7096	7112	7129	7145	7161	7178	7194	7211	7228	2	3	5	7	8	10	12	13	15
.86	7244	7261	7278	7295	7311	7328	7345	7362	7379	7396	2	3	5	7	8	10	12	13	15
.87	7413	7430	7447	7464	7482	7499	7516	7534	7551	7568	2	3	5	7	9	10	12	14	16
.88	7586	7603	7621	7638	7656	7674	7691	7709	7727	7745	2	4	5	7	9	11	12	14	16
.89	7762	7780	7798	7816	7834	7852	7870	7889	7907	7925	2	4	5	7	9	11	13	14	16
.90	7943	7962	7980	7998	8017	8035	8054	8072	8091	8110	2	4	6	7	9	11	13	15	17
.91	8128	8147	8166	8185	8204	8222	8241	8260	8279	8299	2	4	6	8	9	11	13	15	17
.92	8318	8337	8356	8375	8395	8414	8433	8453	8472	8492	2	4	6	8	10	12	14	15	17
.93	8511	8531	8551	8570	8590	8610	8630	8650	8670	8690	2	4	6	8	10	12	14	16	18
.94	8710	8730	8750	8770	8790	8810	8831	8851	8872	8892	2	4	6	8	10	12	14	16	18
.95	8913	8933	8954	8974	8995	9016	9036	9057	9078	9099	2	4	6	8	10	12	15	17	19
.96	9120	9141	9162	9183	9204	9226	9247	9268	9290	9311	2	4	6	8	11	13	15	17	19
.97	9333	9354	9376	9397	9419	9441	9462	9484	9506	9528	2	4	7	9	11	13	15	17	20
.98	9550	9572	9594	9616	9638	9661	9683	9705	9727	9750	2	4	7	9	11	13	16	18	20
.99	9772	9795	9817	9840	9863	9886	9908	9931	9954	9977	2	5	7	9	11	14	16	18	20

Square Root Tables are given at the beginning of the book